McGRAW-HILL OFFICES

New Delhi
New York
St Louis
San Francisco
Auckland
Bogotá
Guatemala
Hamburg
Lisbon
London
Madrid
Mexico
Montreal
Panama
Paris
San Juan
São Paulo
Singapore
Sydney
Tokyo
Toronto

TAXONOMY OF ANGIOSPERMS

V N NAIK
Marathwada University
Aurangabad

TATA McGRAW-HILL PUBLISHING COMPANY LIMITED
NEW DELHI

Seventh Reprint 1994
RZRAARZJRDQXL

ISBN 0-07-451788-0

Published by Tata McGraw-Hill Publishing Company Limited,
4/12 Asaf Ali Road, New Delhi 110 002, and printed at
Pushp Print Services, Shahdra, Delhi 110 053

Dedicated with love and respect to my senior colleague
Prof R M Pai
in recognition of his sound knowledge of angiosperms

Preface

Teaching and research in plant taxonomy has suffered a serious setback in this country. While the revival of the Botanical Survey of India initiated floristic studies in the country, the Indian universities have not given the importance that taxonomy deserves, in their academic programmes. Most of the syllabi stress only a few old systems of classification and characters of the families therein. The science of taxonomy has thus been reduced to cramming of a couple of characters and remembering names of a few plants. In most places, the practical work is confined to the laboratories where the students are kept busy in sketching a few twigs. Botanical excursions do not adequately serve the purpose for which they are meant. Taxonomy is seldom taken to be the basis for all other botanical disciplines. It is often neglected as an old classical science in preference to the newer fields of studies in science. The teaching of taxonomy is often assigned to teachers who have neither the expertise nor the interest in the subject. The fundamentals of taxonomy, its synthetic nature, aims and principles have never been impressed upon the students.

However, of late, efforts are being made to redeem the situation. The Botanical Survey of India and the University of Mysore recently conducted seminars/symposia on floristic studies as well as teaching and research in taxonomy. Among other recommendations, it was emphasised that the university departments be strengthened for teaching taxonomy.

As a followup of these seminars, a few universities attempted to upgrade or revise their syllabi. However, in spite of these efforts taxonomy has yet to receive the attention it deserves. It is therefore felt that the crux of the problem lies elsewhere. At least to me it appears that the students of taxonomy are acutely faced with the difficulty of finding a suitable text which can adequately fulfil their needs. In the absence of such a book they have to consult a large number of reference books as well as research papers. This consumes much of their time and still they cannot be sure of satisfactory collection of data.

In this book an effort has been made to collect and present an up-to-date account of the general principles and modern trends in taxonomy. A systematic treatment of families is not attempted here as there are enough books available dealing with it. A particular stress is given on the definitions, aims, basic principles, methodology and concepts of taxonomy. The most basic as well as synthetic nature of taxonomy is also emphasised. It is hoped that this text will serve as a source book providing adequate information on the fundamentals of taxonomy.

The chapters chosen for inclusion in the text comprise a major part of the syllabus on taxonomy of angiosperms in many Indian universities. In preparation of the draft I have received help from my colleagues. associates and the reviewers who critically read the manuscript and made valuable suggestions for its improvement. I am deeply grateful to them all. I am also thankful to the various copyright holders for their kind permission to reproduce their illustrations which have been indicated at appropriate places accordingly. Lastly, I have pleasure in acknowledging the stimulating inspiration and sincere help of my students in preparation of this book.

I shall be happy to receive comments and suggestions from teachers and researchers in the subject.

V N NAIK

Contents

TAXONOMY OF ANGIOSPERMS

1 Introduction

The rich variety of innumerable objects surrounding us is incomprehensible. It is almost impossible for anyone to have adequate knowledge about each individual object. However, man has a wonderful capacity to discriminate. He often tries to know them by using certain attributes or characters that are common to a large number of objects. In other words, he classifies them into manageable groups. As has been correctly stated by Davis and Heywood (1963), "Classification is a natural occupation of man, recognition one of his most necessary pastime." He must discriminate, whether he likes it or not, between objects that form part of his everyday requirements.

It is often necessary to pinpoint a thing of our interest by noting the similarities or differences with other *things*. Similarly, we also should qualify our statement by indicating the group to which the thing belongs. This is obviously for precision and better communication. A biologist interested in studying a particular organism must know his field of study. It is necessary for him to *identify* it, have a *name* for communication of his ideas about it, and *know the group* to which the organism belongs. These three activities are, in fact, the main functions of *taxonomy*. This is a taxonomic procedure followed by every human being in his daily routine, consciously or subconsciously. Indeed, none can deny his primary occupation as a taxonomist.

For all practical purposes, biologists must know what organism they are working on before they pass on information about it to others. Investigators in certain disciplines of biology other than taxonomy cannot publish their results without the use of a basic classfication of the organism they work on. If their identification is dubious or wrong, the value of the work is greatly diminished and in many cases worthless. Many of the experiments cannot be repeated unless the organisms are correctly identified. Every biologist, whether he realises or not, works with species, and his findings, even on the molecular level, may be largely influenced by the choice of a particular species (Mayr, 1957).

The literal meaning of the term *taxonomy* is "lawful arrangement" or "arrangements by rules" of things (from Greek, *taxis* = arrangement; *nomous* = law, rule). Objects that appear to be haphazard, disorderly or at least innumerable cannot be comprehended properly without their prior arrangement into convenient groups. Thus, plant taxonomy means classification of plants following certain rules or, principles. But it should also be understood that grouping of plants can be possible only when their identity is revealed and they are named for the sake of convenience and communication of ideas about them

When first introduced to the plant science in 1813 by A.P. de Candolle, the term taxonomy meant *the theory of plant classification,* but by constant usage by the later botanists the term has become more inclusive. At present it is taken to be a plant science which includes identification of plants, their nomenclature and classification. It is often considered to be synonymous with the term ***systematics*** or ***systematic botany*** (in respect of plant science). Some authors do not agree with this synonym and hold that taxonomy is a major part of systematic botany. However, it is a matter of opinion but generally the distinction between the two terms appears to be insignificant. Both terms may be used with prefixes such as *cytotaxonomy* (cytologically based taxonomy), ***chemotaxonomy,*** (chemical based taxonomy) *biosystematics* (systematics of living organisms) and others to indicate specialised meanings.

Taxonomy is basic to other sciences and at the same time dependent on them. It has to depend for its improvement, and indeed for its existence, entirely on information from other fields such as morphology, anatomy, embryology, cytology, phytochemistry, physiology, genetics, ecology, phytogeography, etc. It has no data of its own. The different aspects of modern taxonomy have been expressed diagrammatically by Radford *et al.* (1974) (Figs. 1.1 and 1.2).

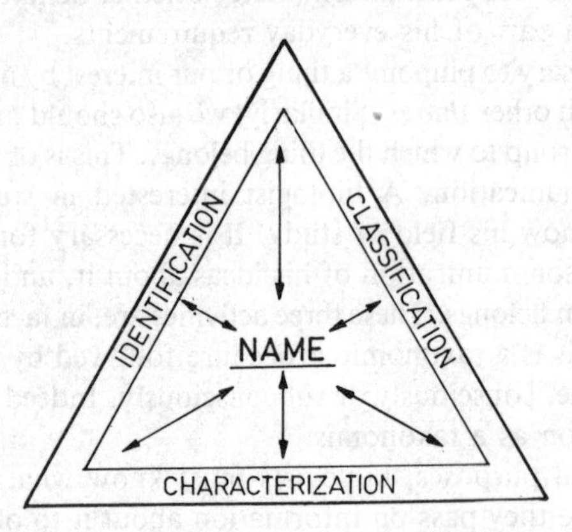

FIG. 1.1 Taxonomic fundamentals. (Redrawn from *Vascular Plant Systematics* by Radford *et al.* 1974, by permission of Harper and Row, New York.)

According to these authors, "Taxonomy is the pedestal upon which biology is built." They further add, "Systematics is a dynamic science. The duties of the taxonomist are never ending.... As long as the plant world exists, there will always be more to learn about plants, plant products and plant taxa, for both practical and theoretical purposes."

The term *taxon,* most probably based on taxonomy, was first used by Adolf Meyer, a German biologist, in 1926 for animal groups. Its use in plant science was proposed by Herman J. Lam in 1948. It was adopted at the seventh International Botanical Congress held in 1950. Taxon means a category or

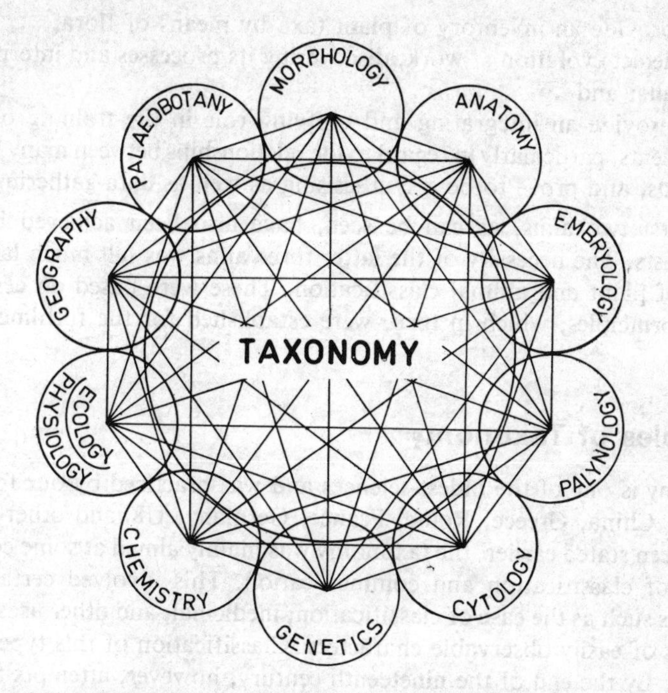

FIG. 1.2 Taxogram showing relationships of various disciplines with taxonomy.

taxonomic group of any rank within the system. It can thus be used to denote a variety, species, genus or any other higher category with equal precision.

Aims of Taxonomy

The three aspects of taxonomic procedure, viz. identification, nomenclature and classification, are included in the aims or purpose of taxonomy. However, there appear to be two main approaches to this science.

1. *The empirical approach:* It is based on practical experience. Observation of facts and characters of organisms ultimately lead to the construction of a basic classification. This is how most of the plants or animals have been classified so far. Keen observation of a large number of characters will obviously facilitate a more acceptable classification.
2. *The interpretative approach:* A classification is constructed in such a way that it can interpret the evolution of a taxon. This is a phylogenetic classification which is rather difficult to achieve in the absence of data from past history of a taxon.

Modern taxonomy attempts to combine these two approaches which can be said to have the following aims:

1. to provide a convenient method of identification and communication;
2. to provide classification which is based on natural affinities of organisms, as far as possible;

3. to provide an inventory of plant taxa by means of flora;
4. to detect evolution at work, discovering its processes and interpreting its results; and
5. to provide an integrating and unifying role in the training of biology students, particularly in regard to the relationships between many biological fields, and prove to be a synthesising as well as data-gathering science.

The first two aims, as can be seen, have also been achieved by earlier taxonomists. The necessity of the latter three aims was felt much later in the history of plant and animal classification. These were based on certain well defined principles, which in turn, were established for the fulfilment of the former.

Principles of Taxonomy

Taxonomy is one of the oldest sciences and was practiced by our forefathers in India, China, Greece, Rome, France, Germany, UK and other countries As has been stated earlier, the taxonomy was mainly aimed at some convenient method of classification and communication. This involved certain simple principles such as the ease of classification, medicinal, and other uses of plants and a set of easily observable characters. Classification of this type is purely *artificial.* By the end of the nineteenth century, however, attempts to classify plants gradually shifted from purely artificial systems to natural or phylogenetic ones. Thus, with the shifting of functions, there has been a change in principles also. It can be said that the principles of taxonomy are concerned primarily with the criteria employed in classification. However, certain *basic* principles have been formulated (Cronquist, 1968a), which are as follows:

1. Taxa are properly established on the basis of multiple correlation of characters.
2. Taxonomic importance of a character is determined by how well it correlates with other characters. This means that the taxonomic importance of a character is determined *a posteriori* rather than *a priori.*
3. An important feature of taxonomy is its predictive value.

The first principle states the importance of correlation of characters. This is probably the most important principle of taxonomy. It implies that no character of a taxon should be considered singly for the establishment of it's relationship with the other taxa but it should always be considered along with other characters. Secondly, the characters chosen should exhibit maximum correlation with other characters. The importance of a character depends upon the degree of correlation. A character with no obvious correlation with other characters is often taken to be an anomalous one and it is usually not taxonomically important. Thus, a zygomorphic flower in Ranunculaceae; only five stamens in Tiliaceae, alternate leaves in Oleaceae, actinomorphic corolla in Scrophulariaceae, simple leaves in Bignoniaceae, and numerous such characters are taken to be anomalous since they are not correlated with other general characters of the taxa. Obviously they are not taxonomically significant.

They may, however, be considered important from their diagnostic point of view, but the relationship must be considered on overall resemblances. Anomalous characters often help in predicting probable relationship of the taxa with other groups where these same characters are considered normal.

Phases of Classification

Classification of a taxon, based on the above principles, is generally achieved in four successive phases, as formulated by Davis and Heywood (1963).

1. *The pioneer (or exploratory) phase:* In this phase, different members of a taxon have to be collected from all over the world (exploration) and identified, at least provisionally.
2. *The consolidation phase:* The plant material is studied in the field as well as in the herbarium and a range of variation is determined in this phase. All the new groups, if invented, are described. Thus a compilation of a flora or a monograph is done.
3. *The biosystematic phase:* This deals with a more thorough knowledge of a taxon based on the first two phases as well as on the geographical variation, cytogenetic studies, physiological features and other population studies. This phase of plant classification has been achieved with great success in certain western countries such as the USA, the UK and others, particularly at and below the generic level. There has been no significant contribution from India in the field of biosystematics. This is mainly because investigation of this nature is painfully slow, requires a team work of specialists and is rather difficult, if not impossible, at higher levels of plant groups.
4. *The encyclopaedic phase:* This is a coordination of the three phases mentioned above.

The first two phases which are mainly descriptive and based on gross morphological features correspond to the ''alpha'' classification by Turrill (1938). In many countries, taxonomic studies have not made even this much progress. Although a large number of floras have been compiled, there are very few monographs worth mentioning. Revisions of certain families have been attempted by some.

The last two phases correspond to the ''omega'' classification by Turrill (1938). The data for these phases are accumulated from researches in the fields, laboratory, garden, herbarium and library and may be analysed with the help of computors. The distinction between alpha and omega classification, according to Davis and Heywood (1963), is one of knowledge. In alpha taxonomy, little is known about the groups of organisms being studied, while in omega taxonomy the groups are more thoroughly studied.

Terminology in Taxonomic Procedure

The three functions of taxonomy, namely, *identification, nomenclature* and *classification* are explained in detail here.

Identification

It is the determination of a taxon based on overall similarities and differences with other taxa. Proper and correct determination of a taxon is a prerequisite for any study based on it. Identification is generally done by comparing a representative specimen of a given taxon with that of another which has been authoritatively predetermined (a direct method) or with the help of keys, descriptions, illustrations, etc. (an indirect method). In most cases, the characters derived from the gross morphology are sufficient for provisional determination of a taxon. Confirmation of such a determination may then be carried out by considering other characters as well. Sometimes, the specimen in question may not agree or compare with the existing predetermined specimen. In such instances it is taken to be new to science. It is the most exciting situation for a student of plant taxonomy to discover a "new" plant. In this process of identification no names are involved.

Nomenclature

It is the naming of a taxon correctly. Once the taxon is determined on the basis of a set of certain dependable characters, it becomes necessary to give it a scientific name. The name, given in accordance with the rules of botanical nomenclature, becomes an effective tool for communication of ideas in respect of the plant group in question. The rules for naming the plants are framed by the International Botanical Congress which meets at regular intervals of five or ten years. A new name is given to a new taxon. Thus, as more and more areas are explored, more and more plants become known to the scientific world and bear new names. These are then added to an already existing list of plants known so far.

Classification

It is highly impossible for any one to study all plants individually that cover the mantle of the globe. It is, therefore, necessary to place them into small or large groups on the basis of their similarities and differences. These groups are then arranged according to their levels into categories in a sequential manner and each category has a name which is in accordance with the rules of nomenclature. Thus, similar individuals may be grouped under a "species", similar species under a "genus", similar genera under a "family", and so on. (These categories are dealt with in more details in Chapter 3.)

It is often easy to refer a single individual or a few plant specimens to their respective species but the difficulties gradually increase as one proceeds from lower categories to the higher or larger ones. This is mainly due to the enormously high number of plant species (approximately 300,000 species of flowering plants) exhibiting a wide array of variability.

There are basically three kinds of classification: ***artificial, natural*** and ***phylogenetic***. These however, are not mutually exclusive but often overlap in practice.

Artificial Classification

When plants are classified for the sake of convenience, using some arbitrary or at least easily observable characters, often irrespective of their affinity, the classification is called artificial. Early systems of classification were mostly artificial. Linnaeus, for instance, used only one attribute, i.e. the number of stamens, for grouping plants into 24 classes. Naturally, his class Monandria includes *Canna* (Cannaceae) as well as *Salicornia* (Chenopodiaceae). Today we know that these two taxa are not at all related and are similar in one respect only. The sexual system of Linnaeus is a good example of artificial classification. A *special* classification is a particular kind of artificial classification in which one or a few attributes of the plant are used to the exclusion of others. All special classifications are designed for a particular purpose, i.e. to show breeding behaviour.

Natural Classification

The theory of evolution proposed by Charles Darwin (1859) postulates that the present day plants have descended from those existing in the ancient past through a series of modifications in response to changing environmental conditions. This means that all plants existing today are related to each other in one way or another. The closely related ones should naturally be grouped together. This is called natural classification. Later pre-Darwinian systems have mostly attempted to be natural in the sense that they are based upon overall resemblances, mostly in gross morphology. It is presumed that larger the number of characters shared by different taxa, more closely are they related to each other. This is the basis of modern classifications. The information needed for arriving at a satisfactory natural classification is now gathered from various sources or disciplines of science mentioned earlier.

Phylogenetic Classification

The classification systems proposed after Darwin's theory, are mostly claimed to be phylogenetic. These are based on known or inferred phylogeny of taxa and are expressed in the form of phylogenetic trees or shrubs showing presumed evolution of the groups. In the case of angiosperms, the phylogeny is nearly always inferred and the phylogenetic classification is usually constructed on the basis of natural classification which in turn is a two-dimensional one. The third dimension, i.e. past history or ancestral history is often presumed on the data available from the remaining two dimensions. Natural classifications are often termed as ***horizontal*** classifications, i.e. based on data available at any one time, while the phylogenetic ones, which rely also on the presumed ancestry, are termed as ***vertical*** classifications. ***Evolutionary*** classification is yet another term usually preferred in place of the phylogenetic one.

The practical value of classification depends on how it stands the test of time. The form of a classification is determined by the purpose for which it is constructed. Therefore, a particular classification may be called better than another only in relation to its purpose. However, the natural classification, since it is multi-character classification, serves the greatest number of purposes. It will therefore be the most generally useful one and be equivalent to what is often called a "general" classification.

In the classification of living organisms, discontinuities serve to distinguish the groups. These are expressed as contrasting characters, e.g. petals present or absent. But it should be noted that these discontinuities do not occur in isolation but are correlated with other characters. The pre-evolutionary concept of these discontinuities presumed them to be special creations. However, it is now well known that they occur due to extinction of certain groups during the course of evolution. Evolutionary divergence has been accompanied by the extinction or survival of the ancestral types. Classification is based on character correlations and discontinuities and cannot cope easily with continuous variation or absence of close correlation.

2

A Review of Pre-Darwinian Classification

Human beings in general are so much dependent on the plant kingdom that people all over the world have been interested in them in some way or the other. Food, clothing and shelter, the three major necessities of human civilisation, are met with by plants alone. They, therefore, have been the subject of various kinds of studies. Medicinal value of plants was recognised as early as the Vedic age. The well known *Atharva Veda,* written around 2000 B.C. contains a wealth of information on medicinal plants and their specific uses. Treatises on medicinal plants had been prepared by the Chinese, Egyptians, Assyrians, Aztecs and others long before the Christian era. But these works do not appear to have had much influence on the modern systems of plant classifications. The systematic account of certain well-defined groups may be found in *Vrikshayurveda* of ancient India, which was compiled by a competent botanist, Parashara. This treatise was the basis of botanical teaching preparatory to medical studies in those days. It deals with the external morphology, nature and properties of soil, description of 14 forest types in India and even the internal structure of leaves, study of cells, etc. Some of these descriptions indicate that Parashara must have had a device such as a microscope of some kind. A system of classification was provided based on a comparative morphology of plants. A large number of families (*ganas*) are also clearly defined as to be easily recognisable today (Majumdar, 1927, 1946).

It appears, however, that due to lack of knowledge of the Sanskrit language, even in this country, the wealth of information compiled by Parashara remains poorly known till today.

On the contrary, the ancient Greek philosophers like Plato, Aristotle, Theophrastus and others, who compiled the principles of plant classification in Greek and Latin (around 400 to 285 B.C.) have been generally credited to be the founders of botany. Theophrastus is considered "the Father of Botany" in the western countries and it is astounding to learn that he did the job of classification by observing a few plants grown in the garden of Lyceum in Athens, and did not travel beyond the walls of the garden!

A review of plant classification from this time onward indicates that the pre-Darwinian systems fall into three main types: systems based on habit, sexual system and systems based on form-relationships.

Systems Based on Habit

The writings of Theophrastus include *Enquiry into Plants* and *The Causes of Plants.* He classified plants on the basis of their habit—Trees, Shrubs, Undershrubs and Herbs and listed about 480 plants in his *Historia Plantarum.* He also distinguished between centripetal (racemose) and centrifugal (cymose) types of inflorescence, superior and inferior ovaries, and polypetalous and gamopetalous corollas.

Similar classification was also given by Pliny (A.D. 23–79) in *Historia Naturalis* (A.D. 77). Better classifications considering certain medicinal properties and usefulness appeared during this time. Dioscorides, a contemporary of Pliny, was a physician and travelled extensively to study plants. His *de Materia Medica* (A.D. 1) includes information on roots, stems, leaves and sometimes flowers of about 600 species of plants. This work was illustrated and served to be one of the most authentic books for Europeans for the next 1500 years.

Albertus Magnus (1193–1280) accepted the classification of Theophrastus in major respects but is credited for determining the differences between monocotyledonous (Corticatae) and dicotyledonous (Tunicatae) seeds for the first time. Tunicate plants were further divided into herbaceous and woody. He named and described garden vegetables in *de Vegetabilis* which was widely read for the next 200 years.

Fifteenth and sixteenth century botany experienced the great general awakening in the field of medicine and classification. This was the period of plant description and illustration. Many of the world famous herbals appeared during these 200 years. This period is sometimes called the Age of Herbals. *Materia Medica* of Dioscorides, which was being used widely for many years, soon became inadequate for identification of plants collected from various parts of the world. The movable-type printing was invented in 1440 in Europe, which aided the compilation of books on medicinal plants (herbals). The authors of these books are called *herbalists.*

Herbarum vivae Eicones, written by Otto Brunfels (1489–1534) which appeared in 3 volumes (1530–1536) is not much valuable from the classification point of view but is well known for illustrations of living plants. Jerome Bock (1498–1554), a contemporary and friend of Brunfels, Leonhart Fuchs (1501–1566), P. Mathiola (1501–1577), the Italian herbalist, Carolus Clusius (1526–1609), Methias de l'Obel (1515–1568), known as the 'father of British botany', John Gerard (1545–1612), an English surgeon and physician and a few others are among the well known herbalists whose contribution to botany of medicinal plants is significant.

The Oriental civilisations like China and India also had their herbals compiled long before the dawn of European botany. *Cheng lei pen ts'ao* written by T'ang Shen wei was printed in 1108 and ran into a dozen editions, the last being printed in 1600. *Pen ts'ao kangmu* by Li Shi Chen (1590) *Pen ts'ao fa hui* by Hsu Yung Cheng (1450) and some others are some of the famous herbals from China.

Attempts of the herbalists referred to above, although commendable in their own way, have been unsuccessful at arrangement of plants into major groups. Thus, the systems adopted by them had very little systematic basis.

It is from the sixteenth and seventeenth centuries onwards that the science of botany developed as an independent discipline. As a result, there were attempts to study more and more plants and a large number of characters in order to arrive at a satisfactory classification.

Andraea Caesalpino (1519–1603), a contemporary of Mathiola, was the first Italian botanist to give a methodical classification of plants based on definite morphological criteria. His famous work, *De Plantis* (1583) contains descriptions of about 1,520 plant species arranged into woody and herbaceous. He also used characters of fruits and seeds. His most important conclusion was that the flowers and fruits were more reliable in classification of plants rather than the habit.

Jean Bauhin (1541–1613) and his brother Gaspard (Caspar) Bauhin attempted their classification in *Historia Plantarum Universalis* (published later in 1650–1651), *Phytopinax* (1596), *Prodrumus theatri botanici* (1620), *Pinax theatri botanici* (1623) and other publications.

The principal advance in taxonomy was made by an Englishman John Ray (1628–1705) who travelled throughout Europe for investigating plants. He closely followed Caesalpino and further formulated a principle that *all parts of the plants* should be considered for classification—a principle now recognised as the cornerstone of a natural system. His *Methodus Plantarum* (1682) and the largest work *Historia Plantarum* (1686–1704) are famous contributions.

He divided the plant kingdom into herbs and trees (after Theophrastus) and further divided herbs into Imperfectae (with mostly non-flowering groups like algae, fungi, ferns, etc.) and Perfectae (the seed plants). Seed plants were further classified into monocotyledons and dicotyledons. In his final system there are 25 classes of dicotyledons and four of the monocotyledons. Some of these groups correspond to the present day families such as Umbelliferae, Verticillatae (Labiatae), Tetrapetalae (mostly Cruciferae), Leguminosae, Staminae (grasses), etc. The work included about 18,000 species.

J.P. de Tournefort (1656–1708) developed an interest in the collection of medicinal plants right from his school days. While working in Paris as a Professor of Botany, he travelled to various parts of Europe to collect plants, and in 1694 he published the *Elements de Botanique* and in 1700, the *Institutiones Rei Herbariae* in which the descriptions of about 698 genera were given. Tournefort was the first to give names as well as descriptions to his genera, many of which were later validated by Linnaeus (e.g. *Betula, Castanea, Fagus, Quercus, Ulmus, Abutilon*). But his system of classification is in many respects inferior to that of John Ray.

The Sexual System

The gradual accumulation of plant material by the eighteenth century posed a serious problem as regards their identification. This situation was faced by a Swedish botanist, Carolus Linnaeus (1707–78), often named as Carl von Linne. He had tremendous enthusiasm and took it as his mission to record the works of the Creator.

By the end of the seventeenth century, Rudolf Jacob Camerarius experimentally proved sexuality in plants (1694). Linnaeus became acquainted with the functions of stamens as male organs and he considered this as the most important character to classify plants. He could note constancy in their number in various groups and constructed his basically arithmetical, so-called Sexual System of classification (Stearn, 1960). The era of systems based on habit, thus came to an end. While working in the University of Uppsala as a student under the guidance of Dr. Rudbeck, he published in 1729 his first paper on sexuality of plants. Subsequently, he published an enumeration of plants in the Uppsala Botanic Garden (*Hortus Uplandicus,* 1730). In this list, the plants were arranged according to the system of Tournefort. However, the number of plants in the garden soon exceeded in kinds and could not be classified readily by Tournefort's system. In the revised edition of *Hortus Uplandicus* (1732) the plants were classified according to a system of his own. This served as a basis for his later publications such as *Systema Naturae* (1735), which provided the foundation for the classification of all plants and animals including minerals, *Critica Botanica* (1737a), *Flora Lapponica* (1737b), *Hortus Cliffortianus* (1737c) and his famous *Genera Plantarum* (1737d). This latter work is of importance in modern taxonomy as a source of descriptions of 935 genera. It was published in five editions plus two supplements called *Mantissae* and in all a total of 1336 genera were diagnosed. These were grouped into 24 classes which were almost entirely based on the number and morphological arrangement of their stamens. Following is an outline of classes of the Linnean system of classification:

Class 1. Monandria—Stamen one—*Canna, Salicornia*
" 2. Diandria—Stamens two—*Olea, Veronica*
" 3. Triandria—Stamens three—many grasses
" 4. Tetrandria—Stamens four—*Protea, Galium*
" 5. Pentandria—Stamens five—*Ipomoea, Campanula*
" 6. Hexandria—Stamens six—*Narcissus, Lilium*
" 7. Heptandria—Stamens seven—*Trientalis, Aesculus*
" 8. Octandria—Stamens eight—*Vaccinium, Dirca*
" 9. Enneandrial—Stamens nine—*Laurus, Butomus*
" 10. Decandria—Stamens ten—*Rhododendron, Oxalis*
" 11. Dodecandria—Stamens 11-19—*Asarum, Euphorbia*
" 12. Icosandria—Stamens 20 or more on the calyx—*Opuntia*
" 13. Polyandria—Stamens 20 or more on the receptacle—*Ranunculus*
" 14. Didynamia—Stamens didynamous—many Labiatae
" 15. Tetradynamia—Stamens tetradynamous—*Brassica*
" 16. Monadelphia—Stamens monadelphous—Malvaceae members
" 17. Diadelphia—Stamens diadelphous—legumes
" 18. Polyadelphia—Stamens polyadelphous—*Theobroma, Hypericum*
" 19. Syngenesia—Stamens syngenesious—many composites
" 20. Gynandria—Stamens united to the gynoecium—Orchids
" 21. Monoecia—Plants monoecious—*Carex, Morus*
" 22. Dioecia—Plants dioecious—*Salix, Juniperous*
" 23. Polygamia—Plants polygamous—*Acer, Nyssa*
" 24. Cryptogamia—Flowerless plants—*Pteris. Agaricus,* Lichen

Since only one or two characters were chosen, the system was simple and convenient. Many botanists during that time were mainly interested in listing plants and were obviously greatly influenced by this system. However, this cannot be considered to show natural affinities of plants, as admitted by Linnaeus himself.

While working in the University of Uppsala as a professor of botany and medicine, he published his *Species Plantarum* (1753) in which he diagnosed nearly 6000 species in 1000 genera. This work is considered to be the most important in the botanical world.

The most significant contribution of Linnaeus to botany was a new and precise system of naming plants. Linnaeus gave the generic name and a trivial name to each plant plus a polynomial description (intended by Linnaeus as a specific name), references to previous publications or his herbarium specimens and the region where the plant was found. The use of a trivial name was so convenient that the combination of a generic and trivial name came to be generally used and ultimately resulted in the establishment of the *binomial system* of nomenclature. Linnaeus was not the first to use binomials but he used them consistently. In fact, the binomial nomenclature consisting of a generic and specific (trivial) epithet was founded by Gaspard (Caspar) Bauhin, more than a century before its use by Linnaeus. But obviously there was no consistency in Bauhin's work in application of binomials. Linnaeus followed it carefully throughout his *Species Plantarum*. This is the reason why the book *Species Plantarum* and the date 1st May, 1753 have been chosen by the modern botanists as a starting point of the present day botanical nomenclature.

Linnaeus had a large number of enthusiastic students who set out to explore the world. He died in 1778 and his collections were sold by his widow to an English botanist, J.E. Smith. Later, these became the property of the Linnean Society of London, founded in 1788.

Species Plantarum underwent repeated revisions and remained the most important system of classification until the beginning of the nineteenth century. The fifth edition was revised by Karl Ludwig Willdenow (1765–1812), the Director of Berlin Botanical Garden (1801–1812), who included a large number of plant species from all over the world and published it in four large volumes.

After acquainting ourselves with the Sexual System and works of Linnaeus, let us try to understand his philosophy and concepts. Cain (1958, 1959a) and Hopwood (1959) have shown that Linnaeus was brought up in the tradition of Aristotalian philosophy. He classified plants by using two principles:

1. logical division (the rules of dichotomy—the given character or object is present or absent) following Theophrastus; and
2. certain *a priori* reasoning employing functional organs of the plants. He considered reproductive structures like the stamen to be the most important. Stearn (1959) has, however, pointed out that there was a conflict in the mind of Linnaeus in his choice of *a priori* reasoning and modern empirical approach. His problem was: (i) should things be put together because they conform to a definition already framed or, vice versa separated because they do not do so, irrespective of other resemblances

and differences, or (ii) should they be linked to things with which they agree in their characteristics generally, despite lack of agreement with the definition? Linnaeus followed the first course, thus achieving an artificial system. At the same time he delimited some of his taxa following natural affinities.

This conflict of approaches continues even in modern taxonomy. Certain groups are classified by definitions, irrespective of their natural affinities while certain others are classified on the basis of an empirical approach. Linnaeus considered genus to be the basic unit of classification and the genera were grouped into classes and orders. He also divided them into species. He was of the opinion that botanists should be able to memorise the characters and names of all genera. Although his generic description was based on a single species, he must have thought of genera as groups of related species. He firmly believed that it is the genus that gives the characters, and not vice versa. Thus his genera were well defined and mostly natural.

Linnaeus did not take his Sexual System very rigidly and quite often included species within a genus which did not agree with his original definition of it. He recognised plants by their general facies and technical characters were used by way of confirmation. This policy accounts for the naturalness of many of his genera.

According to Linnean concept, species were static entities, monotypic, genetically unitary (i.e. true breeding) and equivalent. He recognised variation within species, but believed it to be due to soil or climate, i.e. phenotypic. In his later life, however, Linnaeus modified his views and maintained that many species and genera had arisen by hybridization. But this concept of Linnaeus has been largely neglected. He believed that the best classification would bring together those plants that were essentially alike. He realised that his Sexual System was artificial and in 1738 made his first attempt at natural classification in his *Classes Plantarum*. In the sixth edition of his *Genera Plantarum* (1764) he proposed 58 natural orders with their included genera, many of which correspond to modern families (Palmae, Gramineae, Umbelliferae, Compositae, etc.). He retained the Sexual System, only for its practical value of identification.

There are obvious deficiencies in the work of Linnaeus. His Sexual System is artificial and his species concept inferior to that of John Ray. Although floral parts were emphasised in the descriptions, vegetative parts were largely neglected. This retarded the development of a natural system.

His achievements, however, outweigh these limitations. He put the nomenclature of the past in order; provided a practical way of identifying all plants known at that time, delimited mostly natural species and a few genera being very accurate in his description of floral parts, firmly established the binomial system of nomenclature, and provided taxonomy with a more exact technical terminology. He instilled great enthusiasm in his students, many of whom made valuable collections and became leading botanists in their own right.

A Brief History of Plant Exploration

With a convenient tool such as a Sexual System in hand a large number of enthusiastic students of Linnaeus set out to explore the plant kingdom. Many others also were influenced by the easy method of plant identification and nomenclature and went out collecting plants in different parts of the world. Certain others had already developed an interest in medicinal plants. Thus, there was an outbreak, so to say, of plant explorers in the New as well as in the Old World.

Hans Sloane (1660–1753) from England was probably the first man to move out of his country to distant parts of the globe for plant collection. His *Catalogue Plantarum* (1696) contains 800 species new to science. Mark Catesby (1679-1749), also from England, explored parts of America and published the *Natural History of Carolina, Florida and the Bahama Islands* in two volumes (1731, 1743) and an appendix (1748) to it.

It was about this time that another great botanist George Eberhard Rumpf, (popularly known as Rumphius, 1628-1702) was engaged in the rich tropical flora of Indonesia. He explored the riches of the Island of Amboina between 1653 and 1670. However, most of his collections and illustrations were destroyed in a fire. Even the manuscript he had compiled got lost. A reconstructed manuscript was published by J. Burmann as the *Herbarium Amboinense* (1741–1755). It contains descriptions of about 1,750 species out of which 1,060 were illustrated.

The enthusiastic apostles of Linnaeus include Christopher Ternstrom, who set out for the East Indies, Peter Kalm who selected North America, Fredrik Hasselquist, who left for Palestine, Petrus Loefling who went out to Spain, Peter Forskal, who went to Egypt and Arabia and discovered about 100 new species and 30 new genera, and Carl Peter Thunberg, who went to the Cape of Good Hope and described many new species in his *Prodrumus Plantarum Capensium* (1794–1800) and *Flora Japonica* (1784).

Many other naturalists joined John Ellis and Peter Collinson on the ship *Endeavour*, commanded by Lt. James Cook and accompanied by Daniel Solander and Sir Joseph Banks in 1768. This team of naturalists after three years of exploration made some marvellous scientific discoveries. They also brought a vast collection of plant specimens.

A large number of botanists explored North America and the huge collections made by them were determined by the great botanists, John Torrey (1796–1873) and Asa Gray (1810–1888), who were also responsible for the publication of monumental works like *A Flora of North America* (1838–1842), *Synoptical Flora of North America (1878), and Manual of Botany (1848),* the 8th edition of which appeared in 1950.

South America, which was under the control of Spain and Portugal, was explored by several investigators such as Joseph de Jussieu, J.C. Mutis, Hipolito Ruiz, Jose Pavon, Alexander von Humboldt, Richard Spruce, Karl Friedrich Philip von Martius and others. Many important publications came out as a result of their explorations, some of which include Ruiz and Pavon's *Florae Peruvianae et Chilensis* (1798–1802), Humboldt, Bonpland and Kunth's *Nova Genera et Species Plantarum* (1788–1850), and Martius's *Flora Brasiliensis* (1829–1906), which accounts for 22,767 species and 3,805 plates in 20,000 pages.

Tropical Africa was explored by Michel Adanson (1727–1806), who published the *Histoire naturelle de Senegal* in 1757 and *Famille des Plantes* in 1763. Other botanists who explored Africa were Friedrich Martin Josef Welwitsch (1807–1872), William Paterson (1755–1810), William John Burchell (1782–1863) and a few others.

Lt. James Cook, Sir Joseph Banks, Daniel Solander and others made several trips to Australia for collection of plants. Other explorers of Australia include Sir Thomas Mitchell, von Muller and George Bentham.

The European botanists also came to India and in fact, they are mainly responsible for the development of plant science in this country.

Juan de Loureiro (1715–1769), Karl Ludwig Blume (1796–1862), Sir Stanford Raffles (1781–1826), Dr. Joseph Arnold, Pierre Sonnerat (1745–1814) and E.D. Merrill are some of the most well known botanists who contributed to the study of botany in Southeastern Asia. China also was intensively explored by a large number of plant explorers who contributed significantly to the knowledge of plant science. Various other botanists were engaged in other parts of the world in exploration, description and publication during the seventeenth and eighteenth century.

The wealth of plant material collected by these botanists could not be identified satisfactorily with the help of Linnaeus's Sexual System and its replacement by a better system was urgently felt. This resulted in the development of still better systems (but this time based on form-relationships) in the following century.

Systems Based on Form-Relationships

Michel Adanson (1727–1806) while exploring the plant wealth in Africa, realised the inadequacy of the Linnean system and developed his own system in *Familles des Plantes* (1763). He rejected all artificial systems in favour of a natural one. His groupings are equivalent to the modern orders and families.

Bernard de Jussieu, a contemporary of Linnaeus, was not satisfied with the sexual system and tried to improve it but never published it. His nephew, Antonie Laurent (1748–1836) published his uncle's system, with some improvements, in *Genera Plantarum* (1789). This book may be said to have marked the beginning of the natural systems of classification. In this book all plants were classified into hundred orders which are equivalent to many of the modern families. A solitary class of cryptograms and 14 classes of flowering plants were recognised as follows:

1. Acotyledons — Fungi, Algae, Musci

Monocotyledons

2. Stamina hypogyna — Cyperoideae, Gramineae
3. Stamina perigyna — *Lilia, Narcissus,* Iridales
4. Stamina epigyna — Musae, Orchideae, Dicotyledons

Apetalae

5. Stamina epigyna — Aristolochiae
6. Stamina perigyna — Proteae, Lauri, Polygoneae
7. Stamina hypogyna — Amaranthi, Nyctagines

Monopetalae

8. Corolla hypogyna — Labiatae, Solaneae, Borragineae
9. Corolla perigyna — Rhododendra, Ericae

Corolla epigyna

10. Antheris connatis — Cichoraceae
11. Antheris distinctis — Rubiaceae

Polypetalae

12. Stamina epigyna — Araliae, Umbelliferae
13. Stamina hypogyna — Ranunculaceae, Cruciferae
14. Stamina perigyna — Rosaceae, Leguminosae
15. Diclines irregularis — Amentaceae, Coniferae

Augustin Pyrame de Candolle (1778–1841) further developed the system of A.L. de Jussieu in his *Theorie Elementaire de la Botanique* (1813) in which expressed his approach to plant classification. He introduced the term *Taxonomy* to designate the theory of plant classification. His monumental work, *Prodrumus Systematis Naturalis Regni Vegetabilis* began in 1824 and during his lifetime published seven volumes of it. Ten more volumes were published by others after his death. It was his intention to classify and describe every known species of vascular plants. The plan of his system published in 1819 was:

I. Vasculares (Vascular plants with cotyledons)
  Class 1: Exogenae (vascular bundles in a ring, dicotyledons)
    A. Diplochlamydeae (both calyx and corolla present)
      a. Thalamiflorae (polypetalous, hypogynous)
        Orders 1–46 including Ranunculaceae, Cruciferae, Malvaceae, etc.
      b. Calyciflorae (perigynous or epigynous, polypetalus or sympetalous)
        Orders 47–84 including Rosaceae, Leguminosae, etc.
      c. Corolliflorae (gamopetalous, hypogynous)
        Orders 85–108 including Primulaceae, Labiatae, etc.
    B. Monochlamydeae (calyx only present)
      Orders 109–128 including Chenopodiaceae, Coniferae, etc.
  Class 2: Endogenae (vascular bundles scattered, monocotyledons)
    A. Phanerogamae (flowers present)
      Orders 129–150 including Liliaceae, Iridaceae, Orchidaceae, etc.
    B. Cryptogamae (flowers absent, hidden or unknown)
      Orders 151–155 including Ferns, etc.

II. Cellulares (Plants without vascular bundles or cotyledons)
  Class 1: Foliaceae (leafy, sexuality known)
    Orders 156, 157 as mosses, Liverworts
  Class 2: Aphyllae (not leafy, sexuality unknown)
    Orders 158–161 as Algae, Fungi, Lichens, etc.

It should be noted that ferns were considered as a coordinate group with the monocotyledons and gymnosperms were included among the dicotyledons.

Candolle's son, Alphonse de Candolle (1806–1893) published the rest of the ten volumes of *Prodrumus* with the help of specialists, and in the last edition of *Theorie Elementaire* (1844) included 213 families. The *Prodrumus included* descriptions of 58, 975 species of dicotyledons and gymnosperms known at that time.

The families were arranged in a linear sequence starting from the polypetalous (Ranunculaceae)—gamopetalous—apetalous groups. According to Davis and Heywood (1963), "the lucky choice of Ranalian group as the starting point in linear sequence of the families had done much to popularise the systems ...." The Candolle system dominated plant taxonomy until 1860, despite the fact that more than two dozen systems were proposed during the period 1825–1845.

George Bentham (1800–1884) and Sir Joseph Dalton Hooker (1817–1911) presented their system in a three-volume work in Latin, entitled *Genera Plantarum* between 1862 and 1883. Bentham was a well-trained and very critical botanist who gave full-time attention to botany. Hooker, who was Director of the Royal Botanic Gardens at Kew, was more a plant explorer and phytogeographer than was Bentham.

Genera Plantarum includes names, descriptions and the classification of all the seed plants known at that time (about 97,205 species), arranged according to Bentham and Hooker's system. It was patterned directly on the system developed by de Candolle who was a close friend of Bentham but differed in many respects from the latter. Every genus known to the authors was described in details with the help of the material in the British and Continental herbaria. Thus a firsthand, accurate information in respect of all the genera was provided. The larger genera were further divided into subgenera and sections. The term "family" of the modern systematists was designated as Order and the term "Order" was named as Cohor or Cohort.

The system has some refinements over that of de Candolle, namely the erection of a new series Disciflorae in their Polypetalae and its incorporation between the Thalamiflorae and the Calyciflorae, revision of the apetalous taxa, etc. The gymnosperms were treated as the third taxon, collateral with and placed between the dicotyledons and monocotyledons. Various genera grouped under "Orders" and different Orders under "Cohors" were based on the overall similarities and differences. Certain Orders which could not be satisfactorily placed by them in any Cohort, were treated as anomalous orders (Ordines anomali). This clearly indicates that Bentham and Hooker attempted at a Natural Classification of seed plants taking into consideration all the data available to them.

The system was accepted throughout the British Empire, the United States and India and certain Asiatic countries but was not popular with some of the continental botanists. It has been retained in the British and Indian herbaria. Many of the British and Indian botanists have followed this system in the Floras compiled by them.

All seed plants were classified into 3 classes, 3 sub-classes, 21 series, 25 cohorts and 202 orders. Originally it was designed to include 200 orders and each order was given a definite number. Orders Vochysiaceae and the Cyrilleae were incorporated later. These were not given separate numbers but were included as 20a and 46a respectively. Rendle (1904) has altered these numbers but the original numbers have been accepted in all the herbaria where this system is adopted. Following is the synopsis of Bentham and Hooker's system of classification.

I. Class: *Dicotyledons*

A. Subclass:— Polypetalae (Corolla of separate petals. Orders 1–82, 20a and 46a)

Series 1: **Thalamiflorae** (Stamens hypogynous and usually many. Orders 1–33 and 20a)

Cohort 1: Ranales (Gynoecium usually apocarpous)

Orders–1. Ranunculaceae
2. Dilleniaceae
3. Calycanthaceae
4. Magnoliaceae
5. Anonaceae
6. Menispermaceae
7. Berberidaceae
8. Nymphaeaceae

Cohort 2: Parietales (Placentation parietal)

Orders– 9. Serraceniaceae
10. Papaveraceae
11. Cruciferae
12. Capparidaceae
13. Resedaceae
14. Cistineae
15. Violaceae
16. Canellaceae
17. Bixineae

Cohort 3: Polygalineae (Ovary 2 locular)

Orders– 18. Pittosporeae
19. Tremendreae
20. Polygaleae
20a. Vochysiaceae

Cohort 4: Caryophyllineae (Placentation free-central or axile)

Orders– 21. Frankaniaceae
22. Caryophylleae
23. Portulaceae
24. Tamariscineae

Cohort 5: Guttiferales (Stamens many, sepals imbricate)

Orders– 25. Elatineae
26. Hypericineae
27. Guttiferae
28. Ternstroemiaceae
29. Dipterocarpeae
30. Chlaenaceae

Cohort 6: Malvales (Stamens many, sepals valvate)

Orders– 31. Malvaceae
32. Sterculiaceae
33. Tiliaceae

Series 2. Disciflorae (Hypogynous disc often present, stamens definite, as many as or twice the number of petals. Orders 34–53 and 46a)

Cohort 7: Geraniales (Androecium obdiplostemonous, ovules pendulous, raphe ventral)

Orders– 34. Lineae

35. Humariaceae
36. Malpighiaceae
37. Zygophyllaceae
38. Geraniaceae
39. Rutaceae
40. Simarubeae
41. Ochnaceae
42. Burseraceae
43. Meliaceae
44. Chailletiaceae

Cohort 8: Olacales (Androecium diplostemonous, ovules pendulous, raphe dorsal)

Orders– 45. Olacineae
46. Ilicineae
46a. Cyrillaceae

Cohort 9: Celastrales (Androecium haplostemonous, ovules erect, raphe ventral)

Orders– 47. Celastrineae
48. Stackhousieae
49. Rhamneae
50. Ampelideae

Cohort 10: Sapindales (Androecium diplostemonous, ovules ascending, raphe ventral or inverted)

Orders– 51. Sapindaceae
52. Sabiaceae
53. Anacardiaceae

Ordines anomali– 54. Coriareae
55. Moringeae

Series 3: Calyciflorae (Sepals united, stamens peri- or epigynous. Orders 56–82)

Cohort 11: Rosales (Stamens indefinite, often twice or more the number of petals, styles distinct)

Orders– 56. Connaraceae
57. Leguminosae
58. Rosaceae
59. Saxifrageae
60. Crassulaceae
61. Droseraceae
62. Hamamelideae
63. Bruniaceae

Orders– 64. Halorageae

Cohort 12 : Myrtales (Stamens, definite, rarely, indefinite, flowers perigynous or epigynous)

65. Rhizophoreae
66. Combretaceae
67. Myrtaceae
68. Melastomaceae
69. Lythrarieae
70. Onagrarieae

Cohort 13: Passiflorales (Placentation parietal)

Orders– 71. Samydaceae
72. Loaseae
73. Turneraceae
74. Passifloreae
75. Cucurbitaceae
76. Begoniaceae
77. Datisceae

Cohort 14: Ficoidales (Perianth undifferentiated, ovules on axile or basal placentas)

Orders– 78. Cacteae
79. Ficoideae

Cohort 15: Umbellales (Inflorescence umbellate)

Orders– 80. Umbelliferae
81. Araliaceae
82. Cornaceae

B. Subclass: Gamopetalae (Corolla of united petals. Orders 83–127)

Series 4: Inferae (Stamens as many as petals and alternating with them, ovary inferior. Orders 83–91)

Cohort 16: Rubiales (Stamens epipetalous, anthers distinct, ovary 2–many locular, locules 1-many ovuled)

Orders– 83. Caprifoliaceae
84. Rubiaceae

Cohort 17: Asterales (Stamens epipetalous, anthers distinct or united, ovary 1 locular, 1-ovuled)

Orders– 85. Valerianeae
86. Dipsaceae
87. Calycereae
88. Compositae

Cohort 18: Campanales (Stamens not adnate to corolla, ovary 2–6 locular, locules many ovuled)

Orders– 89. Stylideae
90. Goodenoveae
91. Campanulaceae

Series 5 : Heteromerae (Stamens as many as corolla lobes or many, ovary superior or inferior, carpels more than 2, generally isomerous with the corolla lobes. Orders 92 - 103)

Conort 19: Ericales (Stamens twice as many as corolla lobes or isomerous and alternating with them)

Orders– 92. Vacciniaceae
93. Ericaceae
94. Monotropeae
95. Epacrideae
96. Diapensiaceae
97. Lennoaceae

Cohort 20: Primulales (Stamens as many as corolla lobes and opposite them, ovary 1 locular)

Orders– 98: Plumbagineae
99. Primulaceae
100. Myrsineae

Cohort 21: Ebenales (Stamens as many as corolla lobes and opposite them or many, ovary 2–many locular)

Orders– 101. Sapotaceae
102. Ebenaceae
103. Styraceae

Series 6: Bicarpellatae (Stamens as many as corolla lobes and alternating with them or fewer, ovary mostly bicarpellary and superior. Orders 104–126)

Cohort 22: Gentianales (Corolla actinomorphic, leaves mostly opposite)

Orders– 104. Oleaceae
105. Salvadoraceae
106. Apocynaceae
107. Asclepiadaceae
108. Loganiaceae
109. Gentianaceae

Cohort 23: Polemoniales (Corolla actinomorphic, leaves mostly alternate)

Orders– 110. Polemoniaceae
111. Hydrophyllaceae
112. Boraginaceae
113. Convolvulaceae
114. Solanaceae

Cohort 24: Personales (Corolla zygomorphic, posterior stamen often reduced to staminode, ovules often more than 4)

Orders– 115. Scrophulariaceae
116. Orobanchaceae
117. Lentibulariaceae
118. Columelliaceae
119. Gesneriaceae
120. Bignoniaceae
121. Pedaliaceae
122. Acanthaceae

Cohort 25: Lamiales (Corolla zygomorphic, posterior stamen reduced, ovules 4)

Orders– 123. Myoporineae
124. Selagineae
125. Verbenaceae
126. Labiatae

Ordo anomalous– 127. Plantagineae

C. Subclass: Monochlamydeae (Perianth 1 or two seriate, mostly sepaloid, minute or absent. Orders 128–163)

Series 7: Curvembryeae (Seeds mostly with mealy endosperm, embryo curved, lateral or peripheral; ovary mostly one ovuled)

Orders– 128. Nyctagineae
129. Illecebraceae
130. Amaranthaceae
131. Chenopodiaceae
132. Phytolaccaceae
133. Batideae
134. Polygonaceae

Series 8: Multiovulatae aquaticae (Immersed aquatic herbs, ovary syncarpous, many ovuled)

Order– 135. Podostemaceae

Series 9: Multiovulatae terrestris (Terrestrial herbs, ovary syncarpous, many ovuled)

Orders– 136. Nepenthaceae
137. Cytineae
138. Aristolochiaceae

Series 10: Micrembryeae (Carpels 1–2 ovuled, ovules with copious endosperm and minute embryo)

Orders– 139. Piperaceae
140. Chloranthaceae
141. Myristiceae
142. Monimiaceae

Series 11: Daphnales (Ovary monocarpellary, rarely syncarpous and 2–4 ovuled, plants woody or herbaceous, perianth mostly sepaloid, stamens perigynous)

Orders– 143. Laurineae
144. Proteaceae
145. Thymelaeaceae
146. Penaeaceae
147. Elaeagnaceae

Series 12: Achlamydosporeae (Ovary 1 locular, 1–3 ovuled, seeds endospermic, without testa)

Orders– 148. Loranthaceae
149. Santalaceae
150. Balanophoreae

Series 13: Unisexuals (Flowers strictly unisexual or polygamous)

Orders– 151. Euphorbiaceae
152. Balanopseae
153. Urticaceae
154. Platanaceae
155. Leitnerieae
156. Juglandaceae
157. Myricaceae
158. Casuarinaceae
159. Cupuliferae

Series 14: Ordines anomali–
160. Salicineae
161. Lacistemaceae
162. Empetraceae
163. Ceratophyllaceae

Gymnospermae–

Orders– 164. Gnetaceae
165. Coniferae
166. Cycadaceae

II. Class–*Monocotyledons*

Series 15: Microspermae (Inner perianth petaloid, ovary inferior, seeds minute, numerous)

Orders– 167. Hydrocharitaceae
168. Burmanniaceae
169. Orchideae

Series 16: Epigynae (Inner perianth petaloid, ovary inferior, ovules large and few to many)

Orders– 170. Scitamineae
171. Bromeliaceae
172. Haemodoraceae
173. Irideae
174. Amaryllideae
175. Taccaceae
176. Dioscoreaceae

Series 17: Coronarieae (Inner perianth petaloid, ovary free)

Orders– 177. Roxburghiaceae
178. Liliaceae
179. Pontederiaceae
180. Philydraceae
181. Xyridaceae
182. Mayaceae
183. Commelinaceae
184. Rapataceae

Series 18: Calycinae (Inner perianth sepaloid, rigid or herbaceous)

Orders– 185. Flagellariaceae
186. Juncaceae
187. Palmae

Series 19: Nudiflorae (Perianth absent or reduced)

Orders– 188. Pandaneae
189. Cyclanthaceae
190. Typhaceae
191. Araceae
192. Lemnaceae

Series 20: Apocarpae (Perianth 1–2 seriate or absent, carpel solitary or gynoecium apocarpous, seeds non-endospermic)

Orders– 193. Triuridaceae
194. Alismaceae
195. Naiadaceae

Series 21: Glumaceae (Flowers in dense inflorescences subtended by bracts or glumes, perianth reduced, glumaceous or absent, ovary or locules 1-ovuled)

Orders– 196. Eriocauleae
197. Centrolepideae
198. Restiaceae
199. Cyperaceae
200. Gramineae

The pre-Darwinian systems were based on the dogma that the species are special creations and therefore constant and immutable. Charles Darwin was a close friend of Hooker, and both Bentham and Hooker had a knowledge of the theory of evolution. In fact, Hooker was inclined to reorganise the whole system on the basis of this theory but was objected to by Bentham who did not accept the essentials of Darwin's work. Although the publication of the *Origin of Species* was earlier to that of the above system, the latter remained pre-evolutionary in concept.

3 Hierarchy of Categories in Plant Classification

It has already been pointed out that there was appreciable improvement in plant classification at the hands of the Bauhin brothers in the sixteenth century. The younger of the two, Gaspard (Casper), published a few books, the most important of which is *Pinax* (1623). In this book, Bauhin fully recognised the distinction between genera and species, a distinction which was lacking in the earlier works. Thus it can be said that this was the beginning of recognition of smaller (species) and larger (genus) groups of plant classification. Linnaeus (1737d) provided descriptions to the genera and indicated the species with trivial names included under each genus. Bernard de Jussieu and his nephew A.L. de Jussieu (1789) may be credited with the recognition of still larger groups—orders—which are equivalent to families in the present-day classification.

As more and more areas were explored and a tremendously large number of plant species were collected during the subsequent two centuries, the grouping of plants into still larger groups was felt necessary. Later taxonomists have recognised several groups at various levels and with the recent studies of the living populations of plants, several smaller groups have come into being.

The different levels of groups so produced are recognised as a series of hierarchical *categories*. This series has been termed as a taxonomic structure (Mason, 1950). Categories are the levels or ranks in a hierarchy to which groups are assigned. It should be clearly understood that categories are defined by taxonomists and thus are purely artificial. They are subjective and have no basis in reality. Blackwelder (1962) states that they are arbitrarily chosen before groups are assigned to them. Categories can be defined only by their position relative to other categories. The groups placed in the categories on the other hand, represent discrete sets of organisms in nature and thus are objective or non-arbitrary.

Species, genus, family, etc., are the names given to both levels (categories) as well as groups (taxa). Thus a group placed at the genus-level is called a genus, at the species-level, a species, and so on.

Groups that are more inclusive are considered to be at a higher level than those which are less inclusive or at a lower level. The level of the category is obviously decided by the level of groups included under it. It is important to note that a plant may be a member of several taxonomic groups (taxa), each of which is assigned a taxonomic category, but is not *itself* a member of any taxonomic category—plants are not classified into categories but into groups. A taxon such as a species, for instance, belongs to a genus and to a family etc but it can be a member of only one category, i.e. species. The common characters of all members of the groups placed at a lower category provide the characters of group of a category immediately above it. The similar or common characters of a group of species, for example, provide characters of a genus and common characters of genera provide characters of a family and so on. Consequently, the higher a group is placed in the hierarchy, the fewer will be the characters shared by all the subordinate units. A taxon can have only a few characters that are distinct from the other taxa of the same or higher rank. At higher levels of the hierarchy, no single character may be diagnostic. The family, for example, can be distinguished from other families, not by a single diagnostic character, but by a combination of many characters, all of which may not apply to any single individual.

In short it can be said that the *taxonomic group* is any assemblage of individuals or small discrete groups sharing some common characters. Taxonomic *category* is a level or *rank* assigned to that group. Taxonomic *unit* may be defined as any group of individuals sharing a maximum number of characters among them and exhibiting the greatest continuity of characters within them. At the same time, it is discontinuous from any other group in respect of those characters. *Species* therefore, are taken to be basic units of classification in taxonomic procedures, while *ecotypes* are considered to be basic units in biosystematic studies.

Each category represents a group of plants but no one of these is defined in a strict manner. Their delimitation or circumscription varies and each is subjective in character. The categories of higher level such as Division, Class, Order, etc. are referred to as the *major* categories while those at lower level such as species, variety, etc. are called the *minor* categories. A minor category may be considered to be one whose name is also a part of the name of a particular taxon. A major category, on the other hand, may bear any name which is not a part of the name of the plant included under it.

In the first chapter of *International Code of Botanical Nomenclature* (1961), Article 2 states, "Every individual plant is treated as belonging to a number of taxa of consecutively subordinate ranks, among which the rank of species is basic", and Article 3 indicates *species, genus, family, order, class* and *division* as principal ranks of taxa in the ascending sequence. The number of ranks can be increased by adding the prefix *sub* to the terms denoting the ranks or by introducing supplementary terms, e.g. subspecies, subgenus, subfamily, etc. or super class, infra class and so on.

The Plant Kingdom or *Regnum Vegetabile* is further divisible into the following subordinate ranks—divisio (division), subdivisio (subdivision), classis (class), subclassis (subclass), ordo (Order), subordo (suborder) familia (family), subfamilia (subfamily), tribus (tribe), subtribus (subtribe), genus, subgenus, sectio (section), series, subseries, species, subspecies, varietas (variety), subvarietas (subvariety), forma, subforma, and a few more. These are arranged in a descending manner from higher to lower categories. Article 5 states that this relative order of ranks must not be altered.

Major Categories

The term "Divisio" or Division has been prescribed by the rules to represent the category of the highest magnitude within the plant kingdom while a more or less equivalent term "phylum" is prescribed for the animals. Some authors (Hutchinson, 1926; Tippo, 1942) have used this latter term for plant groups as well. The number of divisions within the plant kingdom is rather variable. Eichler (1883), for example, grouped all plants known to him into five divisions while Engler and Prantl (1887–1915) have as many as 14 major divisions in their system. All seed plants are generally grouped under one division—Spermatophyta—which is characterised by the dominant sporophytic generation and presence of ovules that develop into seeds. The closely related divisions may have originated either from a common ancestor or different ones and therefore the boundaries between them may not always be sharp. The ending for the name of a division has been recommended as *phyta* (Pteridophyta, Bryophyta, etc.).

A division may be further divided into two or more subdivisions or this latter category may altogether be dropped and it may be composed of two or more classes. The division Spermatophyta is often divided into two subdivisions, Gymnospermae and Angiospermae. But other divisions such as Pteridophyta are considered to be composed of no subdivisions but directly classes. The recommended ending for the name of a subdivision is *phytina* (Pterophytina).

Class is the next category subordinate in rank to division. The names applied to classes are Latin as for all other categories and ordinarily have the ending *-opsida* (Pteropsida) or *-ae* (Magnoliatae, Angiospermae, etc.). The subdivision Angiospermae is composed of two classes, monocotyledons and dicotyledons. The class may be further divided into subclasses just as dicotyledons are divided into Polypetalae, Gamopetalae and Monochlamydeae. There has been no strict rule in the selection of names applied to this category but an ending *-opsideae* has been recommended. Some of the authors have added categories such as super class, infra class, etc. (c.f. Takhtajan, 1969; Treub, 1975; Dahlgren, 1975 and Thorne, 1976).

The class or subclass may include one or more orders. This category is the next in line and subordinate to that of class. The use of this term in lieu of the term Family, as adopted by certain earlier authors (Bentham & Hooker, 1862–1883), is taken to be illegitimate by the rules of Nomenclature. The names of orders have the ending *-ales* and are generally based on one of the constituent families, e.g. Malvales, Rosales, etc. However, some of the earlier names of orders, adopted before the existence of currently accepted rules of Nomenclature, do not have such an ending but instead have it as *-ae* (e.g. Polygalineae, Caryophyllineae, Centrospermae, Tubiflorae, etc.). Since these names are old and in long use, they have been allowed, but for those who wish to follow the rules strictly, alternative names have been provided, such as, Polygalales, Caryophyllales, etc. An order is considered to be more homogeneous or possessing a degree of phyletic unity than the higher categories.

An order may be further divided into suborders which have the ending *-ineae* as in Malvineae of the order Malvales. Authors including Takhtajan (1969) have divided their subclasses in certain cases not into orders but instead into super orders and the latter into orders. An order generally comprises one or more families.

The Family is considered as the smallest of the major categories and is most commonly encountered in the taxonomic studies. The names of the families are based on any of the constituent genera with a suffix *-aceae,* e.g. *Malva*-Malvaceae, *Ruta*-Rutaceae, etc. Certain family names, however, have irregular terminations. But these names have been allowed by the rules as exceptions. They are Cruciferae, Guttiferae, Leguminosae, Umbelliferae, Compositae, Labiatae, Palmae and Gramineae. These names were in use long before the present rules of nomenclature were accepted. Due to their common usage since a long time, they have been retained or conserved by the rules. However, those who wish to follow the rules even in respect of these families, have been provided with the *alternative* names proposed for them. They are as follows:

Old name	*Alternative name*
Cruciferae	Brassicaceae
Guttiferae	Clusiaceae
Leguminosae*	Fabaceae
Umbelliferae	Apiaceae
Compositae	Asteraceae
Labiatae	Lamiaceae
Palmae	Arecaceae
Gramineae	Poaceae

There are, broadly, two kinds of families recognised by Walters (1961)—"definable" and "indefinable". Definable families are very natural ones, like Cruciferae, Umbelliferae, Acanthaceae and Gramineae and which are clearly delimited. Many of these represent the "adaptive peak" in evolution (Stebbins, 1951) and include some of the large and successful families containing a large number of genera which are often difficult to delimit. The indefinable families are represented by Ranuculaceae, Rosaceae, Saxifragaceae, where a great diversity of structure is seen. The genera are often very distinct. In other words, they contain many well defined genera. The question is: "Are *they* comparable to definable families or their *genera*?" Many of the relict genera, whose closer relatives have become extinct are certainly comparable with the homogeneous families. It is, therefore, advisable to split indefinable families into more natural smaller groups as has been done for Magnoliaceae, Saxifragaceae and various other families.

If the family is large enough, it is subdivided into subfamilies. Names of subfamilies are based on one of the constituent genera and end in *-oideae*. When

*If the three subfamilies of Leguminosae are raised to family level then the alternative name given above is used for the Papilionaceae and others are named as Caesalpiniaceae and Mimosaceae.

the Leguminosae are considered as comprising three subfamilies, their names are Faboideae, Caesalpinioideae and Mimosoideae. Large subfamilies are divided into tribes, which have names based on any one constituent genus with a suffix *-eae,* e.g. Caesalpineae, Andropogoneae, etc.

Minor Categories

The name of any minor category forms a part of the name of the plant. This may be a genus, a species or any other category of subordinate rank. Genus is the category of highest magnitude among the minor categories. It is subordinate to the family. Each family includes one or more genera. It is generally considered that various genera within the family are closely related and very often have a common ancestral stock. The genera are precisely delimited by a set of well-defined characters. The generic name of a plant is the first of the two words comprising a binomial, for example, *Crotalaria retusa* is a binomial in which *Crotalaria* is the generic name. The Latin names of genera are substantives (or adjectives used as such), always capitalised, in the singular number and may be taken from any source. They have no uniform endings.

The genera were recognised as groups of plants of common affinity in the eighteenth century much before the present concept of the genus was established. J.P. de Tournefort (1716) developed the thesis in his *Institutiones rei herbariae* that the genus is a fundamental category of classification. Plants naving two or three characters in common were regarded as belonging to the same genus. Carolus Linnaeus (1737d) was the first to give a generic description and form limits of the groups. The genera described by Linnaeus, Rafinesque, Hooker and other botanists were delimited on morphological basis alone and it was held that their components (i.e. species) have more characters in common with each other than those of the components of other genera of the same family. This concept is largely followed by several taxonomists even to date. Very often, therefore, it is experienced that the characters that are taxonomically important in separating the components of one genus may not be equally so for another genus of the same family. In spite of this shortcoming, the concept has served the practical need of plant identification and nomenclature.

Certain botanists hold that the genus is more than a mere taxonomic category and the components of the genus indicate phyletic relationships among themselves as well as those of the other genera of the same family. Thus, the genus is considered as a biological category and the taxonomic studies of the genus should take into account not merely the morphological similarities but also the origins, migrations, genetic, cytologic, physiologic and ecologic behaviours, and geologic history of its components. A re-evaluation of existing genera using these tenets is necessary.

A large genus may be divided into subgenera and these into sections, subsections and series.

The next category, *species,* has been considered to be the basic unit of all taxonomic work. This is mainly due to the reason that the species were treated as special creations and therefore, quite immutable entities. However. according to the theory of evolutionary development, no single category is a basic phyletic unit and all categories must be considered as somewhat artificial. However, nomenclaturally the species is a category on which the binomial system has been based.

Many botanists have attempted to define the species in their own way but no one definition is altogether satisfactory. The most acceptable view about the species appears to be that which considers it as a concept—a product of each individual's judgement.

Species Concept

Why are species so important? Not just because they exist in huge numbers and because each species, when properly studied, turns out to be different from every other, morphologically and in many other respects? Species are important because, according to Mayr (1942), "they represent an important level of integration in living nature. This recognition is fundamental to pure biology. An inventory of the species of animals and plants of the world is the base line of further research in biology." Further, he states, "whether he realizes or not, every biologist—even he who works on the molecular level—works with the species or parts of species." The communication of his results will depend on the correct identification of the species involved, and thus, on its taxonomy.

In the history of biology, two names are most intimately connected with the problems of *species definition,* namely Linnaeus and Darwin. The former believed in the constancy and sharp delimitation of species while the latter believed in variation and overlapping or ever-changing pattern of species. But the views of both underwent a change during the life of each. Linnaeus became less and less dogmatic with statements on the constancy of species, while Darwin found it impossible to delimit species with his idea of evolution. He finally regarded species as something purely arbitrary and subjective. He concluded, "In determining whether a form should be ranked as a species or a variety, the opinion of naturalists having sound judgement and wide experience seems the only guide to follow" (Darwin, 1859).

Biologists subsequent to the publication of *Origin of Species* (1859) were clearly divided into two camps, namely the followers of Darwin and those of Linnaeus. The discovery of the Mendelian laws resulted in an even more unrealistic species concept among the experimentalists. None of these, however, studied species in nature as natural populations.

A study of natural populations, later became the prevailing preoccupation of naturalists and as a result a number of controversies arose. These may be summed up as those considering nature of species as either:

1. subjective or objective
2. scientific *versus* purely practical
3. degree of difference *versus* degree of distinctness
4. consisting of individuals *versus* consisting of populations
5. only one kind of species *versus* many kinds of species, and
6. morphologically defined *versus* biologically defined.

Of these, three aspects are stressed in most modern discussions on species, that: (i) they are based on distinctness rather than on difference and therefore are to be defined biologically rather than morphologically; (ii) they consist of populations rather than unconnected individuals; (iii) they are more succinctly defined by isolation from nonconspecific populations than by the relation of conspecific individuals to each other. The crucial species criterion is thus not the fertility of individuals, but rather the reproductive isolation of populations.

Most of the early definitions of species regarded it as aggregates of individuals, unconnected except by descent. Depending on the choice of criteria, it leads to a variety of "species concepts" or "species definitions". Mayr (1942) considered them under five headings, namely, practical, morphological, genetic sterility and biological. Meglitsch (1954) distinguished three concepts, the phenotypic, genetic and phylogenetic. Mayr (1957) subsequently considered three basic concepts, namely, ***typological, non-dimensional*** and ***multi-dimensional*** species concept.

Typological Species Concept

This, according to Mayr (1957), is the simplest and most widely held species concept. Typological thinking holds the dogma of the constancy of species. Variation, under this concept, is merely an imperfect manifestation of the idea implicit in each species. If the degree of variation is too great to be ascribed to imperfections of our sense organs, more than one species must be involved. Thus the species status is determined by degree of morphological difference.

The application of the typological species concept to practical taxonomy results in the morphologically defined species. The "degree of morphological difference" is the criterion of species status. Species are defined on the basis of their observable morphological differences.

Most systematists found this typological-morphological concept inadequate and have rejected it. Its defenders, however, claim that all taxonomists, when classifying the nature into species, follow the typological method and distinguish a "ground plan" or archetype. The utilisation of morphological criteria is valuable and productive in taxonomic practice. A strictly typological-morphological concept is, however, inadequate to cope with the intraspecific variations such as differences in larval stages of animals, sporophytes and gametophytes in plants and polymorphic populations. It is equally incapable of distinguishing absence of visible morphological differences between natural populations which are nevertheless distinct and reproductively isolated and therefore to be considered species. The frequent occurrence of such *cryptic* or *sibling* species in nature has been substantiated by various genetic, physiological or ecological methods. Further, typological species concept treats species as random aggregates of individuals which have the "essential properties of the type" of the species and "agrees with the diagnosis". This static concept ignores the dynamic nature of species populations. Morphological difference between two populations is normally correlated with a given amount of genetic difference. Yet it must be kept in mind that the biological distinctness is primary and the morphological difference secondary. This caution has been exercised, consciously or unconsciously, by nearly all proponents of the morphological species concept.

Non-dimensional Species Concept

The essence of this concept is the relationship of two co-existing natural populations at a single locality at the same time (sympatric and synchronous). It was introduced by John Ray and confirmed by Linnaeus. The relationship of two different species here can be defined as reproductive isolation. It has been realised since long that the species is more than an aggregate of individuals held together by a biological bond. The interbreeding within the species is more conspicuous than is the reproductive isolation against other species. Jordan (1905) was the first to state the non-dimensional species concept in its full extent. This concept, however, is limited to sexually reproducing species.

Multi-dimensional Species Concept

It considers species as groups of populations, namely, such groups as inter-breed with each other, actually or potentially. Thus, it is not clearly demarcated from other similar groupings. The so-called genetic species concept shows that all the three basic concepts can be expressed, on this level, in genetic terms.

It is evident that both morphological and genetic species concepts are attempts to deal directly with the discontinuities in nature.

Species Definition

The most accepted definition of species for higher plants is that of the biological species. Grant (1971) defined biological species as "the reproductively isolated system of breeding populations". Mayr (1969a) defined it as "groups of inter-breeding natural populations that are reproductively isolated from other such groups". Dobzhansky (1935) was apparently the first geneticist to define species in terms of interbreeding and reproductive isolation and other recent definitions are variants of the same theme. According to Simpson (1943) "a genetic species is a group of organisms so constituted and so situated in nature that a hereditary character of any one of these organisms may be transmitted to a descendent of any other". Dobzhansky (1950) defined species as "the largest and most inclusive-reproductive community of sexual and cross fertilizing individuals which share in a common gene pool."

Grant (1971) and Love (1964) have expressed their view on the applicability of the biological species definition to plant groups. Grant has pointed out the difficulties involved with sibling species (biological species but morphologically indistinguishable). Therefore, he has suggested that the groups of non-interbreeding populations be considered biological species while groups of morphologically distinct populations be considered taxonomic species, regardless of their breeding relationships. The taxonomic species, according to this definition, is a unit of convenience for the purpose of identification. Love is of the opinion that the biological species definition is applicable to all organisms, even those that reproduce asexually.

Proponents of the biological species concept rest their case on the contention that there are objective discontinuities in nature which delimit the units. These should be recognised as species. These discontinuities are formed by restriction of gene flow between actually and potentially interbreeding populations. Valentine and Love (1958) hold that the species of the biosystematists is defined in terms of gene exchange—if two populations are capable of exchanging genes freely under either natural or artificial conditions, they are conspecific. If on the other hand, there are internal barriers to gene flow, the populations are ecospecifically distinct.

But if one looks closely to various definitions of biological species, it will be found that they are not founded on sound concepts. The major theoretical and practical difficulties in accepting these definitions are: In the first instance, the reproductive isolation may be internal, genetic or genetic-physiological mechanism; that means the species are intersterile and test for fertility or sterility has to be undertaken experimentally. But many a times, genic changes may cause morphological differentiation earlier than causing intersterility. Thus, genetic differentiation and sterility changes do not always go hand in hand. Consequently, discontinuous groups which are generally accepted as good species may not be given a specific status because of their interbreeding in nature. In case of two species of *Chlorophytum,* viz. *C. glaucum* Dalz. and *C. glaucoides* Blatt., there appears to be only a genic difference causing various morphological changes together with reproductive isolation. But this isolation, has been shown (Naik & Nirgude, 1980) to be a post-zygotic phenomena allowing frequent exchange of genetic material in nature. Thus, the species in question are not completely or strictly intersterile but are otherwise quite distinct.

Secondly, in allopatric populations, there is no question of interfertility, since they can never have occasion to cross. If such populations are shown to be interfertile under cultivation, that cannot be the only criterion to consider them conspecific.

Again, the fertility-sterility test has no meaning in predominantly inbreeding or apomictic groups.

Even the reproductive isolation taken in a wider sense, is not always consistent or rigid. It may break down suddenly in certain instances, as in *Chlorophytum* referred to above.

Sokal & Crovello (1970) are of the opinion that the biological species definition is extremely difficult and often impossible to apply to natural groups.

According to them, the local populations are valuable for studying evolutionary and ecological processes and in taxonomic practice the most useful species concept is a phenetic one. Many of the phenetic data are morphological in nature and can be analysed by computors through the methodology of numerical taxonomy.

Ehrlich & Raven (1969) have pointed out that the exchange of genetic material, or gene flow, in sexually reproducing organisms may be considerably more limited than has been suspected. They have suggested that although a species may have some form of common gene pool, it is selection rather than gene flow that maintains the general phenetic nature of the species. They have demonstrated that even within a population, actual gene exchange or gene flow may be very limited. The biological species definition has also been criticised on the grounds of both hybridization and ethological isolation. Some populations belonging to different plant species are able to hybridize and produce fully or partially fertile offspring. Yet such populations are distinct enough to be called species by taxonomists. Similarly, some distinct groups of populations that are recognised as species are behaviourally isolated under natural conditions, and do not interbreed, although they are capable of producing fertile offspring under laboratory conditions.

Davis & Heywood (1963) hold that taxonomic and biological species, although based on differently conceived abstractions, may coincide in practice. The role of morphology has been clearly stated by Simpson (1961), who distinguishes between the *definition* of a species in genetical terms and its *recognition* in morphological terms. In other words, morphology provides the evidence for putting the genetical definition into practice.

This compromise between the two concepts of species appears to be further resolved in a recent article by Lewin (1981), who states that in an evolutionary continuum there can be no discontinuities delimiting species. He further considers three more or less distinct ways of considering the species concept.

A. The species as perceived by the organisms themselves, whether or not we recognise their specific distinctions.
B. The species as we ourselves perceive it, with our limited but extending field of experience and techniques.
C. The species as designated by a specific name, which does not necessarily correspond to B.

On the basis of these considerations he recognises three species concepts as: the *Biological species* (concept type A); the *Taxonomists species* (concept type B) and the *Nominal species* (concept type C). Since all the three types are discussed above they need no further elaboration. Lewin concludes that as our knowledge grows, our concepts of taxonomic species (concept B) can be expected to approximate more and more closely to biological species (concept A) and the names we use to designate them (concept C) will also correspond more and more closely. These are ends to which we aspire, even if we can never fully achieve them. This clearly appears to be a practical consideration of the problem offering its solution in an indirect way.

Irrespective of the definitions of the concept of the species, this unit has to be fitted into the binomial system of nomenclature. It must have a Latin name composed of two words—the generic name and the specific epithet. In a binomial *Crotalaria retusa* the first is the generic name and the second is the specific epithet.

Infraspecific Categories

Any category below the rank of species is an infraspecific category. These categories were limited in the earlier taxonomic work and were considered as abnormalities. They were described as an appendage to the species. With the development of biosystematic studies, the species is considered to be represented by the initial binomial and all subsequently described variants ascribed to that binomial. When more than one infraspecific taxon is present, a trinomial form of nomenclature is followed. Rarely, the nomenclature may run into a polynomial. For example, *Amaranthus lividus* ssp. *polygonoides* is a trinomial while *Amaranthus hybridus* ssp. *cruentus* var. *paniculatus* is a polynomial.

The rules of nomenclature provide for the infraspecific categories such as ***subspecies*** (abbreviated as subsp.), ***variety*** (var.), ***subvariety*** (subvar.), ***forma*** (f.) ***forma biologica, forma specialis*** and ***individuum.*** Of these the three most commonly used are ***subsp. var.*** and ***f.***

The subspecies has been considered as the next subordinate rank of the species and has been used by various workers with different circumscriptions. Mainly there have been three concepts: (i) a species of small magnitude that is distinguished by less significant morphological features than are the species within the same genus; (ii) a major morphological variation of a species that has distinct geographical distribution other than that occupied by other subspecies of the same species; or (iii) counterparts of the ecotype. More recently the second concept of the subspecies has been favoured by a large number of taxonomists.

The variety (Latin—*varietas*) has been used rather indiscriminately to designate infraspecific category. It has been considered either as

1. a morphological variant of the species without regard for distribution;
2. a morphological variant having its own geographical distribution;
3. a morphological variant sharing areas common to one or more varieties of the same species, and
4. a variant representing only a colour or habit phase.

The forma is the smallest category used in the taxonomic literature. It is generally applied to trivial variants occurring among the individuals of any population. Smaller categories than forma rarely appear in the taxonomic works and therefore are not considered here.

4 Concept of Taxonomic Characters

Taxonomy of living organisms or even of material objects is mainly concerned with their characters. In living organisms it is concerned with variations observed in them. The words "similarity", "dissimilarity", "resemblance", "difference", etc. are mainly employed with regard to the characters. In the natural classification of living organisms evidence is provided by the characters. It is therefore, obvious that the number of characters observed and employed for classification will determine its nature. Taxonomists have been in search of characters which would provide them sound evidence for construction of natural and more acceptable classification of living organisms. This has naturally resulted in the accumulation of vast amount of data pertaining to taxonomic characters. It has been possible for some to use only a few characters while others could employ hundreds of them. Pre-Darwinian classifications have derived their data mainly from exomorphology while the post-Darwinian systems are largely based on characters taken from anatomy, cytology and physiology, in addition to the traditional discipline of exomorphology.

It should be noted here that although a larger number of characters should lead to the construction of more natural classifications, at least in theory, in practice this has not always been the case. Certain classifications, on the contrary, based on a few characters, have proved to be equally, if not more, acceptable and natural, than those based on numerous characters. This situation leads one to believe that it is not merely the number of characters that matter but often their quality that has greater significance. Davis & Heywood (1963) state that ideally the whole organism with all its attributes should be employed for its classification, but since each individual possesses thousands of potential characters, practical limitations impose a restriction on the numbers used. The problem of *selection* then has to be considered. Lam (1959) believes that it is probably not possible to make a fully relevant choice if natural classification is to be ultimately achieved. Further, selection of a few characters at random, at any one time, may lead to different classification every time. The selection of attributes will depend largely on the purpose of classification, patience of the investigator, availability of characters and traditional usage.

Multi-Attribute Classification

When only a convenience is aimed at in the construction of a classification, a few obvious characters are enough. But this is contrary to the aims of taxonomy. It is widely accepted that for general purposes the multiple-attribute classification is most useful. Gilmour & Turrill (1941) think that such a classification allows the maximum number of generalisations to be made from it. According to Bremekamp (1939) it is most serviceable as it conveys the maximum possible amount of information about the groups it contains.

Such Adansonian classifications, as they are frequently called, have two essential features: (i) each attribute selected for constructing the classification is given equal weight; (ii) taxa are based on correlations between these attributes. The taxonomic groups derived by using such multiple attributes are termed as *polythetic* (Sneath, 1962). In these groups no single attribute is sufficient and necessary for membership in the group so long as the members share a high proportion of characters (Sneath & Sokal, 1962). Although Adansonian classifications have been thus modified or elaborated by *numerical taxonomists,* they are not accepted by evolutionary taxonomists. It is considered by this latter group of biologists that a few but phyletic, logical or otherwise important characters can be more satisfactorily employed for classification than multiple and non-evolutionary ones. This means that they use some sort of weighting principles which can justify construction of *special* classifications and serve a special purpose (i.e. phyletic). But according to Davis & Heywood (1963) these are not compatible with the aims of *general* classifications. They further state that by giving greater weight to a particular evidence a classification ceases to serve general purpose. At the same time it may be said that general classifications constructed by employing Adansonian principles have also not proved to be natural in all instances. Merits and demerits of numerical methods are discussed in Chapter 8.

Natural classifications are based on overall similarity between the groups. But such similarities are often difficult to ascertain due to various factors such as convergence, functional correlation and difficulties of understanding homologies. The taxonomic value of various characters should be determined on the basis of their role in natural as well as phyletic classifications. Equal weighting of character may not always be adequate to construct both phenetic as well as phylogenetic classifications. There has to be a differential weighting or at least a different set of characters.

One of the most important questions causing great difficulties is the comparison and evaluation of frequently conflicting information derived from different sources. In many cases there are contradictions in the conclusions reached by different authors on the basis of different characters. The Australian genus *Emblingia* (Emblingiaceae of the Sapindales), for instance, was studied by four different authors considering different parts of the plants. The authors (Erdtman *et al.,* 1969) reached four different conclusions on its systematic position. This example, as many others, proves that satisfactory decision can be reached only after the appropriate taxonomic and phyletic weighting of the characters, which is a competence of a systematist. For a systematist, characters have different information content, and many of them, if not most, are merely "noise" (Mayr, 1969). Besides, the same characters could have different weights in various related taxa. It is also well-known that weighting can be only *a posteriori,* i.e. based on experience. Takhtajan (1980) emphatically states that weighting is a specific taxonomic problem, which can be solved only by the systematist himself. The higher the rank of a taxon, the more important weighting becomes (Mayr, 1969).

Heterobathmy

The problem of weighting would not be so difficult if all the characters of an organism evolved harmoniously, at an equal rate, and occupied the same level of the evolutionary development. But it is a well-known fact that different organs have evolved at different rates. This phenomenon of unequal rate of evolution of different features within one lineage is known as "Mosaic evolution" (De Beer, 1954). Mosaic evolution results into different evolutionary stages or grades. The difference in these grades is termed *heterobathmy* (from Greek *bathmos* = step, grade; see Takhtajan, 1959, 1966, 1980).

An organism may present a mosaic combination of characters of quite different evolutionary levels because of heterobathmy. Thus, for example, the genera *Trochodendron, Tetracentron* and *Sarcandra,* with their primitive, vesselless wood have rather specialised flowers, whereas in the genus *Magnolia,* which possesses a comparatively much more primitive type of flower, the wood is rather advanced with vessels having simple perforation plates.

The more strongly heterobathmy is expressed, the more contradictory is the taxonomic information provided by different sets of characters. In such cases, only the application of various methods can reveal those "critical characters" and "critical tendencies" (Wernham, 1912) which are reliable phyletic markers. Correct weighting of the characters and their evolutionary tendencies gain special significance in such cases.

Presence or Absence of a Character

Cronquist (1968a) points out one of the interesting things in evaluating the significance of taxonomic characters. He states that the presence of a structure or a substance is likely to be more important than its absence, and in support of this statement he provides a genetic explanation. It is amply demonstrated that individual phenotypic characters are commonly governed by a complex system of genes, rather than a single gene unaffected by others. The appearance of a particular characteristic in the phenotype requires the whole genetic system and if two individuals or two allied taxa share the same structure then they probably also share the same genetic system governing its development. If any one of the essential genes in the system is lost, then the structure fails to develop, and a plant which lacks a particular structure may differ by only a single gene from the one which has it. It has been shown that actinomorphic forms of the common snapdragon *(Antirrhinum majus* L.) differ from the ordinary bilabiate form in only a single pair of genes, but this does not mean that the complex, irregular corolla of the snapdragon arose from a regular-flowered ancestry by a single mutation; a complex system of genes is certainly required instead.

It is of course also clear that the absence of a character may reflect the complete absence of a genetic system which would be required to produce it. Thus there is no reason to believe that gymnosperms could be induced to form an angiospermous ovary merely by supplying a missing gene or so.

He concludes that on both theoretical and practical grounds, the absence of a character is a less reliable guide to taxonomic affinities than its presence.

Definition of a Character

Overall similarities can be judged by a combination of characters. The natural selection operates on these combinations of characters. But it is convenient to deal with unit characters which can be treated quantitatively. The choice of such unit characters is largely a matter of experience. This naturally raises the problem of definition of unit characters. However, Davis and Heywood (1963) have attempted to give a general definition, which may be considered quite satisfactory in the absence of any other suitable one. According to the authors, a character is *"any attribute* (or *descriptive phase) referring to form, structure or behaviour which the taxonomist separates from the whole organism for a particular purpose such as comparison or interpretation."* They further state that characters as such are strictly speaking, abstract entities, it is their *expressions* or *states* that taxonomists deal with. "Number of petals", for instance, may be considered as a character, but "petals five" is an expression of that character. When these expressions are variable in character, they serve the purpose of comparison. It may therefore be said that for practical purposes a character may be defined as any feature whose expression can be measured, counted or otherwise assessed. *Unit character,* as defined by Sneath & Sokal (1962), is "a taxonomic character of two or more states, which within the study at hand cannot be further divided logically.... " But in practice, it is rather difficult to divide characters into units owing to lack of skill and perception. Although comparison of characters may be objective, their selection is largely subjective. Thus it may be possible to define a character in a precise manner but it can be considered in individual cases and for definite purposes.

Analytic vs. Synthetic Characters

In taxonomic preocedure characters may be employed for two main activities: (i) identification, characterisation and delimitation of species, and (ii) classification of these species into higher taxa. Corresponding with these activities, characters may be regarded as *analytic* or *synthetic*. There are diagnostic or *key* characters used for identification and characterisation. These are often restricted in their occurrence so that they alone are enough to reach a correct diagnosis. They are most useful and easy for the process of identification and must be included in the floras and manuals.

Analytic characters which are mostly diagnostic ones, are useful in identification, characterisation and delimitation of lower taxa, as stated above. On the other hand, synthetic characters are useful in grouping these taxa into higher groups. Synthetic characters gradually decrease in number as one goes from lower to higher groups. This is obvious because only a few characters become increasingly constant at higher position of the group in the hierarchy. The characters such as sympetalous versus polypetalous condition, superior versus inferior gynoecium, etc. are quite constant and do not vary within smaller groups or within populations of the same species. They are also termed as *constitutive* or *organisational* characters.

Qualitative vs. Quantitative Characters

The characters relating to form and structure are termed as *qualitative* while those features assessed by size, length, breadth, etc. are termed *quantitative*. Both of these are used in descriptions. The characters such as presence or absence of corolla, position of ovary, union of stamens, etc. can be clearly said to be qualitative. In the quantitative description, the number of parts and their range (e.g. seeds 10 to 15; stamens 8 to 10 etc.), size as expressed as length, breadth and its range (e.g. leaves 5 to 10 cm long and 2 to 6 cm broad), shape, colour, indumentum, sculpturing and similar other features are used. Qualitative characters are generally more useful to distinguish taxa of specific or higher ranks while quantitative ones are often useful to separate lower taxonomic categories at infra-specific levels.

Although theoretically all characters are useful in classification, their use, as often experienced, appears to be limited to a small number. This is because certain characters are considered to be *good* or more reliable than others. Good characters are those that: (i) are not subject to wide variation within the samples being considered; (ii) do not have a high intrinsic genetic variability; (iii) are not easily susceptible to environmental modification and show consistency, i.e. agree with the correlations of characters existing in a natural system of classification. All these conditions may be summed up by stating, "a taxonomic character is only as good as its constancy"

Character Weighting

This obviously leads to search those characters which are more constant and to give more weight to these, i.e. to exercise ***character weighting***. Characters are weighted by taxonomists for four main reasons:

1. because they are most easily observed;
2. because they show highest correlation with others in a natural group;
3. because they are believed to have some known or inferred phylogenetic importance or they are shown to be more conservative characters. and
4. because they were left out characters while constructing a natural group.

Of these, the second method of weighting, i.e. weighting based on correlation of characters, is termed ***correlation weighting*** or ***a posteriori weighting*** (Davis

& Heywood, 1963). This is the only type of weighting which should be used for classification. Characters abstracted in this manner will be the ones that diagnose the group and these markers will probably be the most likely characters to use for the keys. The character or a feature which shows the highest average correlation with other similar characters has been called the *indicator character* or simply *indicator* (Smirnow, 1924, 1938; Terentjev, 1931). The indicator is maximally correlated with other characters and therefore has the highest taxonomic significance. A set of such indicators constitute the so-called taxonomic coefficient.

Correlation weighting can be illustrated by the well-known example of the Leguminosae. Whether this group of plants is considered as an order or a family is a matter which can be discussed elsewhere. But it is certain that any member of this group has a characteristic monocarpellary gynoecium with marginal placentation. This very character, therefore , can be considered as the marker or indicator character. Various other characters such as a predominantly woody habit, alternate, often compound, stipulate leaves, racemose or racemose-derived disposition of flowers, basically polypetalous corolla and diplostemonous condition are also considered as important diagnostic characters of the group. Further, each of these characters also shows close correlation with other characters. The gynoecial character, thus, can be taken to have the highest correlation with other characters or the highest taxonomic significance for Leguminosae, and this character together with other characters constitute the taxonomic coefficient. Legumes, therefore, are taken to be constituting one of the most natural groups of flowering plants.

An interesting correlation between the basic chromosome number, ploidy level, duration of the aerial shoot, ecology and secondary thickening on the lateral walls of the metaxylem vessel elements of various species of *Chlorophytum* (Liliaceae) from India and Africa has been shown recently (Naik & Nirgude, 1981a, b). Here also the set of characters showing this correlation may be considered to have the highest taxonomic significance. This has been further supplemented by the fact that change in any one of these characters concomitantly brings about a corresponding change in the other characters as well. The diploid species with basic chromosome number $x=8$, for instance, have spiral thickening on the lateral walls of their metaxylem vessel elements, short-lived aerial shoots and are distributed in the semi-arid situations. But the diploid as well as polyploid members with $x = 7$ have a scalariform or pitted thickening on the lateral walls of their metaxylem vessel elements, a relatively long-lived aerial shoot and are distributed in the humid situations.

Saxifragaceae (*Sensu lato*), Euphorbiaceae, Oleaceae and a few others, unlike Leguminosae, are well-known examples of heterogeneous assemblages. This is mainly because there are hardly any characters which can be designated as indicators of these families. Unisexuality and tricarpellary gynoecium of the majority of Euphorbiaceae and the number of stamens (often 2) and bicarpellary gynoecium of the Oleaceae are very often considered as diagnostic characters of these groups but it is experienced that many a times they are not constant and/or correlated with other characters. Thus they do not have high taxonomic significance and the groups which possess them may be described as having the low taxonomic coefficient.

The third method is regarded as *a priori phyletic weighting* as distinct from *a posteriori weighting*. The former is often employed for the construction of a phylogenetic or vertical classification while the latter is employed for a natural or horizontal classification. It is a well-known fact that the phylogenetic value is difficult to assess in the absence of reliable fossil evidence. Most of the times such an importance is presumed on a dubious evidence or even deduced from some hypothetical ancestors. Many of the so-called phylogenetic classifications suffer from over-estimations of phylogenetic value of certain characters and are far from natural classifications. The classification at generic and sectional level is particularly riddled with *a priori weighting*.

The reliable evidence from the fossil records only can establish primitive characters in a group beyond dispute. When such an evidence is available, it can be used and assessed as an additional character. But unfortunately this is seldom applicable to angiosperms.

The last, method, also termed as *rejection weighting* or residual weighting is useful for a natural classification. The characters that are found to be more variable than the others are often not useful for diagnosis or for construction of keys and are therefore rejected. But it is also experienced that some of these variable characters prove to be specialisations for a particular mode of life. Thus the acceptance or rejection of characters largely depends on the discretion of the employer developed by him through intimate association of the group concerned. Thus it is also *a priori* weighting.

Biological Characters

Taxonomists often distinguish characters as either biological or fortuitous (Wernham, 1912). Biological characters are those that are related to some vital function or advantage and mostly are floral ones such as sympetaly, zygomorphy, epigyny, etc. These characters are considered to be involved in progressive evolution of angiosperms marked by two fundamental tendencies, viz. economy in production of reproductive parts and adaptation to insect pollinators. Fortuitous characters, on the other hand, show no such functional relationship.

Most of the pre-Darwinian systems of classifications were based on characters that were regarded as having high physiological or functional value. Cain (1958, 1959b) therefore, considers these classifications as more natural. But it will be realised that much of the natural phenomena and functional value of many characters is not clearly understood even to day. This was probably correctly understood by A.P. de Candolle and later taxonomists who gradually rejected many such biological characters and employed instead those features which are termed fortuitous. Adansonian taxonomy and its recent elaboration into numerical methods is another extreme where characters, whether biological or otherwise, are not weighted at all.

Basic Characters

According to Stebbins (1950), the relative simplicity of plant structure makes for a large amount of parallel variation and families are made up, as regards floral features, of a combination of characters such as presence or absence of sepals and/or petals, polypetaly versus sympetaly, actinomorphy versus zygomorphy numerous floral parts versus few parts, apocarpy versus syncarpy, hypogyny versus epigyny and a few others. Nearly half of the total 438 families considered by Davis and Heywood (1963) falls into one of these combinations. Such characters, as mentioned earlier, were regarded by Diels as constitutive or organisational characters. They are constant throughout a wide range of individuals, species, genera, etc. Their taxonomic value is high and according to Sporne (1956), they are characteristic of large areas of affinity.

Thus, it may be said that the number of basic characters in angiosperm flowers is limited. But it should be noted that they evolved more than once in separate lines. Features such as sympetaly, epigyny, etc. may, therefore be considered as adaptive convergences in the angiosperms. Occurrence of such characters alone should not be taken as an indication of taxonomic affinity when the groups in question are otherwise regarded as unrelated. Such specialised features, occuring sporadically in otherwise unspecialised groups (e.g. zygomorphic flowers in Ranunculaceae, sympetaly in some Annonaceae, etc.) should be regarded as exceptional features and should not be weighted for considering taxonomic affinities.

Although most of the twentieth century biologists such as Straw (1956) and van der Pijl (1960) have considered functional aspects of characters to be more useful in natural classification, the exact nature of functional or adaptive significance of many of the characters, as mentioned earlier, is not yet clearly understood. The herbarium taxonomists, on the other hand, are not concerned with functional value of the character but regard diagnostic character for the purpose of classification. They are more concerned with the constancy of the features chosen by them for discrimination of groups (Heywood, 1959). Borrill (1961) considers that the functional value of characters taken to be adaptive is doubtful and cannot be employed for taxonomic separation. The flowers of Orchidaceae and Zingiberaceae, Polygalaceae and Papilionaceae, for example, may be regarded as convergent adaptations in response to similar methods of pollination and hence cannot be used for taxonomic separation.

In conclusion we may agree with Cain (1959b) that the taxonomic value of the character should not be judged, for purpose of comparison, mainly in terms of their function. At the same time we cannot afford to deny taxonomic value of characters which can be demonstrated as functional in contrast to those which have no apparent functional value. Davis & Heywood (1963) state that the constant characters are, most probably, selected by the nature as such. Whether we understand their functional value or not is largely a matter of our knowledge about them.

5
The Origin of Angiosperms

Angiosperms, more commonly known as flowering plants, are the dominant seed-bearing plants of the present day, consisting of a vast and varied assemblage of about 300,000 species. They are commonly considered "modern" seed-plants and geologically young. Eames (1961), however, regards them not to be of recent origin. He further remarks that the accumulated evidence from the fossil record and from critical morphological studies, indicates that angiosperms are an old group in which there was early differentiation along several lines. At the same time, in their dominance, angiosperms have not "crowded the gymnosperms from the face of the earth". In fact, all other groups of plants also persist today along with angiosperms.

In all characters, gross and minute, external and internal, sporophytic and gametophytic, the angiosperms show great diversity of form, as a result of adaptive specialisation in response to great climatic changes. Some forms became highly elaborated in their vegetative as well as floral features while others became specialised by "reduction, retrogression or suppression". These latter forms have been considered by some to be primitive, not realising that simplicity is often secondary.

Definition of an Angiosperm

The term angiosperm, in Greek, literally means *vessel seed*, in allusion to the seed borne or produced within a vessel or ovary. Bessey (1915) treated this group as a phyllum, the *Anthophyta* (also from Greek, meaning flower plant). Thus angiosperms may be defined as a group of flowering plants whose *seeds are enclosed within the carpel* or *carpels,* the upper portion of which becomes differentiated into a style and stigma. Further, they are characterised by the presence of vessels in the stems and by the possession of a *complex reproductive structure,* the *flower* (Eames, 1961).

There are, however, exceptions to these characteristics of angiosperms. Members of certain families such as Winteraceae, Tetracentraceae, Trochodendraceae, etc. are believed never to have had vessels, while in others the vessels have been lost through specialisation and suppression. In some members, the carpels are open and the ovules are not completely enclosed within the ovary. The presence of a flower, as a character to distinguish angiosperms from gymnosperms, is a matter of artificial definition since it is impossible to define a flower with morphological precision as to exclude the cone or cluster of fertile sporophylls that characterises gymnosperms. Despite these exceptions, the taxonomic validity of angiosperms as a group is not subject to serious challenge.

There has been considerable difference of opinion as to the facts about the origin of angiosperms. Neither the time nor the place of their origin is known for certain. The nature of their ancestors is yet another problematic aspect. Some morphologists have sought their possible ancestors among seed plants of the Carboniferous or Permian periods, some 200–250 million years in the past, some others consider the Jurassic about 150 million years ago, to be the more probable period of their origin and still others regard them to be more recent, not older than the Cretaceous, about 100 million years ago. Accordingly, at one time or another, all major groups of plants including Lycopodiales, Filicales, Cycadales, Pteridospermales, Bennettitales, Gnetales, etc. have been considered as ancestral to angiosperms. Even algae have been taken to be possible precursors by some (see Takhtajan, 1969). Thus, there are three aspects of the problem: *time, nature* of ancestors and *place* of their origin.

The First Traces of Angiosperms

For the determination of the first traces of angiosperms, we have to depend almost entirely upon fossil evidence. Unfortunately, palaeobotanical studies during the past few decades have not been able to solve the mystery about the earliest angiosperms. This lack of palaeobotanical knowledge may be due to their limited distribution in the long past and an insignificant role that they might have played in the vegetation of the world. Or, as Seward (1933) has remarked, the complete absence of their fossil deposits in the earlier rocks might be due to their failure to be preserved as fossils because they occupied a tract of country remote from the localities where the conditions were favourable for fossilization. In the opinion of a great many authors (Just, 1948; Eames, 1961; Takhtajan, 1969), angiosperms undoubtedly originated long before the Cretaceous period. According to them, an early Mesozoic, about 200 million years ago, seems the most likely period for the origin of angiosperms. But at the same time, it can be said that there is no dependable fossil record from the pre-Cretaceous period (Scott, Barghoorn & Leopold, 1960).

The pollen from the pre-Cretaceous deposits, e.g. from the Lower Carboniferous, some 300 million years ago, are very problematic and in most cases have proved to be pollen grains of gymnosperms. Some deposits of this period, considered at one time to be pollen grains of angiosperms, have been suggested to be the unicellular green alga *Tetraedron*. Similarly, certain leaf impressions from Triassic and Jurassic deposits which have been attributed to angiosperms are also disputable.

Early Cretaceous Angiosperms

As early as 1894, Saporta described several leaf fragments from rocks of Aptian age in Portugal, which were interpreted as angiosperms. From the Albian horizon of Portugal; a significant number was recorded including *Salix, Aralia, Braseniopsis, Myrica, Laurus, Viburnum, Eucalyptus, Magnolia* and *Sassafras*. Seward (1926) described an interesting assemblage of fossil plants from Cretaceous horizons in Western Greenland which include *Artocarpus, Quercus, Platanus* and others.

In a comprehensive study of plants from many localities of the lower Cretaceous age in Western Canada, Bell (1956) described genera including *Populites, Ficus, Trochodendroides, Cinnamomoides, Celastrophyllum, Sapindopsis*, etc. from the upper Aptian and Albian age.

From the Aptian horizons of England, Marie Stopes (1915) described fossil woods of dicots including those of *Aptiana, Woburnia, Hythia, Sabulia* and *Cantia*. Samylina (1959) reported a Lower Cretaceous flora (Aptian-Albian) from Eastern Siberia. This includes Members of Lauraceae, Cercidiphyllaceae, Rosaceae, Leguminosae, Rhamnaceae, Araliaceae, etc.

Upper Cretaceous Angiosperms

The abundance of genera and families of angiosperms characterises the upper Cretaceous floras of the world. The floras of the Amboy clays of New Jersey (Newberry, 1895), Dakota sandstone near Kansas, Nebraska and Minnesota (Lesquereux, 1891), the basin of the Rocky Mountain system (Dorf, 1936, 1938, 1942), Vancouver Island (Bell, 1957), etc. were particularly rich in angiospermous genera which altogether account for about 700 to 750 forms. Most of them are referable to extant genera.

Subsequently, several fossil forms have been described from the Tertiary floras of Europe and Western United States. These included abundant fruits as well as seeds.

Most authentic angiosperm remains thus are found only from the early Cretaceous onwards. Indisputable dicot fruits have been discovered in the valaughnian deposits of Southern France (Chandler, 1958) and Northern California (Chandler and Axelrod, 1961).

According to Hughes (1961), angiosperms are considered "to have evolved during the Barremian and Aptian (stratigraphic divisions of the Upper Cretaceous) from as yet unspecified gymnospermous groups in certain regions of the world... From Albian to Senomanian times, angiosperms steadily and progressively occupied all vegetated areas of the world; but they were not however types which could be classified in recent families. The whole process took perhaps 25 million years, about half the Cretaceous period; this is considered to be neither fast nor slow and its steady progress is supported by the fossil record." Professor Puri (1967) remarks that if we are critical about the identification of ancient fossil finds, all fossil evidence of Palaeozoic angiosperms will be found wanting and consequently unreliable.

Even the most reliable fossil evidence gathered more than 60 years ago from the Upper Aptian deposits of Southern England, does not indicate the time of the first appearance of angiosperms. These fossil angiosperm woods are thought to belong to the palaeotropical families Dipterocarpaceae and Theaceae. Thus, they are not at all primitive in structure but are woods of specialised types.

From Aptian-Albian times onwards, occurrence of angiospermous woods, leaves, pollen, etc. become considerably more numerous. Up to Albian times, however, angiosperms appear to be comparatively rare. They evidently formed only small populations with smaller number of individuals. At the close of the Albian period or towards the middle of the Cretaceous period, angiosperms came to be widely distributed throughout the world. They appeared in great diversity of form and quickly became dominant. Most of these Cretaceous angiosperms belong to the extant genera and there are representatives both of more or less primitive forms and the highly evolved ones. The vast and rapid spread of angiosperms is one of the most important event in the history of life upon the earth.

The Nature of Probable Ancestors of Angiosperms

It has already been indicated that various plant groups have been considered as ancestral to the angiosperms. However, none of these hypotheses appear to be tenable or based on sound footing. Some of the well-known plant groups that have been deemed to be particularly closely similar to ancestral stock or stocks of flowering plants will be discussed in the following paragraphs.

The Isoetes-Monocotyledon Theory

Ferns, both eusporangiate as well as leptosporangiate and fern allies like Lycopodiales, Isoetales, etc., have been shown to possess many common features with those of the monocotyledons. Engler and his associates have postulated the probable origin of monocotyledons from various groups of pteridophytes through an intermediate and hypothetical group, the protangiosperms. This latter group, according to Engler, is not represented in the fossils because many of them were herbaceous. Engler also postulates direct derivation of monocotyledons, from Ophioglossaceae, on the basis of similarities in their vascular bundles. Similarities in the embryos of monocotyledons and ferns have been recalled by others. Campbell (1928), for example, holds that the herbaceous character in angiosperms is primitive, inherited from filicinean ancestors. According to him, the existing heterosporous genera, especially *Isoetes,* show interesting suggestions of a possible relationship with monocotyledons. *Isoetes* is predominantly herbaceous and geophilous. It is also either aquatic or amphibious. Like most of the Filicineae, it is found in humid tropics, a habitat which is also characteristic of a large number of monocotyledons. While discussing the relationships of *Isoetes,* Campbell suggested "the marked similarity in habit and resemblances in the embryo and anatomy of the older sporophyte between *Isoetes* and some of the lower aquatic monocotyledons" like *Najas flexilis* but has also indicated that the differences between the simplest angiosperm flower and the sporophylls of *Isoetes* are great and more evidence is necessary to support his hypothesis.

It will be readily acceptable that there is no factual basis of any kind to attempt to derive the angiosperms directly from ferns or other lower vascular plants without a transitional gymnospermous stage. The evidence available so far indicates that the seed-habit and seed-plants were in all probabilities, the seed-ferns or pteridosperms. It will be further interesting to note that, in spite of the great diversity amongst seed-plants, the morphology of seed itself in these various groups has much in common. It is, therefore, likely that all seed-plants have a common ancestry in ferns by way of the most primitive representatives, the seed-ferns.

Other groups of pteridophytes like Lycopodiales and Equisetales are now considered to represent completely separate and independent evolutionary lines. Ovules, and therefore seeds, are found only in pteridosperms, gymnosperms and angiosperms. These ancestors of angiosperms must thus be sought amongst pteridosperms or gymnosperms.

The Coniferales-Amentiferae Theory

Some of the higher gymnosperms like conifers, Cordaitales and others were then considered to be the probable ancestors of angiosperms. Engler (1882, 1892a, b) and later on Rendle (1904, 1930) pointed out the resemblances of angiosperms to conifers and considered the amentiferous group as the most primitive dicotyledons in their taxonomic treatments. The inflorescences of the amentifers like Casuarinaceae, Salicaceae, Fagaceae, etc. with their simple and naked flowers were compared with those of the conifers. Further similarities were seen in the stamens and bisporangiate microsporophylls of many conifers. Hagerup (1934, 1936) compared the seed-scale complex of *Juniperus* with the gynoecia of Amentiferae. Further, the covered nature of seed in *Agathis* and *Araucaria* also support their closeness with angiosperms. Doyle (1945) has shown that the fertilisation in these and other conifers, where the pollen grains are deposited on the scale and only the pollen tube enters the micropyle, is similar to that in angiosperms.

It is now very well documented that the resemblances as seen above are only superficial and due probably to parallelism. The inflorescence of amentiferous families exhibit a specialised structure. The so called "simple" flowers of these families are not primitively simple but are highly reduced. Similarly, some of the vesselless angiosperms like *Trochodendron, Tetracentron* and others have a structurally more primitive secondary xylem than conifers as well as amentifers. These latter angiosperms are now considered to be rather specialised and not primitive. Further, the ovuliferous scales of conifers and carpels of angiosperms follow distinctly different lines of evolutionary specialisation. Whereas the carpels of angiosperms are modified leaves (phyllosporous), the seed-bearing organs of conifers are never so and probably represent modified telome-systems. It is now believed that the primitive angiosperm flower is bisexual whereas cones of conifers are uniformly unisexual.

The Gnetales-Angiosperm Theory

Richard von Wettstein in his *Handbuch der Systematische Botanik* (1901), rearranged and modified Engler's system and emphasised a close relationship of Gnetales with angiosperms. Markgraf (1930) and later on Fagerlind (1947) strongly supported this view and the latter demonstrated the morphological homology between the flowers of *Gnetum Ephedra* and *Welwitschia* and postulated that these and pro-angiosperms have evolved from a common ancestor.

The Gnetales resemble angiosperms in many respects. They have two cotyledons and unlike all other gymnosperms have vessels in their secondary wood. Ovules of Gnetales differ from those of most gymnosperms and have close resemblance with those of most angiosperms in possessing two integuments instead of only one. Leaves in *Gnetum* are typically net-veined like those of many dicotyledons. The unisexual inflorescences of *Gnetum* can be easily compared with the catkins of many amentiferous angiosperms.

The male flowers of *Welwitschia* are truly bisexual and show that they are derived by reduction of the female parts. The stamens of the three genera of Gnetales are apparently similar to those of angiosperms. The female flowers of all the three genera have two or more envelops round their nucelli which have been variously homologised with perianth or carpels of angiosperms. In all the species of *Gnetum* and *Ephedra* the inner envelop around the nucellus forms a microphylar tube so that sometimes pollen grains germinate inside the tube. Maheshwari and Vasil (1960) have compared this situation with the open stylar canals of some angiosperms and with the intra-ovarian germination of pollen grains. The gametophytes of *Gnetum* and *Welwitschia*, like those of angiosperms, are greatly reduced. In the former, the embryo-sac is tetrasporic. Both the male nuclei fuse with the nuclei of female gametophyte in this plant and free nuclear divisions are absent in *Gnetum, Welwitschia* and also one other gymnosperm, namely *Sequoia sempervirens* (Buchholz, 1939).

Unfortunately, these outward resemblances are not borne out by anatomical and developmental studies. The members of Gnetales, in several respects, have attained an evolutionary level higher than that of some of the primitive angiosperms. For example, they have vessels in the secondary wood while a few genera of angiosperms mentioned earlier in this chapter have xylem completely devoid of them. Further, Thompson (1918) has shown that the vessels of Gnetales originated in an entirely different way from those of angiosperms. In this group, typically scalariform pitted tracheids met with in primitive angiosperms, are eliminated from both the primary and secondary xylem and circular bordered pits appear in the ontogeny of the secondary xylem. This development of vessels is unique in type and is entirely different from that of vessels in angiosperms and certain vascular cryptogams (Bailey, 1944; Cheadle, 1953). Similarly, on the same basis, discussed under the conifer-angiosperm theory, the similarity between the Gnetalean strobilus and the aments of certain angiosperms, is now considered as superficial and due to some degree of convergence.

The similarity between Gnetales and angiosperms on the basis of the number of cotyledons also appears to be due to convergent evolution. Angiosperms might have been derived from poly-cotyledonous rather than dicotyledonous ancestors. It is interesting to note the presence of three to four cotyledons in one of the extant primitive angiosperm genus *Degeneria*. The reduction and loss of archegonium in *Gnetum* might have resulted subsequent to the split of that group and angiosperms—due to parallelism.

In spite of certain similarities, the evidence from vascular anatomy strongly refutes any suggestion of a relationship between Gnetales and angiosperms. Further, the ovules of Gnetales are naked, the nature of their envelops is uncertain and they also differ in the general structure. The female gametophyte of *Gnetum,* according to Pant and Kidwai (1971), is unique and not comparable to that of angiosperms.

The Anthostrobilus (Bennettitalean) Theory

Saporta and Marion (1885), and later Arber and Parkin (1907), proposed the *Bennettitales,* the extinct group of gymnosperms related to Cycadophyta, to be the possible ancestors of angiosperms. The resemblance in structure between the strobili of the mesozoic genus *Cycadeoidea* and the flowers of *Magnolia* has been pointed out by these investigators. Both these structures are bisexual and consist of an elongated axis on which the protective bracts, microsporophylls and megasporophylls are arranged successively from below upwards (Figs. 5.1 and 5.2).

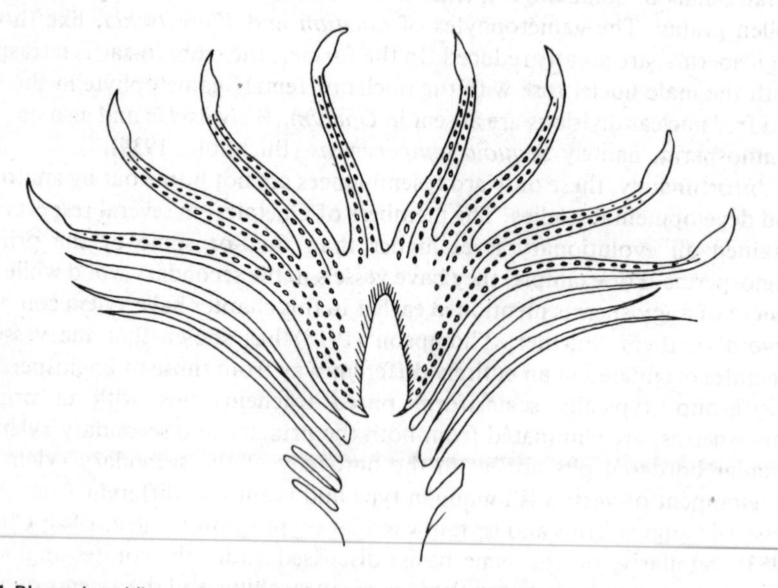

FIG. 5.1 Bisexual strobilus of *Cycadeoidea.* (Redrawn From *An Introduction of Paleobotany* by C.A. Arnold, 1947 by permission of McGraw-Hill Book Co., New York.)

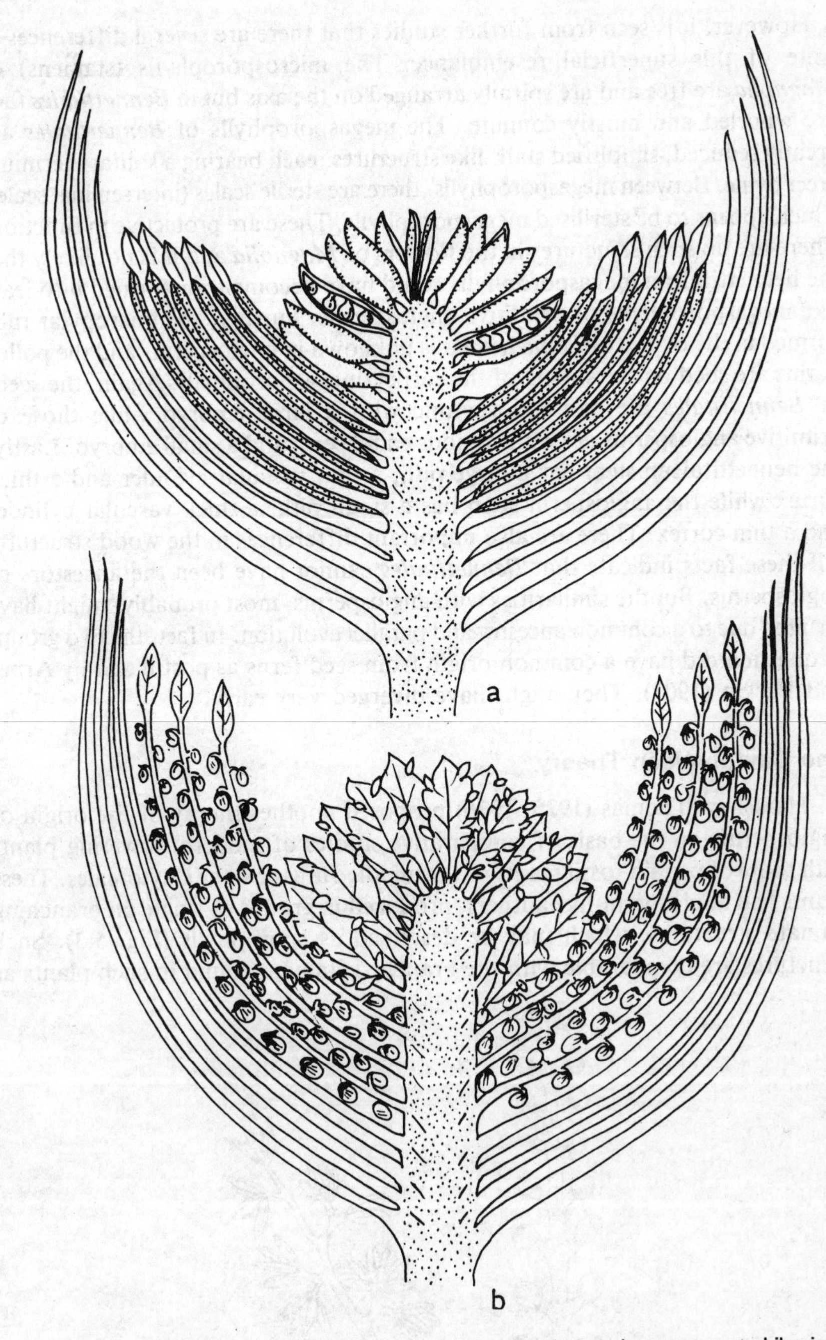

FIG. 5.2 Arber and Parkin's "Hemiangiosperm". (a) Hypothetical angiospermous strobilus in the primitive conditions. (b) The proanthostrobilus of hypothetical Hemiangiospermae. (Redrawn from Arber and Parkin 1907, by permission of the Council of Linnean Society, London.)

However, it is seen from further studies that there are several differences in spite of this superficial resemblance. The microsporophylls (stamens) of *Magnolia* are free and are spirally arranged on the axis but in *Bennettitales* they are whorled and mostly connate. The megasporophylls of *Bennettitales* are greatly reduced, simplified stalk-like structures, each bearing a solitary terminal erect ovule. Between megasporophylls, there are sterile scales (interseminal scales) which appear to be sterilised megasporophylls. These are protective in function. There are no such structures in the flowers of *Magnolia* and it is not likely that the bennettitalean megasporophylls could have become transformed into leaf-like megasporophylls of primitive angiosperms. Further, the micropylar tube formed in the ovules of *Bennettitales* is unknown in angiosperms and the pollen grains are shed on the stigma of the carpel (megasporophyll). Again, the seeds of *Bennettitales* are non-endospermic with a large embryo while those of primitive angiosperms are with copious endosperm and a small embryo. Lastly, the bennettitalean stem has a large pith, a thin vascular cylinder and a thick cortex while the angiosperm stem has a small pith, a thick vascular cylinder and a thin cortex. There are also important differences in the wood structure. All these facts indicate that *Bennettitales* cannot have been the ancestors of angiosperms. But the similarities with angiosperms, most probably, might have resulted due to a common ancestry and parallel evolution. In fact, the two groups in question did have a common origin from seed ferns as postulated by Arber and Parkin (1907). They might have diverged very early.

The Caytonialean Theory

H. Hamshaw Thomas (1925, 1936) proposed another theory of the origin of angiosperms on the basis of comparative studies of modern flowering plants with those of certain fossil plants of the middle Jurassic—the Caytoniales. These plants had angiosperm-like anthers, produced in groups or single on branching pinnate structures, which may be described as sporophylls (Fig. 5.3). Such structures are comparable with the branched stamens found in such plants as

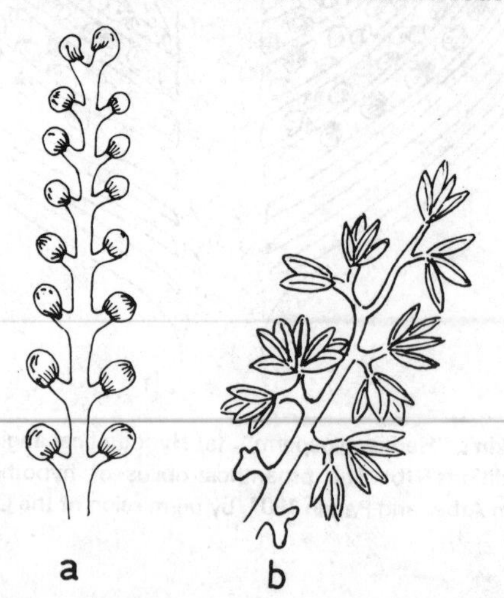

FIG. 5.3 The Caytoniales: (a) Pinnately arranged cupules; (b) branched stamens.

Ricinus, Hypericum and *Calothamnus*. Thomas also explains how angiospermy actually came about, with the help of Caytoniales. It is suggested that the carpel wall of angiosperms may represent a pair of concrescent cupules and that the possible origin of the stigma should be considered in the light of these ancient forms.

Caytoniales, however, are now shown to have affinity with pteridosperms, and they are now classified as Mesozoic remnants of that group. The ancestors of angiosperms must have had open megasporophylls with exposed ovules, as is evident from the morphological studies on the nature of their carpel. Thus the ovary-like pouches of Caytoniales cannot be taken to be the forerunners of angiosperm carpel.

However, more recently, Stebbins (1974) has supported this theory on the basis of homology of the ovules of angiosperms with those of Caytoniales. He has particularly attempted to clarify two problems: (i) why should the primitive orientation of angiosperm ovule be anatropous rather than orthotropous, as is true of the ovules of all other seed plants? and (ii) what are the homologies of the two integuments, in view of the fact that ovules of gymnosperms characteristically possess only one?

Gaussen (1946) and Stebbins (1974) suggested that the ovule of angiosperms is homologous not to the unitegmic, orthotropous ovule of other seed plants but to a cupule of more advanced pteridosperms, particularly Caytoniales, including both the Corystospermaceae and the Caytoniaceae (Thomas, 1933, 1955; Harris, 1951). The position of these cupules relative to their stalks was strikingly similar to that of an anatropous ovule having a well developed funiculus. In Caytoniaceae the cupules were multiovulate and dehiscent but in Corystospermaceae they were uniovulate and indehiscent. If one regards the cupule of this latter family as homologous with the angiosperm ovule, then the outer integument of the latter becomes homologous with the cupule wall and the inner integument with the single integument of the caytonialean ovule as

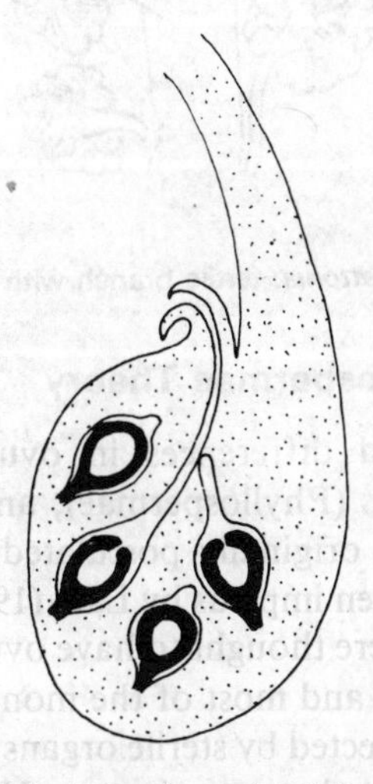

FIG. 5.4 L.S. of cupule of *Caytonia*.

well as with the ovules of the other gymnosperms. Within the "cupule" or anatropous outer integument, the "ovule" of angiosperms has an orthotropous arrangement, corresponding to other gymnosperms.

Further, while clarifying the situation regarding the terminal position of caytonialean cupule on branched axes in contrast to the lateral ovules on flattened sporophylls of angiosperms, Stebbins argues that this situation can be understood on the basis of structure of the fossil *Ligettonia* (Thomas, 1958) found in the Permian strata of South Africa in association with leaves of Glossopteris type. It was suggested that a branched cupule-bearing rachis became adnate to its subtending bract. The carpel is thus regarded as a compound structure, analogous to the ovule-bearing cone-scale of conifers (Florin, 1944). In *Ligettonia,* the elliptic sporophyll apparently bears on its surface two rows of dehiscent cupules (Fig. 5.5). Thus the ancestors of angiosperms were advanced pteridosperms belonging to the Glossopteridalean-Caytonialean alliance that flourished during the Permian, Triassic and Jurassic periods.

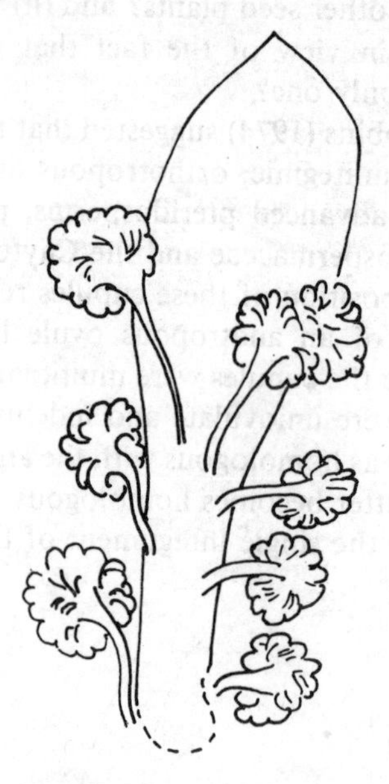

FIG. 5.5 *Ligettonia:* fertile branch with subtending bract.

The Stachyospory-Phyllospermae Theory

On the basis of supposed differences in ovule position borne on stem (Stachyospory) or on leaves (Phyllospermae), an entirely different theory of origin of angiosperms was originally postulated by Sahni (1920) which was redefined, expanded and given impetus by Lam (1948). According to this theory most of the dicotyledons were thought to have ovules enclosed in foliar carpels while the Monochlamydeae and most of the monocotyledons were considered to have megasporangia protected by sterile organs. The two groups were placed in a third group, intermediate between the two. However, Eames (1961) thinks that the theory is valueless because comparative morphology and anatomy show that in angiosperms, all ovules are borne on appendages.

The Pteridosperm Theory

Throughout the Palaeozoic from the Upper Devonian to the Permian, leaves closely resembling those of living ferns are abundant. Some of these leaves were associated with cycad-like stem structure and on the basis of anatomical structure they were considered as forming a distinct group from the ferns. Later they were also discovered with true seeds and have been variously called Cycadofilicales, Pteridosperms or seed-ferns. The mega- and microsporophylls were often borne on the same plant but they were not arranged in definite strobili. On the basis of stem, leaf and seed characters, these have been regarded as probable ancestors of Cycadales and Bennettitales.

The structure of ovule in Pteridosperms, Cycadales, Bennettitales and angiosperms although much diversified, consists of two basic parts, the megasporangium or nucellus and the surrounding protective coverings, the integuments. The morphological nature of nucellus, as established by Hofmeister (1862) is the same for all these groups. The structure of integuments has been variously interpreted. But the most acceptable theory appears to be that formulated by Benson (1904) and later modified by various workers. According to this theory, the ovule is a synangium in which all the sporangia except the more or less central one, have become sterile and have taken on the function of protection for the fertile sporangium. The best evidence for this hypothesis is afforded by ovules of pteridosperms, which show in many forms, well preserved traces of their synangial origin. A similar explanation also applies to the ovules of other groups of plants. In other words, the ovules of all groups of seed plants have probably had a common origin and represent variations of a common structural basis.

According to Long (1966), the first integument of the angiosperm seed is formed by fusion of telomic units but the second integument is an outgrowth, either from the chalaza or the first integument. The angiosperm carpel is regarded as derived from a dorsiventral bivalved pteridosperm cupule by this author.

It has already been indicated that Cycadales or Bennettitales or any other known group of living gymnosperms cannot be considered as ancestral to angiosperms. Thus by way of elimination, the angiosperm ancestry has to be sought in the seed-ferns. According to Cronquist (1968a) "it is a long way, morphologically, from any known seed fern to an angiosperm, but each of the differences could logically be bridged in the course of evolution." The special characters of angiosperms such as double fertilisation and triploid endosperm may be due to extreme reduction of the female gametophyte. Similarly, the origin of sepals from the leaves and of petals from both sepals and stamens, are well-known features in the evolution of angiosperms and therefore, it is not difficult to see the evolution of a flower in this group from cones or cone-like structures of gymnosperms. The most interesting evidence of evolution of angiosperms from seed ferns comes from the fact that some primitive angiosperms lack vessels in the secondary wood, a feature also found in seed ferns. Thus, all the characters in which angiosperms differ from seed ferns could have evolved from a pteridospermous ancestry.

Further, the close external similarity of angiosperms with Bennettitales, also can be explained in terms of common ancestry for both these groups in the pteridosperms. Takhtajan (1969), while concluding his discussion on angiosperm ancestry, states "... that angiosperms arose from some very ancient group of gymnosperms, which must have had primitive secondary xylem of scalariform tracheids at least in the early wood, and primitive bisexual strobili. The strobili must have been of a type that could have diverged to give rise to the primitive bennettitalean strobilus and the primitive angiosperm flower."

According to Melville (1960), the reproductive branch in Glossopteridales—a pteridosperm—is somewhat comparable with that of the present-day angiosperm *Dichapetalum*. On this and other evidences he has proposed a new theory regarding the origin of angiospermic flower known as the "Gonophyll theory". Whether this theory is accepted or not, one thing is clear that angiosperms have some very close connection with pteridosperms. In the absence of any direct evidence, there is a growing tendency among phylogenists to accept the pteridospermic ancestry of angiosperms, at least tentatively.

The Pentoxylales Theory

Meeuse (1961) has listed a number of features of Pentoxylales, a group of fossil pteridosperms, and compared them with those of *Pandanus* (Fig. 5.6). Both

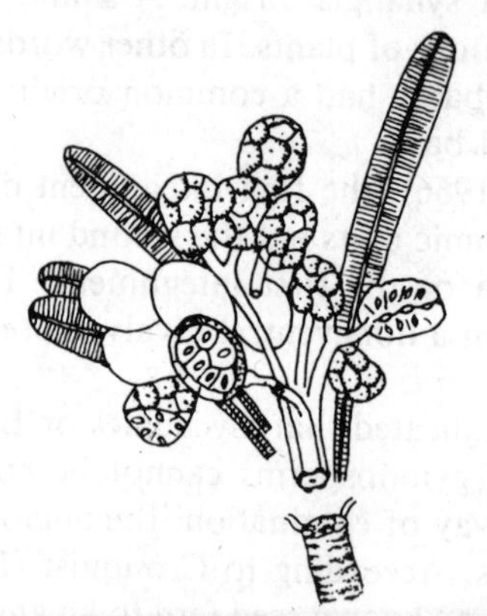

FIG. 5.6 The Pentoxylales: female branch.

these members are erect or suberect dioecious plants with slender cylindrical stems bearing terminal tufts of strap-shaped leaves in spiral arrangement. The inflorescences are borne among the leaves or on short lateral branches in the axils of scaly bracts. The peduncles of inflorescences in both cases contain tracheids with spiral thickenings and others with a kind of bordered pitting. The seeds of the Pentoxylales are enclosed in a fleshy layer, the sarcotesta, and the seed coat consists of two layers. The endosperm is copious and the embryo is minute. All these features are also seen in the seeds of *Pandanus*. Meeuse also listed a number of other comparable characters of Pandanales and Pentoxylales.

In spite of these resemblances, authors like Pant and Kidwai (1971), hold that they could equally be the result of parallel evolution.

The Durian Theory

Corner, with his first hand knowledge of tropical forests, formulated a novel theory (1949) of the origin of angiosperms. This theory is based on the facts of phytogeography, ecology and morphology of angiosperm themselves. Corner suggested that the primitive angiosperm must have been a mesophytic, tropical, cycad-like tree with closely set compound leaves, probably monocarpic and producing a large terminal cluster of arillate follicles (Fig. 5.7). *Durio zibethinus* Murr., a member of Bombacaceae from Burmese and Malayan forests, was taken by this author, as a surviving model of primitive angiosperms. It is a cauliflorous tree and bears large, coloured, loculicidal spiny capsules with fleshy arillate seeds. Corner mentioned that there are about 45 diverse angiospermous families which include arillate genera, mostly distributed in the tropics. Within these families, the reduction series can be traced from genera with arillate fruits to genera having other kinds of fruits. The reduction can further be correlated with a gradual increase in the power of dormancy.

This theory has been criticised by a number of morphologists including Pijl (1952), Parkin (1953), Metcalfe (1954) and Eames (1961) and thus does not find adequate support.

Are Angiosperms Monophyletic or Polyphyletic?

The two terms, monophyletic and polyphyletic have been so frequently used in the classification of angiosperms that it is necessary to understand their exact meaning before employing them in the present discussion.

Davis & Heywood (1963) regard the use of these terms to be purely relative, depending upon how far back in the ancestry one is prepared to go. If life arose only once on earth, all organisms are ultimately *monophyletic* (derived from the common or same ancestor). However, for practical purposes, a narrower definition has to be used for evolutionary interpretation. Simpson (1961) defines monophyly as "*the derivation of a taxon through one or more lineages from one immediately ancestral taxon of the same or lower rank.*" A family, for instance, derived from a family, genus or species. Heslop-Harrison (1958b), following Wernham (1912), defines a monophyletic group as one *derived from an ancestral form which would be regarded as belonging to the taxon in question* (family from family, genus from genus, etc.).

The level of polyphyly, according to Simpson, is specified by *the highest ranking taxa, two or more of which are immediately ancestral to the taxon concerned.*

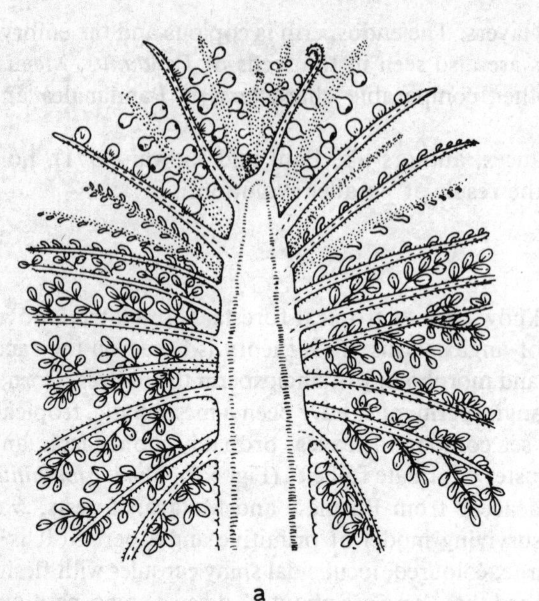

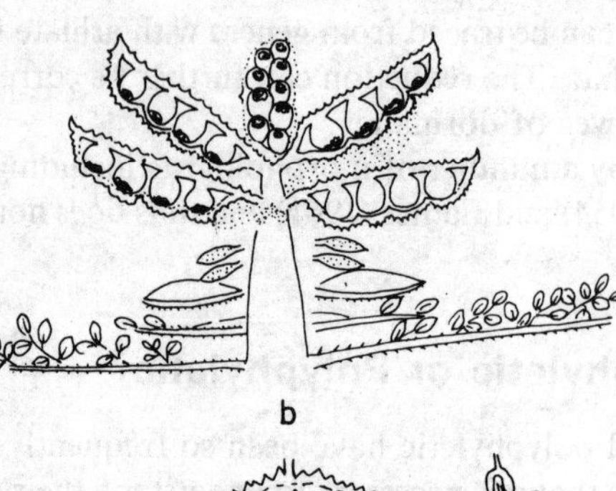

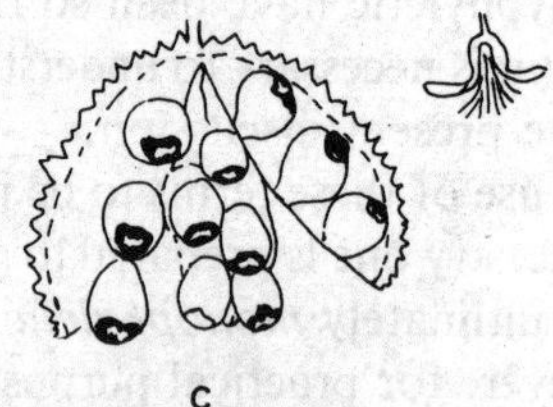

FIG. 5.7 Corner's reconstructions of ancestral angiosperms according to Durian theory: (a) Ancestral pachycaulous spinous flowering plant terminated by flowers and fruits. (b) Primitive fruit with spinous arillate pods. (c) Fruit and flower of *Durio*. (d) Fruit and flower of *Sterculia*. (e) Fruits of *Desmos*. (f) Fruit and flower of *Horsfieldia*. (g) Pods and flower of *Tabernaemontana*. (h) Acorn and flower of *Quercus*. (i) Fruit and flower of Compositae. (Redrawn from *The Life of Plants* by E.J.H. Corner 1964, by permission of University of Chicago Press.)

Thus when these definitions are applied to angiosperms, it should mean their derivation from one (monophyletic) or more than one group (polyphyletic) of plants which can be considered at a lower rank than a sub-division. It could be a Class, Order, etc. or even a species. When they are derived from a class, i.e. a group of immediate lower rank, they may be regarded as *monophyletic* at class-level by Simpson's definitions, but *polyphyletic* at order or family level, as defined by Heslop-Harrison. Thus, the distinction between monophyly and polyphyly rests upon a difference in time level. In the following discussion, we shall adhere to Simpson's definition, so that if angiosperms are derived from any one group below the level of a sub-division, we shall take them to be monophyletic and if they are derived from more than one group below the level of sub-division, we shall regard them as polyphyletic—a practice often followed by most taxonomists.

Angiosperms have undergone intensive evolution in many directions under many different environmental conditions, and as a result, have attained an extraordinary degree of morphological and ecological diversity. It is, therefore, sometimes felt that they must be derived from more than one ancestral source, they must be polyphyletic in origin. Such an outlook was held by a number of phylogenists including Engler (1892) and his followers, Eames (1961), Meeuse (1966, 1970, 1975), Hughes (1976), Krassilov (1973, 1975, 1977) and a few others. Krassilov states that the claim of monophyletic origin of angiosperms arose from the confusion of phylogenetic and taxonomic concepts. According to him, "unpreconceived studies of extant angiosperms point to more than one archetype. Several lines of angiosperms have simultaneously entered the fossil record; monocotyledons, proto-Hamamelidales, proto-Laurales and proteophylls (possibly ancestral to the Rosidae) are recognised among them. Three groups of Mesozoic seed plants—Caytoniales, Czekanowskiales and Dirhopalostachyaceae—are distinguished as major sources of angiosperm character (proangiosperms)...."

The morphological and taxonomic evidence, on the contrary, leads to the conclusion that angiosperms are one natural monophyletic branch of development. The common origin of all the orders and families of angiosperms is demonstrated by their multitude of common morphological characters. It is demonstrated by the uniform staminal structure, with the characterisitic endothecial layer of the anther-wall, by the presence of specialised megasporophylls (carpels) with stigmas, by the constancy of the androecium and gynoecium on the floral axis, by the characteristic male and female gametophytes basically similar throughout the group and accompanied by double fertilisation and the formation of triploid endosperm, and by the presence of sieve tubes (Takhtajan, 1969). Parkin (1923) pointed out that the independent origin of these characters in different taxonomic groups is statistically very unlikely.

Takhtajan (1969) further states that the orders Urticales, Casuarinales and Fagales, so distinct at first sight from Magnoliales, are linked with them by an intermediate group, the Hamamelidales. Thus, the groups which at first sight seem completely isolated and suggest a polyphyletic origin do, in fact, after closer investigation and wider comparison with other groups, sooner or later fall into their natural place in the system of angiosperm classification.

Hickey & Doyle (1977) believe that the paleontological data derived from the monosulcate pollen strongly supports the monophyletic origin of angiosperms.

Faegri (1980), in his recent article, settled the problem of polyphyletic origins of angiosperms. According to him, the question of monophyly or polyphyly must be formulated on the basis of a starting level. In the case of angiosperms this level must be defined as follows: was the immediate common ancestor of all angiosperms also the last non-angiosperm in that line of development, or were several non-angiospermous stages intercalated between the last common ancestor and the proto-angiosperm?

In his definition of proto-angiosperms, he states that this taxon possesses at least one basic feature of angiosperms while the non-angiosperm possesses none. He assumes five basic, mutually independent characters of angiosperms (ABCDE). All these characters, or a syndrome of characters are thought to have been gradually built up in the course of evolution. This is represented schematically in Fig. 5.8.

In this scheme, Example I shows the real monophyletic descent of angiosperms. Example II shows an equally straightforward polyphyletic (or at least diphyletic) descent. Example III is complicated. It shows that "angiospermy" as defined by the full angiosperm syndrome, is clearly polyphyletic but angiosperms, when taken as the acquisition of the first angiospermic character (ABC), can be termed monophyletic. On the other hand, if we demand a full complement of angiosperm characteristic, before accepting the plant as an angiosperm, the group is polyphyletic. Example IV depicts a still more complicated situation of what may have actually happened. It will be seen that there is only one proto-angiosperm taxon ABCD which gives some information about the earlier stage in the ancestry of today's angiospermae, whereas the rest have no known direct ancestors, nor can anything be inferred directly from the other known proto-angiosperms.

Most of us take the monophyletic origin of angiosperms when they have acquired first characteristic of angiospermae—somewhere near the bottom line of the Faegri's scheme.

The Origin of Monocotyledons

Division of angiosperms into two major groups, the monocotyledons and the dicotyledons, has long been maintained, although the differences between the two are not well-marked. Monocotyledons are generally distinguished from dicotyledons by their single cotyledon, scattered vascular bundles in their stems and parallel leaf venation. These, however, are not their exclusive characters. There are other morphological characters of less significance, such as general habit, often underground perennating organs like rhizomes, bulbs or corms and hypogeal germination. In addition, they have many adventitious roots and the floral parts are arranged in whorls of three. Similarly, absence of a typical cambium and presence of septal nectaries are some more characters used to distinguish a few monocot groups. However, all these differences are outnumbered by close morphological resemblances.

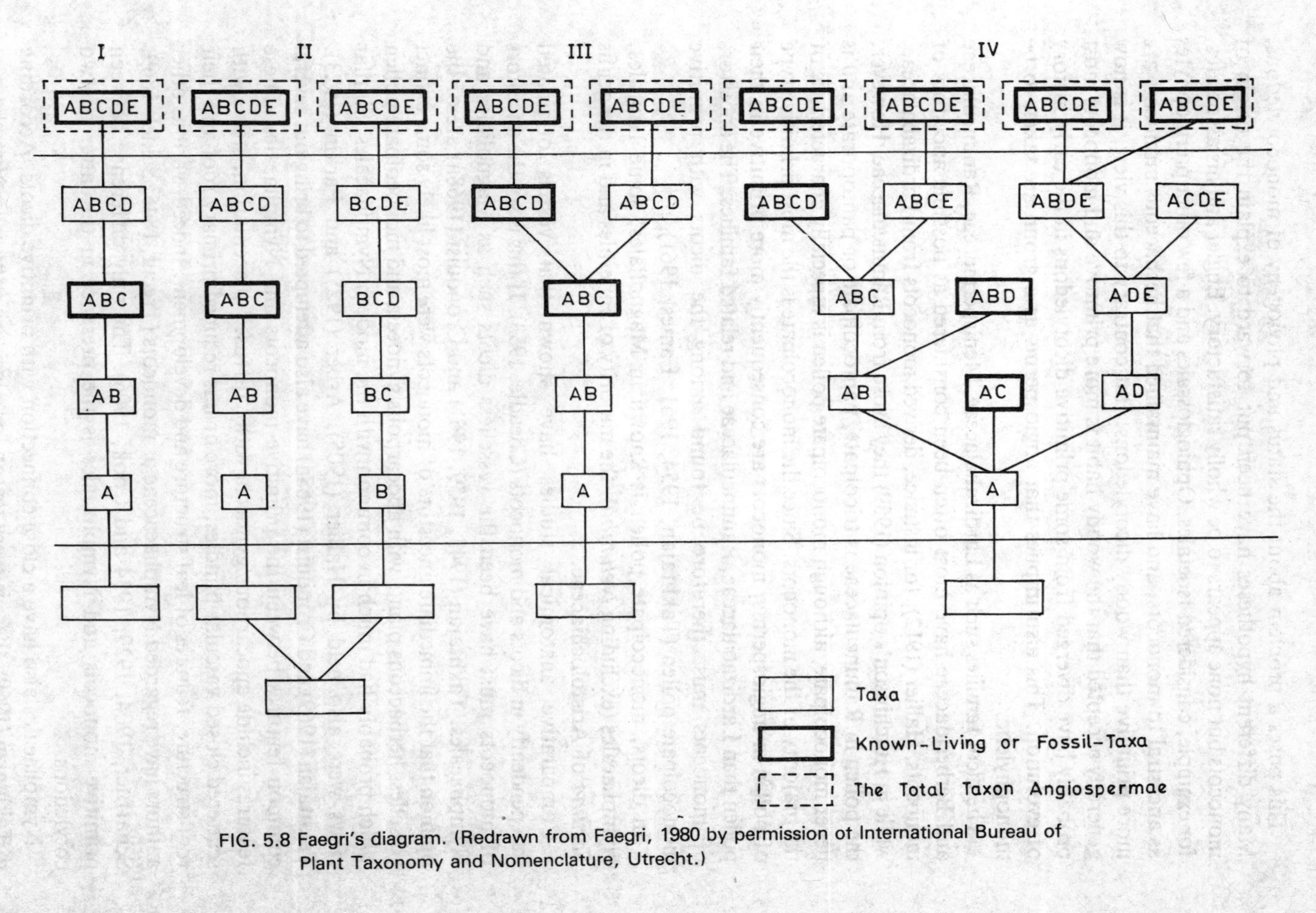

FIG. 5.8 Faegri's diagram. (Redrawn from Faegri, 1980 by permission of International Bureau of Plant Taxonomy and Nomenclature, Utrecht.)

This poses a problem about the status and phylogeny of monocotyledons. Many different hypotheses have been put forward to explain the origin of monocots but none appears to be wholly satisfactory. Engler and his associates, for example, considered Isoetales, Ophioglossales and a few other pteridophytes as ancestral to monocots, and have maintained that herbaceous monocots are more primitive than woody dicotyledons. But contrary to this view, it is now generally accepted that the woody habit is more primitive and monocots most probably have diverged from some primitive dicotyledons in the early history of evolution. This also implies that angiosperms as a group are taken to be monophyletic.

The dicot families such as Lardizabalaceae, Menispermaceae, Ranunculaceae and Berberidaceae have most often been considered as possible ancestors of monocots. Hallier (1912), for instance, derived monocots from Lardizabalaceae, while in Hutchinson's opinion (1959) they arose from Ranunculaceae. However, the pollen in Ranunculaceae is tricolpate, pantocolpate or pantoporate and is never monocolpate, although monocolpate pollen is especially characteristic of the majority of the monocots. Since the monocolpate is the most primitive type of pollen in angiosperms, monocots are consequently more primitive in their pollen than Lardizabalaceae, Ranunculaceae and related families. The ancestors of monocots must therefore be found among the dicots with primitive monocolpate pollen (Takhtajan, 1954, 1961; Eames, 1961).

In dicots, monocolpate pollen is known in Magnoliales, some Laurales, Nymphaeales (excluding *Nelumbo*), the majority of Piperales and in the genus *Saruma* of Aristolochiaceae.

Comparative anatomical studies have shown that vessels originated independently in dicots and monocots (Cheadle, 1953). If this is so, the ancestors of monocots must have been the vesselless dicots such as Magnoliales and Nymphaeales. Takhtajan (1943, 1959, 1961) and Cronquist (1968a) are of the opinion that the immediate ancestors of monocots were most likely some extinct vesselless herbaceous plants with apocarpous gynoecia and monocolpate pollen which probably had much in common with the modern Nymphaeales. Similar views were also held by Hallier (1905), Arber (1925) and Parkin (1923). Takhtajan (1969) and Cronquist (1968a) have also attempted to bring out several common features between the primitive monocots and Nymphaeales. These features include apocarpous gynoecia with "diffuse" placentation, stems with scattered closed vascular bundles, more or less reduced primary root and their root structure, features of leaf structure and development. Indeed, various other authors have regarded Nymphaeaceae as monocots (Trecul, 1845; Seidel, 1869; Schaffner, 1904, 1929, 1934 and Cook, 1906). The only difference between primitive monocots and Nymphaeales is the presence in the latter of two cotyledons.

Nymphaeales also have a close connection with primitive dicots. According to Takhtajan (1969), there is every reason for considering the order Nymphaeales as a hygrophilous derivative of some ancient Magnoliales, the vegetative organs of which have more or less degenerated in an aquatic environment. Such ancient herbaceous dicots of nymphaealean type, but more primitive and less reduced than their present-day representatives, quite probably initiated the monocot line. Thus, monocots have an aquatic ancestry as well (Henslow, 1911; Cronquist 1968a). Sargant (1903, 1904, 1908), however, concluded that monocots have arisen as a result of adaptation to a geophilous (marsh loving) habit. He calls them "aquatic geophytes". Apparently, the common ancestors of both Nymphaeales and monocots were amphibious geophytes in which geophily at first arose under terrestrial conditions—most probably under the forest canopy or in the forest margin.

Monocots are characterised by a single cotyledon in their embryo, while the great majority of dicots have two cotyledons. Hegelmaier (1874, 1878), on the basis of comparative study of various dicot and monocot embryos, suggested that the monocot embryo arose as a result of the failure of one of the two cotyledons of a typical dicot embryo to develop. This abortion-hypothesis was subsequently propagated by Henslow (1893, 1911), Winkler (1931), Metcalfe (1936), Eames (1961) and many others. Stebbins (1974), on the other hand, believes that the single cotyledon of monocots is derived through intercalary concrescence of the petioles of two original cotyledons by way of syncotyly and subsequent reduction of lobes. He does not agree with the nymphaealean ancestry of monocots but proposes that they might have diverged early in the history from a common stock. In his opinion, vessels arose later in the evolution of monocots and the group is most probably derived from *Drymis*-like ancestors with short internodes and vesselless wood. They evolved in open climate which was seasonally wet and dry. The primitive monocot habit thus is exemplified by geophytic habit with radical leaves and branched scapes somewhat similar to the present-day *Aspidistra, Curculigo, Chlorophytum* -like members of the Liliales. Aquatic monocotyledons, as well as xeric forms and those having arboreal growth habit are regarded as secondary derivatives.

On similar grounds, but in an entirely different manner, Burger (1977) proposed derivation of monocots from dicot ancestors very similar to Chloranthaceae of the order Piperales. According to him, Piperales, like Nympheales, are more closely related to monocots than other living dicots. Because Piperales, Arales and some Najadales exhibit relationships that span the most profound dichotomy in angiosperms, it is argued that these plants represent very ancient lineages. Berger developed a hypothesis suggesting that the simple flowers, similar to those of Chloranthaceae, came together by the loss of internodes to form three-parted flowers of Piperales and many monocots. He further postulates that the ancestral simple flowers had a single small bract, two stamens and a single adaxial pistil. He has provided evidence from Lactoridaceae, Saururaceae, Potamogetonaceae, Alismatales and others in support of his hypothesis.

Role of Ecology and Genetics in the Evolution of Angiosperms

Ecology of angiosperms appears to be peculiar, especially with regard to their absence in the fossil remains. The groups that are considered to be primitive are at present localised in the montane situations of the tropics and subtropics. Thus it seems likely that the first angiosperms were inhabitants of the mountains (Berry, 1934; Takhtajan, 1948; Arnold, 1947; Axelrod, 1952, 1960; and Nemejc, 1956). If this conjecture is correct, then the absence of fossil record can be understood. Mountain plants are usually found far from the areas of accumulation of sediments and buried plant remains. Thus, their fossilization is not usually possible. This situation also tells us that the size of their populations, as in the case of most mountain plants, is of small dimensions and often leads to rapid rate of evolution. (For details of population concept, ecological and genetic variations see Chapter 8.)

The population is characterised by free exchange of genes amongst its members. It therefore exists and acts as a unit of evolution. But the effective breeding population is in fact smaller than the size of the entire population. Thus interbreeding is possible between the neighbouring individuals, and those separated from each other by a large number of individuals between them may become isolated from one another. In such a situation they can as well be regarded as members of different populations. In other words, a large population in which individuals at opposite ends are isolated from one another, actually represents a group of small effectively breeding populations. In fact, in nature, species are often represented by numerous small populations such as these. They are particularly characteristic of mountain situations and are effectively isolated from one another by various factors.

In small populations, effect of mutation is more pronounced and there is rapid spread of mutant genes. This causes a "genetic drift" between the two potentially interbreeding populations and evolution of new forms. If this genetic drift countinues in future generations, the new forms become established in nature. If on the contrary the drift discontinues, the population may revert back. Such chance events or accidents have no real significance in large, freely breeding populations. Again, genetically isolated, or rather, mutated small populations may undergo occasional interbreeding giving rise to hybrids of vigorous nature.

On the basis of this information on population genetics, Takhtajan (1947) attempted to explain the origin of angiosperms and their rapid expansion. He states that the transitional groups between gymnosperms and angiosperms existed as small populations in which evolution went on at an accelerated rate. Takhtajan (1969) also postulates the phenomena of *neoteny* to explain the adaptations of angiosperms to varied climatic conditions. *Neoteny* is the cessation of ontogeny at an earlier stage than in the ancestral forms. As a result of such premature completion of ontogeny, the ancestral adult stage disappears from the individual life-histories of neotenic forms. Kolstov (1963) has demonstrated that abrut neoteny involves a marked simplification of the phenotype alone but the genotype retains its complexity.

Genetically, neoteny may be understood to have mutation of genes controlling the speed of ontogenetic development and involve the reduction in the activity of certain other genes. Back mutations which can unlock the neotenic barriers are also possible—thus resulting in evolutionary reversals. Takhtajan has further attempted to explain the morphological peculiarities on the basis of neoteny.

According to him, the flower may be regarded as a neotenic form of the strobilus of ancestral gymnosperms. Similarly, conduplication of megasporophyll into carpel, stamens and even male and female gametophytes are shown to be the results of neoteny.

Stebbins (1974) agrees with the point of population size and their upland inhabitation of pre-angiospermous plants as well as present evolutionary active groups of angiosperms. He believes that montane situations, particularly with semi-arid climate, exposed to seasonal draught, are ideal for the rapid rate of evolution.

Insects and Evolution of Angiosperms

It has been already mentioned that angiosperms most probably evolved during the Lower Cretaceous and spread enormously by the Middle Cretaceous ultimately forming a dominant component of the earth's vegetation by the Upper Cretaceous. This happened within a short evolutionary period of about 25 million years.

The problem before us now is how to explain the origin of angiosperms "long before the Cretaceous period" and "the great expansion of them during middle Cretaceous" (see Takhtajan, 1969). Darwin in 1875 suggested that angiosperms must have been largely developed in some isolated areas, whence owing the geographical changes, they at last succeeded in escaping, and spread quickly over the world. Takhtajan expanded this hypothesis further on a concrete factual basis and concluded that due to great continental uplifts, the intensification of mountain building, the development of arid-climate regions and the general diversification of environmental conditions lead to an abrupt transformation of the organic world. According to him, the Cretaceous, and particularly the late Cretaceous, was marked by a much greater diversity of physico-geographical conditions than the Jurassic and for some reasons it is not fully understood how plants that had been dominant in the Jurassic period gave way to angiosperms. Plants like Bennettitales, Ginkgoales, Cycadales and ferns, did not possess sufficient evolutionary plasticity to enable them to produce new forms adopted to novel conditions of more diverse and rapidly changing environments. Ultimately some of them like Bennettitales and Ginkgoales became totally extinct while certain others like Cycadales and ferns faded into the background. Angiosperms with their great evolutionary plasticity and unusual adaptability, spread rapidly.

An important factor in the rapid development of angiosperms was their complex interrelationship with insects, which is not found in living gymnosperms. The role of insects in the evolution and development of angiosperms has been emphasised by various authors including Arber and Parkin (1907), Seward (1910), Scott (1911) and recently by Ehlrich and Raven (1964).

Some angiosperms that are considered to belong to primitive families are pollinated by beetles. These and similar other insects were feeding on floral parts and as they moved from one flower to the other pollen was transported from one flower to the carpels of others. These flowers generally have many floral parts, so the chewing away of many stamens or carpels may still leave many others unaffected and functional. This primitive insect pollination must have led to protection of the ovules (Gundersen, 1950; Grant, 1950; Percival, 1965; and Faegri & van der Pijl, 1966, 1979) and also economy of pollen. The original attractant in insect pollination was pollen but the necessity for pollen economy leads to a course of evolution in which a flower starts producing a cheaper foodstuff, nectar, as its alternative. Nectar is produced in special structures—nectaries. These appear to have originated independently in diverse groups of angiosperms. Thus, pollen economy, profitable use of nectar and exploitation of insect visitors lead to the perfection of pollination mechanisms.

Entomophily of primitive type, or cantharophily, was gradually replaced by entomophily (small or sucking insects) in some forms and anemophily in others. But according to Cronquist (1968a), wind pollination and insect pollination are not necessarily mutually exclusive. The change from one to the other can take place gradually, without sudden jumps, especially if the adaptation to insect pollination is generalised and does not involve a complex or unusual structure associated with a particular kind of pollinator. The evolutionary trend from entomophily to anemophily is reversible and in a number of cases this has actually happened (e.g. *Ficus, Castanea*).

The protection to ovules against chewing insects was offered successfully by closure of the carpel. Golenkin (1927) pointed out that the development of closed carpels made it possible for angiosperms to simplify the structure of their ovules and this in turn led to smaller ovules. This was a very important advance, as it enabled the angiosperms to have great economy of material in construction of ovule and female gametophyte. Along with the development of carpel, there was formation of stigmatic surface—a further specialisation for further evolution of pollination mechanisms. The stigma can serve as a new barrier to undesirable pollen and thereby assist cross-fertilisation. Finally, the union of carpels and their enclosure, in bud condition, by floral parts had a great adaptive significance. Corner (1964) thinks that these changes were also exceedingly important for the improvement of the seed-dispersal mechanism.

Beetle-pollination was gradually replaced by pollination by other specialised insects such as bees and wasps (Hymenoptera), butterflies and moths (Lepidoptera), flies (Diptera) with sucking mouth parts, and birds. With the development of gamopetalous and zygomorphic corolla, there evolved specificity of insect pollinators and their constancy of visits. The co-ordinate evolution or co-evolution of angiosperms and their pollinators achieved the highest degree of variation and adaptation leading to complex process of mutual selection. Therefore, the families of angiosperms with flowers more highly specialised for pollination show greater species differentiation of floral characters than those pollinated by different insects. With the establishment of more specialised forms of pollination, the rate of angiosperm evolution greatly increased, and has continued gradually to increase (Grant, 1949, 1963).

Adaptive radiation for pollination by animal vectors has been recognised in two families that have been intensively studied, the Polemoniaceae (Grant & Grant, 1965) and the Orchidaceae (van der Pijl & Dodson, 1966). In these families, adaptation to solitary aculeate Hymenoptera and other relatively unspecialised insects is the primitive condition. Several lines of radiation have led to pollination by more specialised Hymenoptera (*Bombus, Xylocopa*), as well as by long-tongued flies (Bombylidae, Syrphidae), day- and night-flying Lepidoptera, Coleoptera and hummingbirds (Trochilidae). Each of these adaptations involves characteristic modifications of the colour, form and odour of the flower. In orchids, two adaptations for attracting male Hymenoptera as pollen vectors have evolved: resemblance of females, which includes pseudocopulation, and chemical sex attractants.

Similarly, diversification of species in some genera such as *Asclepias* (Woodson, 1954) and *Pedicularis* (Sprague, 1962; Macior, 1968) is associated with the evolution of different structural adaptations for pollination by the same vector.

Stebbins (1974) concludes that adaptive radiation for pollen vectors involves the following evolutionary principles: (i) predominant influence of the most effective pollinator; (ii) adaptive syndromes of characters, selection along lines of least resistance, transfer of function via an intermediate stage of double function, and reversals of adaptive trends. Each of these phenomena contributes to the complexity of adaptive radiation in angiosperms.

Cradle of Angiosperms

The third important problem about the origin of angiosperms is to determine *the place* where they might have first evolved. The fossil evidence, just as it is insufficient to decide *the time* as well as *the nature of ancestors* of angiosperms, is also meagre and unsatisfactory to settle the problem of the place of origin.

There appear to be two opposing views in respect of the centre of origin or at least the place of diversification of flowering plants.

Some authors are of the opinion that angiosperms might have originated at high latitudes in the Arctic or the Antarctic region. Heer (1868) first suggested the northern polar region to be the centre of origin of angiosperms and the hypothesis was strongly supported by a large number of palaeobotanists as well as phytogeographers including Saporta (1877), Hooker (1879), Asa Gray, Adolf Engler in the late nineteenth century and later by Thiselton-Dyer, Seward, Berry, Chaney, Just, Arnold and many others in the twentieth century.

This hypothesis holds that angiosperms originated in the polar region of Holarctic and from there spread in successive waves across the whole earth. The beauty of this hypothesis lies in the fact that it provides an easy explanation for the present distribution of many genera in widely separated continents, chiefly the northern America and the eastern Asia. However, this explanation leaves many more phytogeographical problems unsolved. The north polar region is particularly poor in fossil records of the Cretaceous and Tertiary floras. Further, the available evidence indicates the derived nature of the genera found in those parts. Some of the phytogeographers mentioned above, also thought that some time in the past there must have existed a tropical weather in the polar regions which favoured the development of rich tropical forests of angiosperms in those regions. But it is now well known that subsequent to the mid-Mesozoic era, when angiosperms are believed to have originated, there has never been a tropical warm climate in the polar regions and the atmospheric conditions of extremely low temperatures and prolonged darkness certainly do not favour the development of rich tropical forests. In fact, recently, Croizat (1952) and van Steenis (1962) also have strongly criticised the idea of the polar origin of angiosperms. Axelrod (1959) has clearly shown that at the beginning of the Cretaceous, angiosperms were found only between 45° N and 45°S latitudes and not beyond these. It is only at the end of the early Cretaceous that they reached higher latitudes. Takhtajan is therefore of the opinion that "the hypothesis of Arctic (or Antarctic) origin for angiosperms must be firmly rejected. The facts of palaeobotany have been found to be incompatible with it, nor can the present distribution of plants be explained by it."

Since the polar hypothesis of the origin of angiosperms was felt inadequate to explain the present distribution of plants, many authors turned to seek their origin in the lower latitudes—the tropical and subtropical regions.

Hallier (1912) thought the basin of the Pacific Ocean to be the birth place of angiosperms, on the hypothetical continent Pacifica. He considered places such as the Andes, the Hawaiian Islands, New Caledonia and New Zealand to be the probable places where ancestors of angiosperms could be traced. But there is no geological evidence in support of such a hypothetical continent. Bailey (1949) suggested that the present floras of Northern Australia, New Guinea, New Caledonia, Fiji and the adjacent areas are rich in certain primitive forms of angiosperms which serve as missing links in the chain of angiosperm phylogeny. The geographical restriction of most primitive angiosperms to the islands is most striking. Many primitive families such as the Magnoliaceae, Degeneriaceae, Himantendraceae, Eupomatiaceae, Winteraceae, Austrobaileyaceae, Amborellaceae, Gomortegaceae, Lactoridaceae, Calycanthaceae, Trochodendraceae, Tetracentraceae, etc. are concentrated chiefly about the Pacific basin. The western part of the basin is particularly rich in the number of species belonging to these families and covers the wider areas from Assam, Burma, China, Japan to Australia, New Zealand, New Caledonia and the island of Fiji. The cradle of angiosperms, according to Takhtajan, must be sought here in this part in the eastern and south-eastern Asia, Australasia and Malenesia. This part shows the geographical distribution and connections of primitive angiosperms and thus may be taken as, if not a birth place, at least a centre of their diversification, during the Cretaceous period, and this could be very near to their birth place as well. Most probably it was situated in South-East Asia.

However, this does not mean that all primitive angiosperms are concentrated in the South-Eastern Asia. They occur outside this region as well. But the comparative morphological studies reveal that even among the primitive genera, this presumed cradle of angiosperms is characterised by more primitive species. Many such examples within Magnoliales have been quoted in support of the hypothesis, thus making it an acceptable theory.

Unfortunately, there is no direct palaeobotanical evidence which can support this theory. The present acceptance of the theory is based on the study of distribution and comparative morphology of presumably primitive angiosperms. Stebbins (1974), however, argues that the tropical rain forests with equable climate have most probably served as the "museums" rather than "cradle" of angiosperms. According to him, the maximum environmental challenge for adaptive radiation, leading to the origin of diversified groups of angiosperms is likely to occur in marginal or ecotonal regions in which precipitation is intermediate between complete sufficiency and continuous deficiency and in which frosts are minimal but present. The plant communities of these transitional regions are more fragile and are more likely to be altered by changing factors. In the Pacific coast of the United States, he has observed that speciation in marginal or transitional habitats has been more active than in either wet forests or deserts. Thus the tropical rain and cloud forests are not the communities within which angiosperms originated and differentiated, but they have preserved the diversified plant groups because of low rate of extinction. The museum hypothesis is supported by the fact that tropical forests contain a complete spectrum from the most primitive to the most advanced families and the transitional forms are either totally absent or less abundant. He has quoted several examples to show that the derivation of mesophytes from more xeric ancestors might be expected to occur more frequently than the reverse trend. On the basis of the "species pump" hypothesis developed by Valentine (1967) it has been attempted to explain the diversity of tropical plant communities. It is interesting to note that marginal conditions due to increasing drought surround the tropical forests. The more active and rapid speciation takes place in these marginal areas, and the newer populations are "pumped" into the stable communities of tropical forests from time to time. Thus, angiosperms, in all probabilities have developed in semi-arid situations having a marked seasonal drought and a short season favourable for the formation of flowers and seeds. Under such conditions, strong selective pressures would exist for speeding up the reproductive cycle, thereby favouring morphological reductions as well as rapid endosperm and embryo development that results from double fertilisation. The regions in which climatic factors have greatly promoted the diversification of modern flora are the Cape region of South Africa, the Ethiopian highlands, parts of the Indian Peninsula, south-central Mexico, northern Venezuela, the coast of Equador and the northern provinces of Argentina.

In conclusion, as has been summed up by Pant and Kidwai (1971), it may be said that, in spite of these heroic attempts to solve the problem from different angles, there is no convincing evidence in support of either the accepted *time, nature of ancestral stocks* or the *place* of origin of angiosperms and the "abominable mystery" felt by Darwin in 1859, still remains, if not totally, at least in major part "abominable" to the present generation of scientists.

Hypothetical Construction of the First Formed Angiosperm

In the absence of dependable and complete fossil history of angiosperms, their evolutionary history—or how they progressed gradually from simple to the most complex type of organisms—can only be inferred from data existing in living members of the group. The most basic question is to determine the probable nature of primitive angiosperms. Since no such plant is known to be taken as primitive from which various groups are presumed to have evolved it is necessary to construct the same hypothetically. This can be done on the basis of a set of characters presumed to be primitive. If all the assumed primitive characters are put together, that may give some idea of a hypothetical primitive angiospermic plant.

The next problem is to decide as to which characters are primitive and which ones are advanced. Various authors have based their so-called phylogenetic systems on these "dicta" and principles. However, opinions still differ and it would be seen that there are contrasting schools of thought in respect of the consideration of primitive features. Sporne (1948) had defined the term "primitive character", as that which is possessed by its ancestors. An "advanced character" on the other hand, is the one possessed by a present-day taxon and not possessed by its ancestor, that is, it replaced an ancestral character during evolution. However, phylogenists, many a times, are unable to determine the direction in which a particular character has evolved. This results in uncertain situation regarding the primitive feature. Therefore, the most successful methods in determination of primitive or advanced nature, as related to comparative morphology, are the ***doctrines of association, correlation and common ground plan.***

According to Wagner (1962), the common ancestry gives rise to divergent derivatives. Some derivatives will closely resemble their ancestor whereas others will become highly modified and not resemble their ancestors at all. If this is true then it should be assumed that (i) plants which have a large number of characteristics in common have the same common ancestor; (ii) evolution proceeds in various directions; and (iii) evolution takes place at different rates at various times and in different lines. Wagner (1961, 1962) has suggested the ground plan/divergence method for reconstruction of the best estimate of phylogeny, utilising all characters. Accordingly, three aspects of studies are essential. These are: (i) systematic or comparative analysis of plants; (ii) determination of ground plans to find common characters for all or most of the plants; (iii) phylogenetic synthesis to assemble the taxa according to their respective deviations from the ground plant.

With such a philosophy in mind, the dicta or principles proposed by some of the authors are given here for the sake of comparison, and the general evolutionary trends accepted by various recent authors are discussed later in the next chapter.

Bessey's Dicta (1915)

A. General Dicta

1. Evolution is not always upward, but often it involves degradation and degeneration.
2. In general, homogeneous structures (with many and similar parts) are

lower, and heterogeneous structures (with fewer and dissimilar parts) are higher.
3. Evolution does not necessarily involve all organs of the plant equally in any particular period, and one organ may be advancing while another is retrograding.
4. Upward development is sometimes through an increase in complexity and sometimes by a simplification of an organ or a set of organs.
5. Evolution has been generally consistent and when a particular progression or retrogression has set in, it is persisted into the end of the phylum.
6. In a phylum the holophytic (chlorophyll-green) plants precede the colourless (hysterophytic) plants, and the latter are derived from the former.
7. Plant relationships are up and down the genetic lines and these must constitute the framework of phylogenetic taxonomy.

B. Special Dicta (With Reference to Flowering Plants)

8. The stem structure with collateral vascular bundles arranged in a cylinder is more primitive than that with scattered bundles, and the latter are to be regarded as derived from the former.
9. Woody stems (as of trees) are more primitive than herbaceous stems, and herbs have been held to have been derived from trees.
10. The simple, unbranched stem is an earlier type, from which branching stems have been derived.
11. Historically, the arrangement of leaves in pairs on the stem is held to have preceded the spiral arrangement in which the leaves are solitary at the nodes.
12. Historically, simple leaves preceded branched (compound) leaves.
13. Historically, leaves were first persistent (evergreen) and later deciduous.
14. The reticulate venation of leaves is the normal structure and the parallel venation of some leaves is a special modification derived from it.
15. The polymerous flower structure precedes and the oligomerous structure follows from it and this is accompanied by a progressive sterilisation of sporophylls.
16. Petaly is the normal perianth structure and apetaly is the result of perianth reduction (aphanisis).
17. The apochlamydeous perianth is earlier and the gamochlamydeous perianth is derived from it by a symphysis of the members of the perianth whorl.
18. Actinomorphy is an earlier structure than zygomorphy and the latter resulted from a change from a similar to a dissimilar growth of the members of the perianth whorl.
19. Hypogyny is a more primitive structure from which epigyny was derived later.
20. Apocarpy is the primitive structure and from it syncarpy was derived later.
21. Polycarpy is the earlier condition and oligocarpy was derived from it later.

22. The endospermous seed is primitive and lower while the seed without endosperm is derived and higher.
23. Consequently, the seed with a small embryo (in endosperm) is more primitive than the seed with a large embryo (in scanty or no endosperm).
24. In earlier (primitive) flowers there are many stamens (polystemonous) while in later flowers there are fewer stamens (oligostemonous).
25. The stamens of primitive flowers are separated (apostemonous) while those of derived flowers are often united (synstemonous).
26. The condition of powdery pollen is more primitive than that with coherent or massed pollen.
27. Flowers with both stamens and carpels (monoclinous) precede those in which these occur on separate flowers (diclinous).
28. In diclinous plants the monoecious condition is the earlier and the dioecious later.

Thorne's Principles (1958)

1. Existing species have descended with change from pre-existing species and are therefore, the products of evolutionary forces.
2. Ancestral conditions and trends of specialisation are often recognisable in the organs, tissues and cells of living and fossil angiosperms.
3. The primitive, ancestral condition of any given characteristic can be no more specialised than its condition in a derived, existing species most primitive for that characteristic.
4. The presence of vestigial rudiments of organs, or sometimes the presence of vestigial vascular supply to greatly modified or missing organs, often furnishes evidence of evolutionary reduction, loss, fusion or other major modification of structures.
5. The prevalence of parallel and convergent evolution in habit, function and structure is a predictable consequence of the relatively limited means angiosperms have for effective reproduction and for adaptation to available environmental niches.
6. All parts of plants at all stages of their development may produce evidence that is valuable in establishing relationships.
7. Evolution may tend towards elaboration and diversity or towards reduction and simplicity.
8. The role and direction of evolution may vary in different organs and tissues of plants.
9. Most existing angiosperms are highly specialised and greatly modified from their primitive, generalised ancestors.
10. Evolutionary trends are sometimes reversible under the influence of change in environmental factors.
11. Once lost, organs usually are not regained.
12. New angiospermous structures have arisen as modifications of or as outgrowths from pre-existing structures.

13. The sporadic or restricted occurrence of unusual or uncommon characteristics lacking apparent evolutionary significance is often an indication of relationship when correlated with other characteristics.
14. The occasional attainment of certain characteristics of certain levels of evolutionary development is frequently valuable in determining the affinities of families and orders.
15. Embryos and seedlings of related though dissimilar plants often resemble each other more than do the adult plants because of their apparent retention of primitive characteristics.

General Trends (after Hutchinson, 1959)

Primitive	*Advanced*
1. Tropical habitat	Temperate habitat
2. Woody plants	Herbaceous or climbing plants
3. Wood without vessels (Homoxyly)	Wood with vessels (Heteroxyly)
4. Perennial habit	Biennial or annual habit
5. Terrestrial habit	Aquatic, epiphytic, saprophytic or parasitic habit
6. Cylindric arrangement of vascular bundles	Scattered vascular bundles
7. Chlorophyll present	Chlorophyll absent
8. Evergreen plants	Deciduous plants
9. Stipules present	Stipules absent
10. Node unilacunar with two traces	Node various
11. Spiral phyllotaxy	Opposite or whorled phyllotaxy
12. Leaves simple	Leaves compound
13. Flowers hermaphrodite	Flowers unisexual
14. Flowers solitary	Flowers in inflorescences
15. Flowers entomophilous	Flowers anemophilous
16. Floral parts spirally imbricate	Floral parts whorled or valvate
17. Flowers polymerous	Flowers oligomerous
18. Perianth undifferentiated	Perianth differentiated into calyx and corolla or further reduced
19. Flowers with petals	Flowers apetalous
20. Petals distinct	Petals united
21. Actinomorphy	Zygomorphy
22. Hypogyny	Perigyny and epigyny
23. Stamens many	Stamens few
24. Stamens separate	Stamens united
25. Stamens 3-veined microsporophylls with linear embedded sporangia	Stamens variously modified.
26. Pollen monocolpate	Pollen tricolpate
27. Carpels many	Carpels few
28. Carpels distinct	Carpels united
29. Carpels conduplicate, unsealed, styleless	Carpels variously modified
30. Placentation laminar	Placentation various
31. Fruits single	Fruits aggregate
32. Fruit afollicle	Fruit various
33. Seeds large, embryo small, endosperm abundant	Seeds small, embryo large, endosperm scanty or none

34. Cotyledons two	Cotyledons one or three (or more)
35. Ovule anatropous	Ovule various
36. Integuments two	Integuments one or none
37. Endosperm nuclear	Endospern cellular or helobial
38. Ovule crassinucellar	Ovule tenuinucellar
39. Sieve cells slender and long with scattered sieve areas	Shorter sieve-tube elements with specialised sieve plates
40. Chromosome number low; $n = 7$	High number.

Evolutionary trends with regard to other disciplines will be discussed in Chapter 8, "Taxonomy: A Synthetic Discipline".

Sporne (1954, 1974) while discussing statistical correlation between floral and vegetative characters in dicotyledons has suggested the following to be the most reliable indicators of primitiveness: 1. Woody habit, 2. presence of secretory cells, 3. alternate leaves, 4. presence of stipules, 5. actinomorphic flowers, 6. free petals, 7. pleiomerous stamens, 8. pleiomerous carpels, 9. arillate seeds, 10. two integuments, 11. integumentary vascular bundles, 12. nuclear endosperm, 13. free carpels, 14. axile placentation, 15. unisexual flowers, 16. leucoanthocyanins, 17. small number of seeds, 18. scalariform perforation plates, 19. scalariform intervascular pitting, 20. apotracheal wood parenchyma, 21. unstoried wood, and 22. binucleate pollen.

Although most of the trends or dicta as proposed above are in confirmation with the observations of a large number of characters, certain dicta such as the primitive nature of opposite phyllotaxy, the statistical analysis indicating primitive nature of unisexual flowers and small number of seeds, do not appear to be acceptable to many phylogenists. It may well be said that at least in some groups of plants like Gentianales (Contortae of Engler) and Asterales (particularly Asteraceae) the opposite leaves have been interpreted as primitive and certain amentiferous families (not all) may have primitively unisexual flowers.

It is now possible, by the deductive method, to construct a hypothetical plant which shared all primitive characters and from which all other deviations have possibly occurred in different groups. Thus, most phylogenists now agree that the ancestral angiosperm was a dicotyledonous plant with the following features.

It was a low shrub of semi-arid montane tropical forest with harsh climate. The leaves were alternate, simple, stipulate, pinnately net-veined, shining green and coriaceous in texture. They had anomocytic or ranunculaceous stomata with no subsidiary cells and unspecialised guard cells. It had an active cambium which cut elongate, vertically overlapping initials. Wood was without vessels and was uniformly porous. The tracheids were very long and slender with long, tapering ends and numerous scalariform bordered pits. The wood parenchyma was diffused with uniseriate as well as multiseriate rays. The phloem had sieve elements but no true sieve tubes and also lacked companion cells. There was no sclerenchyma. The sieve elements, like the tracheids, were narrow, elongated, and vertically overlapping with the lateral sieve areas, but there was no terminal sieve plate.

The flowers were terminal and solitary on leafy branches, rather large, with numerous, spirally arranged free floral parts. The perianth was undifferentiated into calyx and corolla and wholly calyx-like. Stamens were laminar with embedded microsporangia. All floral parts probably had three leaf traces and three nerves. The pollen was monosulcate and binucleate at the time of transfer. The pollination was cantharophilous (beetles). There were no nectaries or nectar.

Each carpel was stipitate like the petiolate leaf and folded along the midrib on the adaxial surface but the margins were not completely fused with each other. The ovules were borne on the inner surtace of the margins in this unsealed carpel. The margins were provided with glandular hair so that the carpels were effectively closed and the hair served as the stigmatic surface.

The ovules were anatropous, each with two integuments and a massive nucellus. The embryo sac was polygonum type, monosporic and eight nucleate. Double fertilisation resulted into a copious triploid endosperm and a small rather immature embryo at the time of seed discharge. The endosperm was probably of the nuclear type. The embryo had two or more cotyledons and germination was epigeal.

In spite of the fact that such a plant probably never existed, it is useful to take this as a ground plan from which all the existing patterns in flowering plants evolved in the course of evolution.

6

General Evolutionary Trends in Flowering Plants

It has been brought out in Chapter 5, that the fossil record in respect of angiosperms is almost or quite lacking. The numerous fossils that have been discovered are in the form of leaves, wood and isolated remains of fruits and seeds. Many taxonomists therefore feel that the construction of a phylogenetic system of classification of flowering plants is impossible. However, it has been shown by some of the recent systematists, that this is an over-assertion of the opponents of evolutionary classification. When an evolutionary systematist claims his system to be phylogenetic, he means that the hierarchical system of taxa is so arranged as to represent the sequence of repeated branching (cladogenesis) and the degree and the character of evolutionary modifications of branches and their "grades" (Takhtajan, 1980).

This construction of phylogenetic classification has been achieved with considerable success in recent years (Cronquist 1968a Takhtajan, 1969, 1980; Thorne, 1976; Dahlgren 1975, 1977, 1980) by the comparative study of living forms. In most of the cases the study of living flowering plants has revealed their mutual two-dimensional "horizontal" relationships and by logical reasoning, their third dimension or "vertical" relationships have been deduced. Though such a classification is not geochronological, it nevertheless is "as far as possible" phylogenetic.

A beginning was already made as early as the first quarter of the twentieth century, in the development of the evolutionary macrosystem of flowering plants. Hans Hallier (1905, 1908, 1912), for example, constructed a synthetic system based on all available data including data of comparative phytochemistry. However, the data in respect of internal structure was very meagre at that time. But now we are in a much better position. Our knowledge of the plant world has been enriched to a large extent in the recent years. Studies in the comparative embryology, palynology, comparative anatomy of floral and vegetative organs gained a wide scope. Systematists continue using data of comparative phytochemistry and modern advanced methods of comparative serology.

At certain times, however, conflicting information is derived from different sources. In many cases there are discrepancies or even contradictions in the conclusions reached by different authors on the basis of different characters. A satisfactory decision can be reached only after the appropriate taxonomic and phyletic weighting of the characters by competent systematists.

It is, therefore, necessary to understand the general evolutionary trends in the various characters of living forms of flowering plants. Interpretation of most of the features, as mentioned above, must largely depend on their comparative study within various groups.

Habitat and Growth Habit

Majority of the present-day phylogenists consider angiosperms to have first developed in the moist tropics. Even today there are largest number of species occurring in the tropical and sub-tropical regions of the world. The idea of the tropical origin of angiosperms was developed by the palaeobotanist Axelrod (1952, 1960), who concluded. "the tropical uplands probably were principle reservoirs of early, primary angiosperm evolution." Later studies in ecology and plant geography lead to the conclusion that angiosperms originated and for a long period evolved in montane tropical forests (high altitudes in the tropics), under diverse climatic conditions. Stebbins (1974) has supported this later hypothesis and considered semi-arid regions to be the birth place of angiosperms.

A large proportion of species are frost sensitive. The frost lines can be said to be the 45° North and South latitudes beyond which the freezing temperatures occur even at ordinary altitudes. But the greatest number of species are concentrated between the tropic of Cancer in the north and the tropic of Capricorn in the southern hemisphere. The number of species gradually decreases as one moves toward the polar regions. The high competition pressure in the tropics probably caused the poleward migration of angiosperms and adaptation of resistance to cold. This adaptation is clearly seen in the deciduous habit, the herbaceous habit and the sclerophyllous habit (scale-like leaves).

In moist tropical regions with an equable climate, growth is continuous, and thus there is an abundance of tall trees. But in the temperature regions, the evergreen trees of the tropics have gradually made space for the deciduous trees, sclerophyllous trees and herbs. Thus it clearly appears that all these temperate habits of plants are derived from the tropical woody habit.

Over and over again it has been shown by various investigators that herbs are derived from trees, and temperate groups are derived from the tropical ones. The largely temperate and herbaceous members of Umbelliferae, Labiatae, Boraginaceae, etc. appear to be clearly derived from their mostly tropical woody relatives such as Araliaceae, Verbenaceae and Ehretiaceae respectively.

Takhtajan (1969) emphatically stated that the herbaceous habit originated from the woody one essentially by *neoteny*. By neoteny is meant the cessation of ontogeny at an earlier stage than in the ancestral forms. The plant flowers before the vegetative maturation occurs and further growth is curtailed or postponed. The neotenic transformation may affect the whole organism or only parts of it. The evolutionary progression is commonly from large trees to small trees to woody shrubs to smaller shrubs to perennial herbs to annual herbs.

Leaf Structure

The determination of a primitive structure of leaf is rather controversial. According to Corner (1949, 1954a), the earliest angiosperms had pinnately compound leaves like the pteridosperms. It might have been so, but amongst the living primitive angiosperms such leaves are not represented. All extant angiospermous trees with pinnately or even palmately compound leaves are considered as specialised groups. Even Corner's *Durio zibethinus* Murr. (Bombacaceae) is not taken to be a primitive member.

Certain pteridosperms such as *Glossopteris* had simple leaves and this trend appears to have been carried further in most of the primitive angiosperms. Not all simple leaves are primitively simple. However, some of them (e.g. certain Geraniales, Sapindales, etc.) with simple leaves have a compound-leaved ancestry. Similarly, some of the compound leaved forms are derived from simple leaved ancestors (many Asteraceae, *Pedicularis, Sambucus,* etc.)

The general agreement amongst phylogenists seems to be that the simple, entire, pinnately veined, coriaceous and glabrous leaves are primitive. This is so because such leaves are most common amongst the plants that are considered primitive on other grounds. It may be added here that the different organs of plants might have evolved at different rates in the course of evolution and therefore, association of simple leaves with primitive characters need not be taken dogmatically to ascertain their primitive nature, they may well be advanced. But generally, well-defined groups such as Magnoliales exhibit a greater correlation of characters, and thus it seems reasonable to suppose, in the absence of any other convincing evidence, that the common leaf type in the woody members of Magnoliales is a primitive type for angiosperms as a whole. Once this is accepted, it would be further possible to accept pinnate, reticulate venation as more primitive than palmate and/or parallel venation.

Most phylogenists have considered that the leaves of the first angiosperms were stipulate. Here also, the same principle of association of characters is relied upon. There is no direct evidence either from the fossils or from the comparative studies of living members. But generally, stipulate leaves are more commonly met with in presumably primitive members or at least they are absent in presumably derived orders such as Asterales. At the same time, there are a large number of exceptions, and thus the problem cannot be satisfactorily settled.

The stipules appear to be rudimentary structures. They are generally small, with simplified vascular bundles, without stomata and are caducous or quickly wither. They are, therefore, considered as on an evolutionary downgrade.

Phyllotaxy

Alternate arrangement of leaves is by far the most common one within the plant kingdom and appears to be basic for most of the vascular plants with few exceptions, such as Equisetales. If monopodial branching is taken to have been derived from the ancestral dichotomous branching of the primitive fossil pteridophytes by the unequal growth of branches, then it is logical to conclude that an alternate arrangement of subtending leaves is primitive. However, Tomlinson (1970) is of the opinion that dichotomy is not necessarily a primitive feature of the morphology of angiosperms and may prove to be quite frequent in monocotyledons. But in spite of this, it is clear that plants with alternate leaves are more common and also primitive in other respects than those with opposite leaves.

In certain families such as Asteraceae, some Gentianales, Scrophulariaceae, etc. opposite leaves are primitive while the alternate ones are advanced. Many species in these taxa exhibit transitional stage with the lower opposite and the upper alternate leaves. However, instead of considering the opposite phyllotaxy as a basic, it is profitable to consider the origin of opposite leaves from the alternate ones as a reversible trend.

Bessey's conclusion that the opposite leaves are primitive is largely based on the recapitulation principle that *ontogeny is a recapitulation of phylogeny*. According to him, the opposite arrangement of cotyledons is a reflection of the ancestral condition. But this appears to be an overemphasis on the recapitulation theory since there are many exceptions to this. Further, due to the suppression of internodes in a condensed embryo, the cotyledons seem to be opposite, and it does not mean anything else.

Stomatal Apparatus

The evolution of the stomatal apparatus in angiosperms is not clearly understood. Cronquist (1968a) has suggested that the primitive type is the anomocytic or ranunculaceous type in which guard cells are surrounded by ordinary epidermal cells, without specialised subsidiary cells. Evolutionary specialisation led to the differentiation of two, three, four or more subsidiary cells in various arrangements. It also appears that subsidiary cells may be lost at any time so that stoma revert to the ranunculaceous type. Ranunculaceous stomata in such advanced families as Asteraceae and Caprifoliaceae may well be secondary rather than primitive. In the Liliatae (monocotyledons), there appears to be a reduction series from three or four to two to no subsidiary cells. Certainly, in this group, the absence of subsidiary cells is advanced rather than primitive. But according to Takhtajan (1969), the anomocytic type is derivative and it arose from types with subsidiary cells.

On the basis of their development, two types of subsidiary cells are recognised. In the *mesogenous* type, both subsidiary cells as well as guard cells originate from a single common mother cell. In the *perigenous* type, the subsidiary cells do not originate from the primary mother cell of the guard cells. In the evolution of angiosperms, the mesogenous type appears to be primitive and occurs in many primitive families such as Magnoliaceae (Paliwal & Bhandari, 1962; Pant & Gupta, 1966) and Winteraceae (Bondeson, 1952). According to Takhtajan (1969), the stomatal apparatus of mesogenous Magnoliales is of the type known as paracytic (having one or more subsidiary cells on either side of the stoma, parallel with its long axis). Thus the mesogenous paracytic type is most likely the basic type of stomatal apparatus. Payne (1979) reviewed the stomatal patterns in Embryophytes and interpreted their evolution and ontogeny. He recognises three basic ontogenetic types of stoma:

1. *Diameristic:* With stoma at right angles to the wall that formed the guard-cell mother cell (GMC).
2. *Parameristic:* With stoma parallel to the wall that formed the GMC.
3. *Anomomeristic:* With stoma lying at any angle to the wall that formed the GMC.

Simple diameristic, mesoperigenous stoma are hypothesised to be primitive for Embryophyta, generally. This pattern, according to Payne, still characterises all monocots and is a likely candidate for the progenitor of dicotyledons as well.

Nodal Anatomy

Depending upon the number of leaf gaps, the nodes of angiosperms are described as either multilacunar, trilacunar or unilacunar. All ferns and a majority of gymnosperms are characterised by unilacunar nodes, but Cycadales and *Gnetum* have multilacunar nodes (Pant & Mehra, 1964). It is generally accepted that in gymnosperms the multilacunar type has been derived from the unilacunar type in the course of evolution. This trend in gymnosperms is however, not of much use in the interpretation of evolution of the nodal structure in angiosperms. The latter group might have evolved from the gymnosperms with either multi- or unilacunar nodes. In addition to these types, a third type, trilacunar, has been described for certain angiosperms. All the three types have been considered as primitive by different authors. Sinnott (1914), for example, held that the trilacunar type is the most primitive among angiosperms and other types have been derived from it. Ozenda (1949) concluded that at least in the presumably primitive group such as the Magnoliales, the multilacunar and not the trilacunar type is common. In his opinion, the three types form a regressive series from the multilacunar through the trilacunar to the unilacunar. A fourth type, namely, unilacunar with two leaf-traces, was considered later by various authors such as Marsden & Bailey (1955), Canright (1955), and Bailey (1956). This view gained a wider support from a number of anatomists. Although two-trace unilacunar nodes are rather uncommon in angiosperms, they exist in several families of the Magnoliales as well as in certain members of Verbanaceae, Labiatae and Solanaceae. It is also found in the cotyledonary node of various angiosperms. According to Marsden & Bailey (1955), the unilacunar node with a single trace, arose by the fusion of two trees, and the trilacunar and multilacunar types arose by the addition of lateral traces arising from new gaps in the vascular cylinder.

Benzig (1967) has pointed out that two-trace unilacunar nodes are limited to a few families characterised by derived decussate phyllotaxy and many specialised floral characters. He arrived at the conclusion that either the unilacunar node with one trace or the trilacunar node with three traces is more likely to be primitive.

Takhtajan (1964a) is of the opinion that the uneven number of leaf traces arose from an even number, while the number of gaps is always uneven.

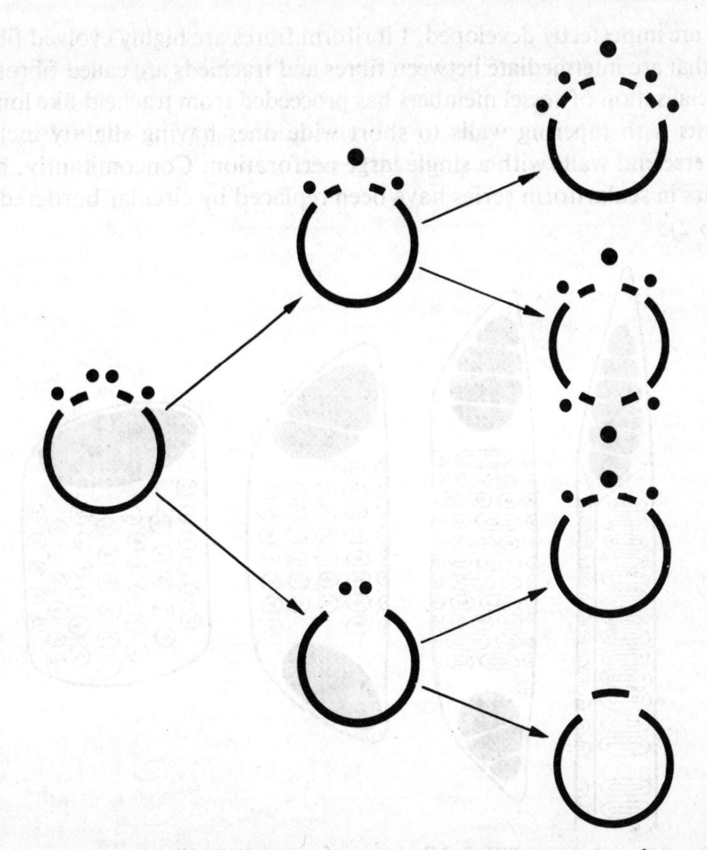

FIG. 6.1 The probable course of evolution of nodal structure in dicotyledons from a primitive trilacunar type (after Takhtajan, 1964a).

According to him, unilacunar nodes with two traces or tri- or multilacunar nodes with two leaf traces from the central gap should be considered as primitive and all other types derived from it (Fig. 6.1).

Xylem

The evolutionary trends of various structural features have been better established for the xylem than for any other single tissue. They are based on the xylem itself and do not depend on preconceived notions of the relationships among the families of angiosperms.

The tracheid is a more primitive element than a vessel member. The primitive angiosperm tracheid is slender and elongate, with long tapering, overlapping ends and numerous scalariform pits divided into rectangular pits in the course of evolution, which in turn became rounded and spirally or irregularly arranged. Specialisation of such tracheids proceeded in two directions according to their function. Those specialised for strength became xylem fibres while those specialised for conduction developed into vessel members.

Fibres are usually more slender than tracheids and have fewer smaller pits which are imperfectly developed. Libriform fibres are highly evolved fibres while those that are intermediate between fibres and trachieds are called fibrotracheids.

Specialisation of vessel members has proceeded from tracheid-like long narrow elements with tapering walls to short wide ones having slightly inclined and transverse end walls with a single large perforation. Concomitantly, bordered-pit pairs in scalariform series have been replaced by circular bordered pit pairs (Fig. 6.2).

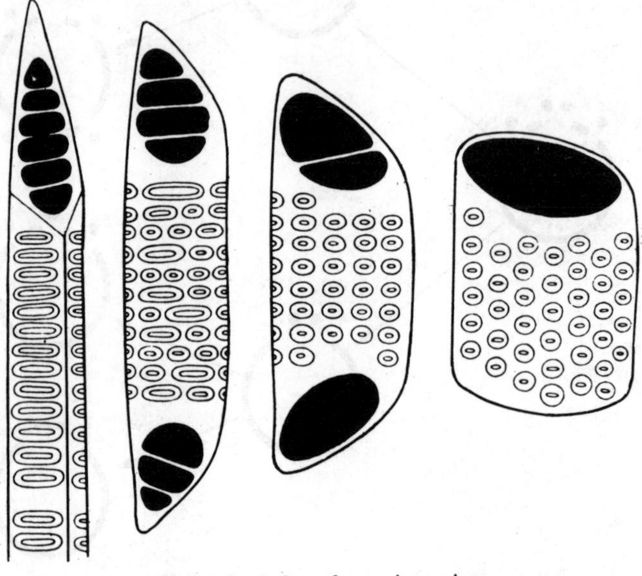

FIG. 6.2 Evolution of vessel members.

Vessel members arose independently in *Gnetales,* dicotyledons, monocotyledons, certain ferns, *Selaginella* and *Equisetum,* through parallel evolution. In dicotyledons, specialisation of tracheids into vessel members occurred first in the secondary xylem and then gradually proceeded into the primary xylem beginning with the latest part of this tissue. In monocotyledons, vessels do not occur in secondary xylem and they developed first in the ontogenetically latest part of the primary xylem. Further, monocotyledonous vessels appeared first in the root and later in other parts of the plant body.

Only a few angiosperms (Amborellaceae, Tetracentraceae, Trochodendraceae, Winteraceae and *Sarcandra* in Chloranthaceae) are primitively vesselless, belonging to the woody group of families of the Ranalian complex. Absence of vessels in certain aquatic and herbaceous members such as Ceratophyllaceae, Nymphaeaceae, Lemnaceae, etc. reflect secondary loss of vessels due to aquatic habitat.

Wood parenchyma in early angiosperms was either scanty and scattered (apotracheal) or totally absent. According to Cronquist (1968a), absence of wood parenchyma is a primitive condition. Rays were either uniseriate or multiseriate. Evolutionary advance leads to a clustering of parenchyma near about the vessels (paratracheal). Absence of rays is an evolutionary advance and is met with in secondary wood of many herbs.

Phloem

Phloem has undergone evolutionary changes that are comparable to xylem. Like the primitive vessel members, the primitive sieve elements are long and slender with groups of minute pores forming scattered sieve areas along the longitudinal walls and very oblique end walls. These elements have progressively evolved into short broad elements with horizontal end walls having a sharply defined single sieve area. The sieve areas on the lateral walls became obscure and finally were eliminated.

Companion cells are absent in the phloem of ferns and gymnosperms and are reported to be absent also from the phloem of *Austrobaileya*. In the rest of angiosperms, one or more companion cells are associated with the sieve elements.

Primitive phloem of angiosperms consists mostly of thin walled cells while more advanced members have little or no parenchyma but have bands of fibres.

Cambium and Vascular Bundles

Long fusiform cambial initials have gradually decreased in length giving rise to shorter xylem and phloem cells. There has also been an overall reduction in the activity and area of the cambium during the course of evolution. Thus there is a gradual change from woody to herbaceous habit and there is a further reduction of cambium in herbs leading to total loss in most of the monocotyledons. The cambium in certain woody monocotyledons might have appeared as a new tissue and probably is not homologous to a typical cambium.

Arrangement of vascular bundles in a ring, typical of most of the dicotyledons, is a primitive feature as compared to the scattered arrangement of vascular bundles in a few dicotyledons and most of the monocotyledons.

Inflorescence

Most of the primitive angiosperms are characterised by rather large and showy flowers which are mostly borne singly at the apices of the main stems or branches. Thus, further vegetative growth is checked. But in the tropics, where the conditions are favourable for vegetative growth throughout the year, the terminal flower might be pushed aside by new branches so that it occupies a lateral position and the axis continues to grow as a sympodium. This is what is generally called a determinate growth, and appears to be the first step towards the formation of an inflorescence.

There are three different views put forward for the explanation of evolutionary trends in the inflorescence types of the present-day angiosperms. Nageli (1883), Celakovsky (1892) and Pilger (1922) supported the theory which postulates that the primitive type of inflorescence was a panicle. All other types can be derived, according to Goebel (1931), from this basic type.

The second theory, that the primitive type was a single flower, was supported by Parkin (1914), who proposed that the inflorescences have developed from this type by addition of lateral flowers by axillary growth.

The third theory, that the dichasium may represent a primitive type, has been accepted by Rickett (1944).

In any case, it appears more acceptable that of the two basic types of inflorescence, namely, the determinate (or cymose) and indeterminate (or racemose), the former is a primitive type. Whether it was a dichasium as proposed by Rickett or a terminal solitary flower, is difficult to say. But since the primitive or advanced characters generally show correlation in plant groups, it would be profitable to accept a solitary terminal flower, most common in the Ranalian complex, as a primitive type. By repeated vegetative growth from below the flower it might have produced a dichasium due to the well-known phenomenon of apical dominance.

Thus, in the strict sense, as long as the flower is solitary, it cannot be accepted as the beginning of the inflorescence but it is only after it has developed lateral branches from below it, to form a dichasium, that one can see the inflorescence. If the assumption of dichasium as a primitive type is held as plausible, then it is possible to derive other types, as shown by Rickett (1944). By slight structural modifications, the types such as bostryches, cincinni, verticels, cymes, etc. can be easily derived, while by apparent elimination of internodes it may give rise to types such as umbel, capitulum, corymb, etc. Further, a compound cyme with its side branches originating at different levels can be converted into a classical panicle which is strictly racemose.

Racemose inflorescences such as simple raceme, panicle, spike, spadix, etc. have thus evolved from cymose types by the reduction of lateral branches. Further, these inflorescence types are rather uncommon in primitive families and are found more commonly in advance families such as Cruciferae, Leguminosae and Scrophulariaceae. In the species of *Campanula* and *Saxifraga*, racemes appear to be derived from mixed panicles by suppression of secondary branches.

In addition to the two main types mentioned above, there are other types which exhibit a mixture of cymose and racemose branches. These can be considered as transitory forms.

Flower

It is now believed by the majority of phylogenists and taxonomists that the most primitive flowers are those of Magnoliales. These flowers are characterised by numerous spirally arranged large and firm tepals, numerous spirally arranged laminar stamens and numerous spirally arranged, unsealed carpels. All these characters are found distributed among the members of Magnoliales but no one individual plant has a combination of all these. However, recently Stebbins (1974) has suggested that on the basis of floral morphology and anatomy, the flowers of *Paeonia* (Paeoniaceae) and certain Winteraceae should be regarded as more primitive than those of Magnoliales. This latter view appears to have gained support from the recent anatomical studies carried out by Gottwald (1977), who has accorded the more primitive state to the Dillenial group.

The flowers of earliest angiosperms had an elongated axis or receptacle on which the parts were spirally arranged. They were radially symmetrical and bisexual and thus resembling cycadicean gymnospermous strobili.

The floral evolution in general appears to have proceeded in the direction of aggregation and reduction of parts. The receptacle is shortened so that all parts are brought closer together in a series of cycles. The number of parts is reduced from many to few and further became connate. Not only this, but parts of different whorls became adnate to each other. In certain instances, the parts were lost altogether.

Certain flowers, on the other hand, have undergone elaboration and differentiation instead of aggregation and reduction. Both these tendencies are clearly noted in nature. It may further be noted that different organs of plants have undergone evolution at different rates. Some have evolved faster than the others. Thus, in certain flowers, sepals have remained distinct while the petals became connate. A sympetalous corolla generally is accompanied by epipetalous stamens but this correlation is not found in certain members of Mimosaceae, Crassulaceae, Cucurbitaceae, etc. where the corolla is sympetalous but the stamens are not adnate to it. In spite of these irregularities, there appears to be some sort of loose correlation in the advances of the different organs.

Unisexual flowers in majority of angiosperms clearly have a bisexual ancestry. Some intermediate forms have well developed parts of both sexes but only one sex is functional. Monoecious and perfectly dioecious groups have evolved from perfect flowered members through a condition termed as polygamy.

Morphological studies indicate that the tepals of primitive flowers are homologous with foliage leaves and the sepals of most of the advanced members are also foliar in nature. Petals are of two different origins. Some are modified tepals, representing the inner whorl of the ancestrally undifferentiated perianth. Others are staminodal in nature. Anatomically, most of the sepals are characterised by three vascular traces while most of the petals have one trace. This, however, should not be considered to be a critical distinction since there are some exceptions. Petals of some primitive flowers have three traces while certain others have a single median trace and imperfectly developed lateral traces.

When there are two whorls of perianth, the outer whorl is regarded as the calyx and is generally green, while the inner whorl, or corolla, is often coloured. In the monochlamydous flowers, the existing whorl of perianth is often called calyx, even when it is corolla-like.

The primitive flower was hypogynous, with the sepals, petals and stamens arising from below the ovary. It has also been mentioned that these parts were distinct as well as free from each other. Lateral connation of members of the same whorl has resulted into synsepalous, sympetalous, monadelphous and syncarpous conditions. These whorls then got adnate to each other resulting in epipetalous stamens, episepalous stamens, episepalous petals, etc., ultimately forming a compound structure—hypanthium—by fusion of all the three outer whorls. Hypanthium resembles calyx in appearance and petals and stamens are described as arising from the mouth of this calyx tube. Such flowers, with hypanthium, are termed perigynous. The perigynous condition is intermediate between the hypogynous on the one hand and epigynous on the other. Complete fusion of the ovarian wall with the hypanthium results into the epigynous condition. This, however, is not the only way in which ovaries become inferior. They can as well become sunken in the cup formed by hollowing out of the receptacle. Thus, the inferior ovary may either be appendicular (fusion with hypanthium) or receptacular (sunken into the receptacular cup) in nature. In certain cases, the inferior ovary may be partly receptacular and partly appendicular in nature.

Generally it would be expected that different floral parts mature in a sequence from outside to the inside, or when the receptacle is elongated, from bottom to the top. However, in reality, it is noted that this sequence is often not allowed. Although the calyx and corolla are the first whorls to mature, in many cases the stamens grow faster than these whorls. But maturation of stamens, i.e. shedding of the pollen grains from the anthers, takes place only after opening of the flower. Carpels should be the last members to mature but instances of protogyny (maturation of carpels before that of the stamens) are not uncommon. The maturation of individual members in a single whorl is rather difficult to determine but when members are arranged in more than one whorl, it is possible to determine the sequence of maturation in these whorls. It might either be from outside to the inside (acropetal or centripetal) or from inside to the outside (basipetal or centrifugal). The centripetal maturation of stamens is more or less a constant feature in Magnoliales and related orders, while it is centrifugal in Dilleniales, Theales and other related orders. In certain groups of plants such as Geraniales, the sequence of development of stamens is reported to be in either direction. Corner (1946) holds that the primitive massive centrifugal androecium must have been derived from the usual centripetal state.

Androecium

It has now been shown beyond doubt that the laminar stamen with embedded microsporangia, as seen in *Degeneria,* is a primitive type (Fig. 6.3). The position of pollen sacs may be adaxial or abaxial, and both these positions are known in the presumably primitive families.

Change in the number of stamens from numerous to few appears to have followed two different trends and might have occurred many times. One of the trends is the cohesion of filaments into one or few bundles as seen in Malvaceae

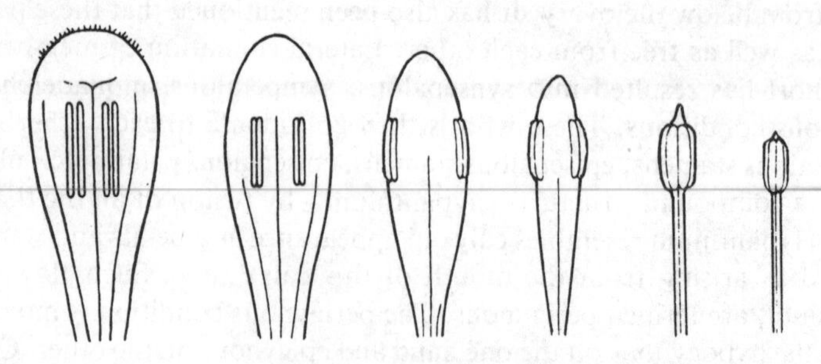

FIG. 6.3 Evolution of stamen.

and Bombacaceae, followed by subsequent loss of individual members leading to isomerous or even oligomerous condition of stamens. The second trend is the formation of spirally arranged stamens into few to many definite whorls followed by the loss of entire whorls. Thus the progression might go from many whorls to few and then to two or one whorl. The whorls of stamens are arranged in the same manner as the sepals and petals, i.e. members of adjacent whorls alternate with each other. The stamens in the outermost whorl alternate with the petals, while the next set is opposite the petals, and so on. During the course of evolution, either the outer or the inner whorl may be dropped out first. In families which have commonly two sets of stamens, the outer whorl is opposite the petals, indicating that the outermost whorl has been lost. When there is only one whorl of stamens, the members generally alternate with the petals, indicating their position either in the first or the third ancestral whorl from outside. In certain families such as Primulaceae, Plumbaginaceae, etc. there is a single whorl of stamens and the members are opposite the petals. This indicates that only the second whorl from outside has been retained. In Celastrales it appears that the outermost whorl has been retained, while in the closely related order Rhamnales, it appears that the second whorl has been retained.

Some botanists believe that at least in some families such as Paeoniaceae, Dilleniaceae, Guttiferae, Malvaceae, etc., the progression has been from few stamens in a single whorl, to fascicled stamens, to numerous separate stamens. On the other hand, Eames (1961) has interpreted the anatomical evidence in these families to indicate reduction series. Cronquist (1968a) has also supported the view of reduction in these families.

The number of stamens in a single whorl may further get reduced so that there are fewer stamens than petals. Increase in the number of stamens, once they have been confined to a single series, is much less common.

Stebbins (1974), on the other hand, has proposed, on the basis of recent morphological studies, that the original androecium of angiosperms consisted of a relatively small number of branched structures, which could have either compound, flattened microsporophylls or small lateral branchlets. Thus neither centripetal nor centrifugal initiation of stamen primordia may be regarded as more primitive or more advanced than the other.

Pollen Grains

There are two principal types of pollen grains in angiosperms. The great majority of dicotyledons have triaperturate or triaperturate-derived pollen. In monocotyledons, on the other hand, the pollen grains have a single aperture, usually situated in a single furrow. Uniaperturate pollen grains are found also in Magnoliales and gymnosperms. Since pollen grains of this kind are associated with primitive characteristics, they have been regarded as more primitive than triaperturate grains.

The longitudinal slit-like aperture is termed *colpus* and the pollen grain with such an aperture as *colpate*, while the more or less round aperture is termed *pore* and the pollen grains possessing them *porate*. Sometimes both these types of apertures are developed in one and the same pollen grain, which is then termed as *colporate*. It is generally believed that the evolutionary progression has been from colpate to colporate to porate condition. There are, however, many intermediate grades, refinements and special conditions.

Most angiosperms have two nuclei in their pollen grains at the time of shedding from the anthers. The nucleus in the smaller cell is a generative nucleus and the one in the larger cell is a vegetative nucleus. The generative nucleus divides later to form two sperm nuclei, but this division usually takes place in the pollen tube after germination of the pollen grain. In a considerable number of groups the generative nucleus divides in the pollen grain before germination of the latter. Thus, the grains are trinucleate. The early division of the generative nucleus represents one more step in the progressive compression of the male gametophyte. Trinucleate pollen is a characteristic feature of the taxa of Caryophyllales. It also occurs in a number of other taxa of different orders. Obviously this character cannot be used to construct taxonomic groups.

Pollination

Most students of botany are familiar with the pollination mechanism in certain common plants through the agency of wind, water, insects, birds and in rare instances even mammals. Many taxa have self-pollinated flowers. Majority of the terrestrial plants are pollinated either by wind or by insects. Plants growing in open situations such as temperate forests, grasslands, etc. favour wind pollination, while insect pollination is common in closed situations such as the tropical forests. The marginal communities may have plants pollinated both by insects as well as wind. Certain plant species, as is well known for members of Asteraceae, are facultative cross-pollinated and on failure of this mechanism may take up self-pollination.

It is interesting to note that there has been a change of pollination mechanism from cross to self in a large number of plants in response to changing environmental conditions. Stebbins (1957) has mentioned numerous examples of this trend in the families such as Brassicaceae, Fabaceae, Onagraceae, Asteraceae and Poaceae. In most of these examples, the flowers do not show considerable morphological changes and a close observation is needed to detect the pollinators. Certain changes, like heterostyly and homostyly, slightly reduced flower size, etc. are notable in certain groups. The most profound changes in floral morphology have been suggested by Ornduff and Crovello (1968) in the Limnanthaceae. Here the cross-pollinated species of *Limnanthes* have large pentamerous flowers while a few self-pollinated members have smaller size of flowers, and a closely related genus *Floerkea* has still smaller flowers which are trimerous. The latter genus apparently has evolved from *Limnanthes* by reduction following the acquisition of self-fertilisation.

Although cross-pollination is commonly carried out through wind (anemophily), insects (entomophily) and water (hydrophily), the mechanism of hydrophily has not been studied in detail. When Amentiferae were generally regarded as primitive angiosperms, wind pollination was also considered primitive. Now it is increasingly regarded that wind-pollination is a secondary condition usually associated with floral reduction. However, it should not be inferred that the shift between insect- and wind-pollination is unidirectional. A large number of instances are known where wind-pollination has given way to insect-pollination. The best example of this trend can be found in *Dichronema* (Cyperaceae), *Olyra* and *Pariana* (Poaceae), *Morus, Broussonetia* and *Ficus* (Moraceae).

It is now generally held that the primitive angiosperms were pollinated by beetles (cantharophily) that chewed and ate bits of the perianth and stamens. This type of pollination exists even today in many magnolialean families. The flowers of Calycanthaceae, Eupomatiaceae, Magnoliaceae, Nymphaeaceae have little or no nectar and no obvious nectaries. It is considered that the nectaries developed later in the course of evolution independently in diverse groups of angiosperms. The beetles are known in fossils as far back as the Permian period. Angiosperms most probably evolved in the Cretaceous, and the pollination was by these beetles (Coleoptera). Thus the primitive angiosperms were most probably cantharophilous rather than entomophilous (other insects such as Diptera, Hymenoptera etc.). The other insects date from the Jurassic but were not the chief pollinators then. In later years, the flowers of angiosperms adopted entomophily and evolved in response to specialised pollinators. Thus, starting from the magnolialean flower with numerous separate tepals, flowers have progressed towards definite and small number of floral parts, sympetaly and zygomorphy, as is witnessed in the flowers of Scrophulariales, Lamiales and Orchidales.

Wind-pollination, as stated earlier, has evolved from insect-pollination many times, usually associated with reduction of the perianth as in Amentiferae.

The most specialised pollination mechanism is that by bats (Chiroptera) who are active during the night, in the tropical forest. It has come to the knowledge of naturalists relatively recently. This type of pollination has been documented in genera like *Parkia* (Mimosaceae), *Ceiba* (Bombacaceae), *Kigelia* (Bignoniaceae) and others. The flowers or inflorescences of these genera are large and have stout stalks which extend out from the foliage or hang down. They have strong odours and ample nectar.

Gynoecium

The morphological nature of the carpel as a modified phyllome or leaf-like megasporophyll has been generally accepted by all evolutionary biologists. Such an interpretation is well documented in families like Winteraceae of the Magnoliales. The evolutionary process involved was chiefly infolding or conduplication. Some species of *Drimys* (Winteraceae) have thin unsealed carpels that are merely folded along the midrib and the ovules are borne on two inner surfaces. Various stages in the development of the closed carpel of most angiosperms are still preserved among various living members of the Magnoliales.

Earlier, it was believed by the proponents of this classical concept of carpel structure that ovules were originally borne along the margin or slightly below the margin of the phyllome. Recent studies by Bailey and Swamy (1951) have indicated that in the primitive carpel the ovules were arranged on its adaxial surface in two rows, situated between the midrib and the margins. Takhtajan (1959) has designated this position as laminar-lateral. The marginal position is regarded by these authors to be secondarily derived through suppression of meristematic activity of the marginal portion of the phyllome.

Primitive gynoecium of angiosperms was made up of several or many carpels, spirally arranged on a more or less elongate receptacle. Each of the carpel also had numerous ovules. Such gynoecia occur even today in many primitive angiosperms. The evolution has proceeded in the direction of reduction in the number of carpels, their fusion to form a syncarpous condition and lastly reduction in the number of ovules. The laminar-lateral position of ovules became marginal and the fusion of carpels resulted into syncarpous gynoecium with axile placentation. This placentation type has been regarded by many as the ancestral type from which other types can be derived. In few groups, however, fusion of incompletely closed carpels might have given rise to parietal placentation. It has also been noted in certain instances that the incomplete partitions have protruded towards the centre eventually meeting each other and resulting into axile condition.

Other types of placentation might have arisen from these two types (Fig. 6.4). Free-central or central placentation, for example, arises from the axile by abortion of the partitions. When the placental column reaches the top of the ovary, it is called central placentation, while the failure of this column to reach the top, results into free-central placentation. Further reduction of the central column may result into a basal position of ovules. Basal placentation may arise also by restriction of the axile or parietal placentas to the base of the ovary. Similarly, apical placentation arises by progressive restriction of the placenta from the base upwards.

The evolution of lamellar type of placentation appears to be rather problematic. It occurs in the primitive families such as Nymphaeaceae and Butomaceae and also in certain advanced families such as the Gentianaceae and Hydrocharitaceae. In the primitive families this appears to be an ancestral condition, while it might have been secondarily derived in the advanced families.

Ovule

The ovules of angiosperms are classified into four main types. They are anatropous, orthotropous, amphitropous and campylotropous. In the anatropous ovule the micropyle and the stalk (funiculus) lie side by side, while they are at opposite ends in the othotropous ovule. The amphitropous ovule has its micropyle situated at right angles to the stalk and in the campylotropous type the ovule is slightly bent, otherwise it is similar to the amphitropous type.

In all the living gymnosperms the ovule is typically orthotropous and is considered to be the most primitive type. On the other hand, most angiosperms

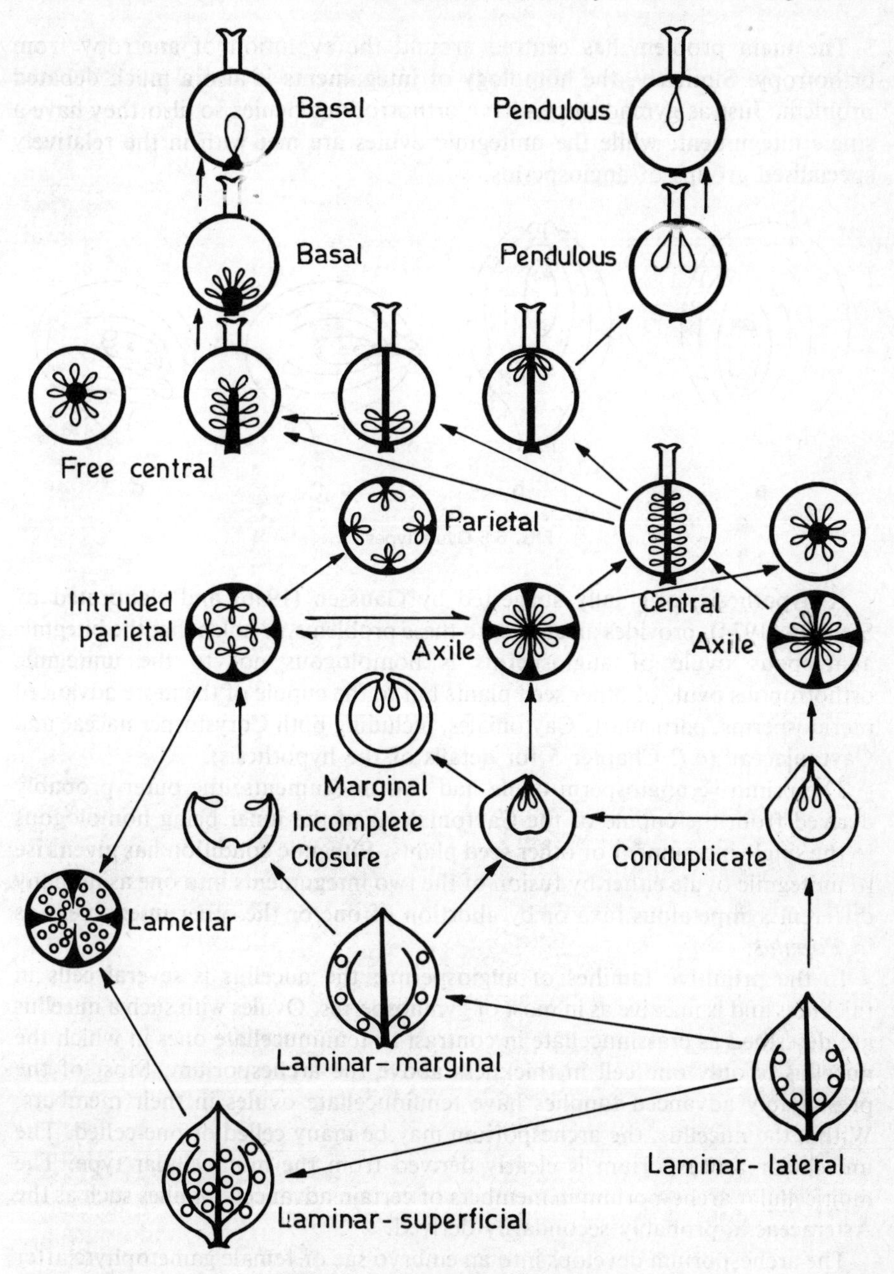

FIG. 6.4 Evolution of placental types.

including the primitive ones, have anatropous ovules. Other types are rather rare and are found in widely separated groups. This situation suggests that anatropy has been achieved very early in the evolution of angiosperms. Campylotropous and amphitropous ovules are derived from anatropous type and many á times they are anatropous at an earlier stage of their development. Orthotropy in certain angiosperms is a secondarily derived condition.

The main problem has centred around the evolution of anatropy from orthotropy. Similarly, the homology of integuments is also a much debated problem. Just as gymnosperms have orthotropous ovules so also they have a single integument, while the unitegmic ovules are met with in the relatively specialised groups of angiosperms.

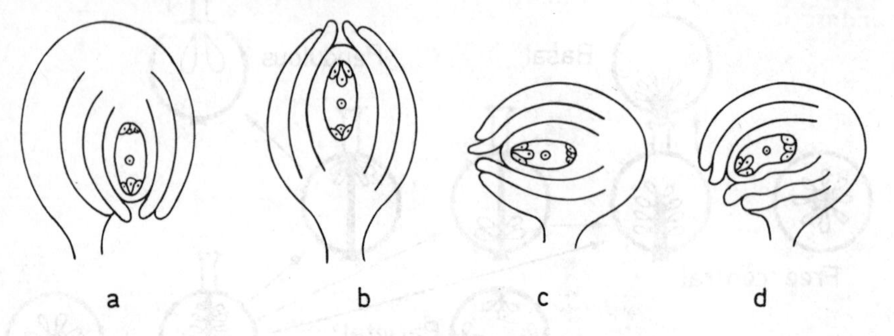

FIG. 6.5 Ovule types.

A hypothesis, originally suggested by Gaussen (1946) and elaborated by Stebbins (1974), provides an answer to these problems. It holds that the bitegmic anatropous ovule of angiosperms is homologous not to the unitegmic orthotropous ovule of other seed plants but to the cupule of the more advanced pteridosperms, particularly Caytoniales, including both Corystospermaceae and Caytoniaceae (*c.f.* Chapter 5 for details of the hypothesis).

The primitive angiosperm ovule had two integuments, the outer probably derived from the cupule of the Caytoniales and the inner being homologous to the single integument of other seed plants. Bitegmic condition has given rise to unitegmic ovule either by fusion of the two integuments into one as in many different sympetalous taxa or by abortion of one or the other integument as in *Populus*.

In the primitive families of angiosperms, the nucellus is several cells in thickness and is massive as in most of gymnosperms. Ovules with such a nucellus are described as crassinucellate in contrast to tenuinucellate ones in which the nucellus is only one cell in thickness above the archesporium. Most of the presumably advanced families have tenuinucellate ovules in their members. Within the nucellus, the archesporium may be many celled or one-celled. The unicellular archesporium is clearly derived from the multicellular type. The multicellular archesporium in members of certain advanced families such as the Asteraceae is probably secondarily derived.

The archesporium develops into an embryo sac or female gametophyte after undergoing reduction division. In majority of angiosperms the embryo sac is formed from one of the four megaspores and is typically eight nucleate or Polygonum type. All the other types of monosporic as well as bisporic and tetrasporic types are derived from this basic type.

Fertilisation, Seeds and Seedlings

The two male gametes enter the embryo sac, one fusing with the egg while the other with the secondary nucleus. This double fertilisation is followed by the development of copious endosperm from the triple fusion with the primary endosperm nucleus in most of the primitive angiosperms. Thus endospermic seeds are primitive. Non-endospermic seeds develop by utilisation of the endosperm by the developing embryo before the seed matures. These are regarded as advanced.

Endosperm is classified into three main types on the basis of its early developmental stages. They are nuclear, cellular and helobial types. In the nuclear type, the fusion nucleus divides repeatedly and nuclear divisions are not immediately followed by cell plate formation. In the cellular type, the nuclear divisions are followed by cell plate formation almost immediately, while in the helobial type the condition is somewhat intermediate between the nuclear and cellular types. There is no unanimous opinion about the primitive nature of any one type of endosperm.

Most of the angiospermous embryos are either mono- or dicotyledonous. But tricotyledonous condition occurs in a few members. *Degeneria* has normally three to four cotyledons in most of the embryos and since this genus is regarded as primitive in other respects, polycotyly also may be regarded as primitive and the reduction in their number to two and one may be regarded as a derived condition. Further, it is also agreed by many evolutionary biologists that monocotyledonous embryos are derived from dicotyledonous ones either by suppression of one of the cotyledons or by fusion along their lateral margins.

The mature seeds, on germination, may throw their cotyledons out of the testa and soil surface (epigeal) or they may retain them within the testa (hypogeal). In the epigeal type, the cotyledons, on exposure to sunlight, may take up photosynthetic activity until the leaves are well developed. In the hypogeal type, the cotyledons function as absorbing organs and utilise the food stored in the endosperm. The shift of the function from photosynthesis to absorption, appears to be an evolutionary specialisation.

The fleshy covering is developed on seeds of certain angiosperms. If it is developed from the integuments then it is termed as *sarcotesta*, while the one developed from the funiculus is called *aril*. Corner (1945a, b) maintains that the arillate seed is primitive in angiosperms, and has developed his famous durian theory, considering the arillate seed of *Durio zibethinus* Murr. (Bombacaceae) to be primitive. This view, however, has not been widely supported.

Fruits

Fruits of angiosperms are variously classified as (i) simple or compound, depending upon whether they are developed from a single flower or inflorescence; (ii) dry or fleshy or (iii) dehiscent or indehiscent, and so on. The evolutionary progress appears to be from fruitlets developed from apocarpous gynoecium to simple fruits to compound or multiple fruits. The primitive fruitlets, such as those of *Magnolia, Michelia* and members of Magnoliaceae, break open along one of their margins at maturity. They are thus dehiscent and are termed as follicles. An apocarpous gynoecium of Magnoliaceae matures into a cluster (Eterio) of follicles. Since this type of fruit is associated with the presumably primitive family, it is regarded as the most primitive by a number of evolutionary biologists, however, Stebbins (1974), states that this condition is hard to imagine as primitive. He believes that the original primitive flower of angiosperms was not large in size and strobiloid in form, as is regarded by several other botanists. According to him, the flower of the modern Magnoliaceae is obviously specialised as is evidenced by the recent anatomical studies (Ozenda, 1949; Canright, 1955; Melville, 1962; Skipworth and Philipson, 1966). He further concluded that there is probably no modern group that has flowers similar to those that existed in the earliest angiosperms.

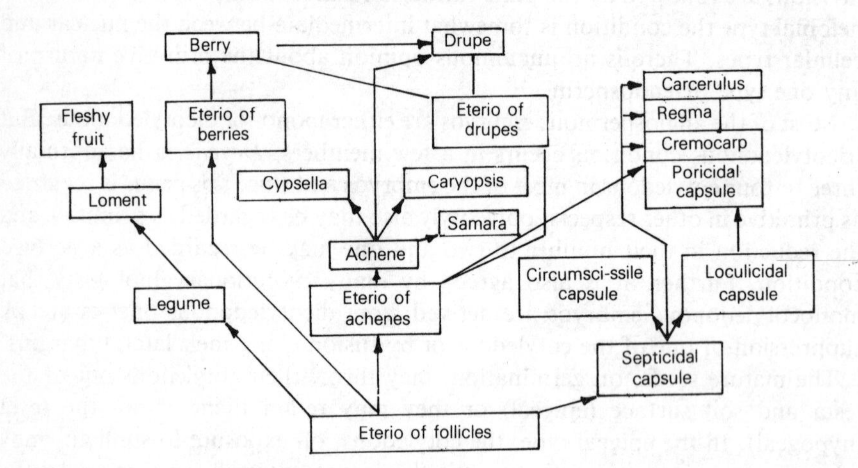

FIG. 6.6 Diagram showing probable evolution of fruit types.

Here it may be proper to regard the magnoliaceous fruit as the most primitive type at least among modern members of angiosperms. It is then possible to develop evolutionary trends from dehiscent fruitlets to indehicent ones and further to fruits developed from syncarpous gynoecium leading to indehiscent and fleshy, few to one-seeded fruits. A probable sequence in the evolution of fruits may be as indicated in Fig. 6.6.

7

Post-Darwinian Systems of Classification

It has already been pointed out in Chapter 2, that the evolutionary theory, proposed by Darwin and Wallace in 1858 influenced taxonomy in various ways. The systems in which plant groups were arranged either haphazardly, in a linear sequence or in a stepwise progressive manner were gradually being replaced by the phylogenetic systems or more natural systems.

The Englerian School

Post-Darwinian systems can be arranged into two main groups based on the supposed nature of a primitive angiospermic flower. The two schools of thought developed widely different concepts regarding the primitive flower and flourished side by side for a considerable period. The first of these concepts was proposed by a German taxonomist, *Alexander Braun* in his *Flora der Provinz Bradenburg* in 1859. This influenced his successor, A.W. Eichler in Berlin and was fully elaborated by Adolf Engler, subsequently.

Braun classified monocotyledons so as to show a progression from more simple organisation to the complex one. Accordingly, he considered naked unisexual flowers of Lemnaceae to be the most primitive and arranged other families to show a gradual complexity, ultimately ending in the highly elaborate Orchidaceae. Similarly, he began the dicotyledons with Apetalae which are followed by Sympetalae, Eleutheropetalae and ending with Leguminosae.

A.W. Eichler modified this system to some extent and proposed his classification in a book entitled *Blutendiagramme* (1875–1878). The monocotyledons were arranged in the same manner as in Braun's system but the families of dicotyledons distributed among Apetalae were classified into Apetalae and Choripetalae, the latter group consisting of families with differentiated sepals and free petals. In the beginning he placed sympetalous families before polypetalae but reversed this position in Kiel *Syllabus* (1876) and later in Berlin *Syllabus* (1880). In the final revision (1883) he began the dicotyledons with the Cupuliferae and ended with Compositae. His system is briefly outlined below:

A. Cryptogamae
- I. Division Thallophyta
  - 1. Class Algae
  - 2. Class Fungi
- II. Division Bryophyta
  - 1. Class Hepaticae
  - 2. Class Musci
- III. Division Pteridophyta
  - 1. Class Equisetineae
  - 2. Class Lycopodineae
  - 3. Class Filicineae

B. Phanerogamae
- I. Division Gymnospermae
- II. Division Angiospermae
  - 1. Class Monocotyleae
  - 2. Cass Dicotyleae
    - (i) Subclass Choripetalae
    - (ii) Subclass Sympetalae

It was for the first time that the seed plants were classified into Gymnosperms and Angiosperms.

H.G. Adolf Engler adopted Eichler's system with some modifications in his *Guide to Breslau Botanic Garden* (1886). This was later modified in his *Syllabus,* the first edition of which appeared in 1892 and underwent several revisions, the last one appeared in 1964 by Melchior. Engler, in collaboration with Karl Prantl, expanded the system in their 23-volume work *Die Naturlichen Pflanzenfamilien* (1887–1915). The revision of this work began in 1924 and various students and collaborators of Engler added detailed generic monographs. This, however, has remained incomplete till today.

Engler never considered his system to be phylogenetic. The plant groups were built up in step-like manner and form a generally progressional series. He maintained and expanded the concept of a primitive flower originally proposed by Alexander Braun. According to this concept, which is generally recognised as the *Englerian concept,* flowers with only stamens or carpels form the lowest grade of organisation. Such unisexual and naked flowers generally borne in ament (catkin inflorescence) are the most primitive within angiosperms and have probably been derived from gymnospermous ancestors with unisexual strobilus bearing either micro- or megasporophylls. Bisexual flowers are derived from a cluster of male and female flowers held in the same inflorescence and simulating a flower (pseudanthium), while a subtending perianth evolved later.

The Englerian school further maintains that these unisexual flowers were wind-pollinated like the cones of gymnosperms and that the different groups of angiosperms have been derived from various groups of gymnosperms as well as from pteridophytes, thus proposing a polyphyletic origin.

Angiosperms are classified into two classes, the monocotyledons and the dicotyledons, together consisting of 303 families. The monocotyledons have been considered more primitive than the dicotyledons and therefore have been placed before them. They are classified into 11 orders and 45 families starting with the unisexual and apetalous Pandanales followed by the aquatic Helobiae, Triuridales, Glumiflorae, Princeps, etc. and ending in the highly evolved Microspermae. The dicotyledons are classified into two main groups: (i) Archichlamydeae and (ii) Sympetalae, which are further divided into 44 orders and 258 families. Archichlamydeae include 33 orders of perianthless as well as polypetalous flowers, while Sympetalae include 11 orders of gamopetalous flowers. The orders Verticillatae, Fagales, Salicales, etc. with perianthless unisexual flowers are placed in the beginning of the dicotyledons followed by the polypetalous orders such as Centrospermae, Ranales, etc. and ending in the Sympetalous orders such as Contortae, Tubiflorae, etc. Compositae is regarded as a highly evolved family. The order Centrospermae is regarded as holding an intermediate position connecting the monocotyledons on the one hand and the dicotyledons on the other.

Melchior, in the 12th edition (1964) of Engler's *Syllabus* made profound changes and rearranged the entire group of flowering plants. A major change was brought about in the arrangement of two main classes of angiosperms. Unlike all the earlier revisions, the dicotyledons were treated as more primitive than the monocotyledons and placed before them. The second major change was effected in the splitting of various orders and rearrangement of families within them. In the 11th edition, a total of 303 families were included in 55 orders. In this last revision however, the number of orders was increased to 62 (48 of the dicots and 14 of the monocots) which include a total of 344 families (291 of the dicots and 53 of the monocots). This has been done in order to bring the system on par with the other contemporary classifications and wherever the systematic treatments were proved beyond doubt.

Nevertheless, the essence of the Englerian concept of the primitive flower is maintained in its original form. Vast data accumulated from various fields has been taken into account in contrast to only morphological and embryological features employed in the earlier revisions. This has altered the systematic position of several orders as well as families. Following is the synopsis of Engler's classification of angiosperms as modified by Melchior (1964). (Figures in parentheses indicate number of families.)

(Divisions I to XVI include all other plants)

XVII Division: Angiospermae

Class: Dicotyledoneae (291)

1. Subclass: Archichlamydeae (227)

Order: Casuarinales (1)
Juglandales (2)
Balanopales (1)
Leitnerales (2)
Salicales (1)
Fagales (2)
Urticales (5)
Proteales (1)
Santalales (7)

Suborder: Santalineae (6)
Loranthineae (1)

Order: Balanophorales (1)
Medusandrales (1)
Polygonales (1)
Centrospermae (12 + 1)

Suborder: Phytolaccineae (6)
Portulacineae (2)
Caryophyllineae (1)
Chenopodiineae (3)

Family of doubtful relationship-Didieriaceae

Order:	Cactales (1)
	Magnoliales (22)
Suborder:	Magnoliineae (8)
	Schisandrineae (2)
	Austrobaileyineae (3)
	Tetracentrineae (2)
	Eupteleineae (1)
	Cercidiphyllineae (1)
Order:	Ranunculales (7)
Suborder:	Ranunculineae (5)
	Nymphaeineae (2)
Order:	Piperales (4)
	Aristolochiales (3)
	Guttiferales (16)
Suborder:	Dilleniineae (6)
	Ochnineae (4)
	Theineae (5)
	Ancistrocladineae (1)
Order:	Sarraceniales (3)
	Papaverales (6)
Suborder:	Papaverineae (1)
	Capparineae (3)
	Resedineae (1)
	Moringineae (1)
Order:	Batales (1)
	Rosales (19)
Suborder:	Hamamelidineae (3)
	Saxifragineae (10)
	Rosineae (3)
	Leguminosineae (3)
Order:	Hydrostachyales (1)
	Podostemales (1)
	Geraniales (9)
Suborder:	Limnanthineae (1)
	Geraniineae (6)
	Euphorbiineae (2)
Order:	Rutales (12)
Suborder:	Rutineae (7)
	Malpighiineae (3)
	Polygalineae (2)
Order:	Sapindales (10)
Suborder:	Coriariineae (1)
	Anacardiineae (1)
	Sapindineae (7)
	Balsamineae (1)
Order:	Juliniales (1)
	Celastrales (13)
Suborder:	Celastrineae (10)

	Buxineae (1)
	Icacinineae (2)
Order:	Rhamnales (3)
	Malvales (7)
Suborder:	Elaeocarpineae (1)
	Sarcolaenineae (1)
	Malvineae (4)
	Scytopetalineae (1)
Order:	Thymelaeales (5)
	Violales (20)
Suborder:	Flacourtiineae (9)
	Cistineae (4)
	Tamaricineae (3)
	Caricineae (1)
	Loasineae (1)
	Begoniineae (2)
Order:	Cucurbitales (1)
	Myrtiflorae (17)
Suborder:	Myrtineae (15)
	Hippuridineae (1)
	Cynomoriineae (1)
Order:	Umbelliflorae (7)
2. Subclass:	Sympetalae (64)
Order:	Diapensiales (1)
	Ericales (5)
	Primulales (3)
	Plumbaginales (1)
	Ebenales (7)
Suborder:	Sapotineae (2)
	Ebenineae (5)
Order:	Oleales (1)
	Gentianales (7)
	Tubiflorae (26)
Suborder:	Convolvulineae (3)
	Boragininineae (3)
	Verbenineae (3)
	Solanineae (15)
	Myoporineae (1)
	Phrymineae (1)
Order:	Plantaginales (1)
	Dipsacales (4)
	Campanulales (8)

B. Class: Monocotyledoneae (53)

Order:	Helobiae (9)
Suborder:	Alismatineae (2)
	Hydrocharitineae (1)
	Scheuchzerineae (1)
	Potamogetonineae (5)
Order:	Triuridales (1)

Order:	Liliiflorae (17)
Suborder:	Liliineae (11)
	Pontederineae (1)
	Iridineae (2)
	Burmanniineae (2)
	Philydrineae (1)
Order:	Juncales (2)
	Bromeliales (1)
	Commelinales (8)
Suborder:	Commelinineae (4)
	Eriocaulineae (1)
	Restionineae (2)
	Flagellariineae (1)
Order:	Graminales (1)
	Principes (1)
	Synanthae (1)
	Spathiflorae (2)
	Pandanales (3)
	Cyperales (1)
	Scitamineae (5)
	Microspermae (1)

Engler's *Syllabus* and *Pflanzenfamilien* covered the whole plant kingdom, and this is the main reason for its widespread adoption. This monumental work began during his professorship in botany at the University of Berlin and directorship of the Berlin Botanical Garden from 1889 to 1921. He and his distinguished associates like Karl Prantl and others provided keys and descriptions to all families from algae to Compositae. For each family they provided an information concerning the embryology, morphology, anatomy, geographic distribution, descriptions of the genera, illustrations and a bibliography of pertinent literature. Thus this is the first angiospermic system to take anatomical data into account. The materials in the American and Continental herbaria were arranged according to this system and numerous floras followed this sequence.

The Englerian concept of primitive flower was strongly criticised by Arber and Parkin (1907). According to these authors: (i) the concept presupposes that the perianth arose *de novo;* (ii) Engler's so-called primitive flowers are invariably accompanied by complicated and highly evolved inflorescences; and (iii) the theory is phylogenetically sterile and does not bring angiosperms in line with fossil plants.

Evidence from anatomy suggests that the "simple" flowers of present-day Amentiferae are in fact highly reduced ones and are probably derived from hermaphrodite petaliferous ancestors with less specialised inflorescences. Similarly, it is accepted by increasing number of phylogenists and taxonomists that dicotyledons are at least as primitive as monocotyledons if not more, and their position in the Engler's system must be reconsidered. This, as can be seen, was done as late as in 1964.

The Englerian concept of primitive flower has, however, been defended by Sprague (1960) who stated, "the conclusion is inescapable that the earliest angiosperms were apetalous and anemogamous. Many of the groups such as

Fagales, Urticales and Piperaceae may have remained in that condition but others like Saururaceae and many Centrospermae may have achieved entomogamy, not by the development of petals but by the development of colour in sepals or bracts". Hamshaw Thomas (1958) is also of the opinion that the appearance of hermaphrodite flowers in angiosperms is relatively late and not a primitive feature. Heslop-Harrison (1957, 1958a) believed that all unisexual flowers need not have arisen by suppression of one set of organs in hermaphrodite flowers and further, in another group unisexuality appears to be a basic attribute and may be a less specialised condition than bisexuality.

A few other authors supported Engler's concept but proposed their own systems with slight modification.

A.B. Rendle published a classification (1904, 1925, 1930, 1938) which was patterned after Engler's system. The monocotyledons were treated as more primitive than the dicotyledons but Palmae which were regarded by Engler to form a separate order, the Principes, were placed under Spathiflorae along with Araceae and were considered more primitive than the latter. Similarly, certain smaller and less important families such as Scheuchzeriaceae, Butomaceae, Cyclanthaceae. Flagellariaceae, Centrolepidaceae, Mayacaceae, etc. were omitted; thus retaining only 32 families in 9 orders. The dicotyledons were grouped into three grades: (i) Monochlamydeae, (ii) Dialypetalae, and (iii) Sympetalae. The monochlamydeae began with Salicales followed by Garryales, Juglandales, etc. ending in Centrospermae. The Dialypetalae began with Ranales followed by Rhoeadales and ended in Umbelliferae. Sympetalae were regarded as the highest grade of floral development which have sprung from various dialypetalous groups. It was considered that generally the woody habit is more primitive than the herbaceous.

One of the most significant merits of this two-volume work lies in the clarity and completeness of descriptions, the recording of exceptional cases and the discussions on relationships of families, etc.

Richard von Wettstein, an Austrian botanist, proposed a system of classification which was mainly based on the Englerian concept of primitive flower. The first edition of his *Handbuch* was published in 1901 and underwent revisions, the fourth and the last one being published posthumously in two volumes (1930–1935).

Wettstein believed that angiosperms have descended from gymnosperms which were very much similar to the present-day Gnetales. Like Engler, he also believed that among the angiosperms the bisexual flowers with well-developed perianth had evolved from ancestors having unisexual perianthless flowers. While arranging various families and orders, he departed further from Engler's system and considered data from much wider fields than any of the earlier workers. Naturally, a system developed in this manner has proved to be more phylogenetic than that of either Engler or Rendle. He further diverged from Engler's system in considering dicotyledons as more primitive than monocotyledons and the latter to have been derived from the Ranalian stocks.

It is evident from this arrangement that Wettstein regarded woody habit to be more primitive than the herbaceous, many flowered inflorescences to be more primitive than few or solitary flowered types and the spiral arrangement of floral parts to have preceded the cyclic.

Within the dicotyledons, Casuarinales were regarded as the most primitive of Amentiferae, and a close similarity between the flowers of *Ephedra* and *Casuarina* was presented as evidence in support of this arrangement. Other dicotyledons were thought to be diverse in origin and several groups were considered primitive and independent. Dialypetalae (polypetalous families) were thought to have been derived from two orders, viz. the Ranales and Euphorbiales, and gave rise directly to Sympetalae. Wettstein also admitted certain cases of perianth reduction.

This system, however, has not been widely accepted. Further, there is no evidence from fossils that Ephedrales or Gnetales existed before the Cenozoic, but angiosperms were abundant as early as the Mesozoic.

In 1938, ***August A. Pulle*** of the Netherlands, published a modification of Engler's system. He accepted Spermatophyta to be a division, but unlike Engler, included four subdivisions in it, namely, Pteridospermae Gymnospermae, Chlamydospermae and Angiospermae. The last subdivisions was further divided into monocotyledons and dicotyledons, which were grouped into eight series. The general arrangement of dicotyledons was patterned after Wettstein. Sympetalae were regarded to be polyphyletic while monochlamydeae were thought to be unnatural assemblage. The system was revised in 1950 in which Gnetales were merged with Centrospermae, a view accepted by most of the recent authors. Following is broad outline of this system of classification:

Subdiv: Pteridospermae (2 extinct families)

Subdiv: Gymnospermae

Class: Cycadinae, Bennettitinae (extinct), Cordaitinae (extinct), Ginkgoinae and Coniferae

Orders: Araucariales, Podocarpales, Pinales, Cupressales, and Taxales.

Subdiv: Chlamydospermae

Orders: Gnetales and Welwitchiales

Subdiv: Angiospermae

Monocotyledoneae

Spadiciflorae, Pandanales, Helobiae, Triuridales, Farinosae, Liliiflorae, Cyperales, Glumiflorae, Scitamineae, Gynandrae

Dicotyledoneae

Series I	:	Most of the Amentiferae, Centrospermae, Polygonales, Plumbaginales, Primulales
Series II	:	Santalales and Balanophorales
Series III	:	Hamamelidales, Ranales, Ebenales
Series IV	:	Aristolochiales, Rosales, Myrtales etc.
Series V	:	Rhoeadales, Batidales, Parietales etc.
Series VI	:	Pandales, Malvales, Tricoccae, Geraniales, etc.
Series VII	:	Celastrales, Umbelliferae, Rubiales
Series VIII	:	Most of the sympetalous orders

Carl Skottsberg of Sweden modified Engler's system (1940), utilising some concepts from Wettstein's system. Within the angiosperms, he thought the monocotyledons to be derived from unknown primitive dicotyledons. In both these taxa, apocarpy was considered as a primitive feature. The apetalous families were regarded to be polyphyletic in origin and were placed in various dicotyledonous orders.

B. Hayata produced a "dynamic system" (1921) of angiosperm classification which was basically a rearrangement of Engler's system. The natural system is thought to be an everchanging one with view of the systemiser. None of the species, genera or families have been regarded to have a fixed natural position but have changeable positions, subject to alterations according to the criterion for comparison. The arrangement points out the reticulate nature of character variation.

The Ranalian School

The second concept of the primitive flower, well known as the ranalian concept, was originated by Charles E. Bessey (1915) and greatly modified by Hutchinson (1926). This view gained a wider support and may be described as follows:

It was regarded that the angiospermic flowers arose from a gymnosperm with a bisexual strobilus bearing megasporophylls above and microsporophylls below. The lower sporophylls developed into sepals and petals by progressive sterilisation. The upper ones developed into stamens and carpels. The axis of the strobilus shortened to form the receptacle. The primitive flower thus had numerous free perianth parts with many free stamens and carpels spirally arranged. The nearest approach to this primitive type of flower is found in *Magnolia* (Magnoliaceae–Ranales *sensu lato*) living today. Arber and Parkin (1907) provided the theoretical basis for this view. These authors suggested that the ancestor of angiosperms was an undiscovered gymnosperm, distantly related to that rare fossil *Cycadeoidea dacotensis* in Bennettitales, a Mesozoic plant that had borne "anthostrobili" in the axils of its cycad-like leaves.

Charles E. Bessey, an American and a student of Asa Gray, while working at the University of Nebraska, proposed a new phylogenetic system (1883) which in many respects was a modification of Bentham and Hooker's system realigned according to evolutionary principles. This was amplified in 1897, and the final treatment appeared in 1915.

Bessey considered seed plants to have had a polyphyletic origin and to be composed of three separate phyla of which he dealt only with *Anthophyta* (angiosperms).

He divided angiosperms into two major groups, *Oppositifoliae* (dicots) and *Alternifoliae* (monocots), and while arranging various taxa in these groups he used the data available from historical, ontogenetical (developmental) and morphological studies of homologies (c.f. Bessey's Dicta in Chapter 4).

Accordingly, Ranales or their ancestors were considered as the most primitive angiosperms. The evolutionary lines of development of various orders were summarised in a tree-like manner, familiarly known as "Bessey's Cactus" (see Fig. 7.1). There are three major series derived from a single stock. The branch on the left represents monocots, the other two branches indicate the two major groupings, Cotyloideae (the rosalean line) and Strobiloideae (the ranalian line) within the dicots.

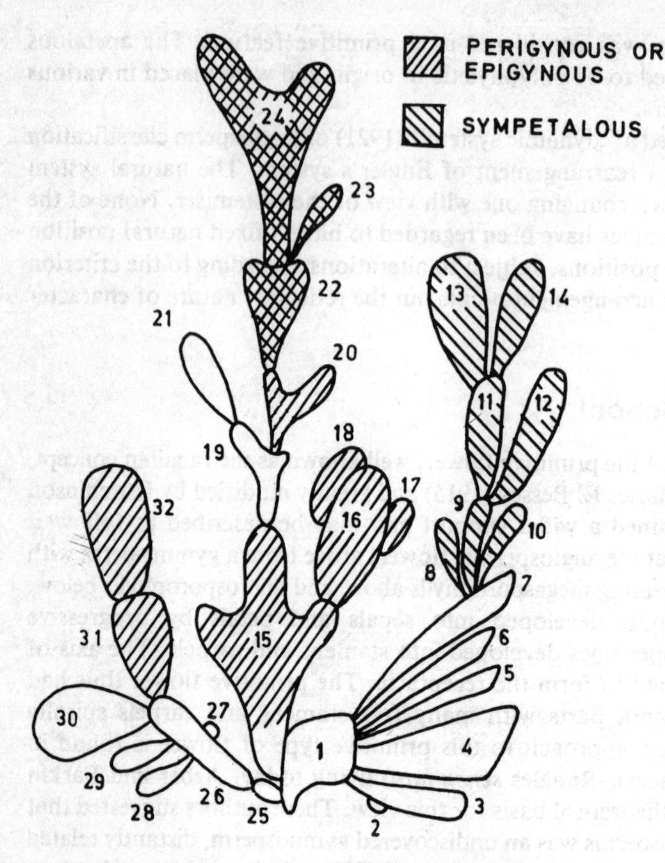

1. Ranales
2. Sarraceniales
3. Malvales
4. Geraniales
5. Guttiferales
6. Rhoeadales
7. Caryophyllales
8. Ebenales
9. Primulales
10. Ericales
11. Gentianales
12. Polemoniales
13. Scrophulariales
14. Lamiales
15. Rosales
16. Myrtales
17. Cactales
18. Loasales
19. Celastrales
20. Umbellales
21. Sapindales
22. Rubiales
23. Campanulales
24. Asterales
25. Alismatales
26. Liliales
27. Hydrales
28. Arales
29. Palmales
30. Graminales
31. Iridales
32. Orchidales

FIG. 7.1 Bessey's cactus.

Following is the synopsis of his classification (figures in parantheses indicate number of families).

Division: Anthophyta (300)
  Class: Oppositifoliae (Dicotyledoneae–255)
    Subclass: Strobiloideae (146)

Superorder:	Apopetalae–Polycarpellatae
Order:	Ranales (24)
	Malvales (12)
	Sarraceniales (2)
	Geraniales (21)
	Guttiferales (21)
	Rhoeadales (7)
	Caryophyllales (17)
Superorder:	Sympetalae–Polycarpellatae
Order:	Ebenales (5)
	Ericales (6)
	Primulales (5)
Superorder:	Sympetalae–Dicarpellatae
Order:	Gentianales (6)
	Polemoniales (6)

Scrophulariales (10)
Lamiales (4)

Subclass: Cotyloideae (109)

Superorder:	Apopetalae
Order:	Rosales (23)
	Myrtales (15)
	Loasales (5)
	Cactales (1)
	Celastrales (24)
	Sapindales (15)
	Umbellales (3)
Superorder:	Sympetalae
Order:	Rabiales (5)
	Campanulales (4)
	Asterales (14)

Class· Alternifoliae (Monocotyledoneae–45)

Subclass: Strobiloideae (31)

Order:	Alismatales (9)
	Liliales (13)
	Arales (3)
	Palmales (1)
	Graminales (5)

Subclass: Cotyloideae (14)

Order:	Hydrales (1)
	Iridales (11)
	Orchidales (2)

As has been stated earlier, the Bessey system has been supported by a large number of taxonomists in the recent years with a few modifications. Much more information of phylogenetic nature is now available than was known in the first quarter of the twentieth century. The system gained support not because of the fact that it was claimed to be phylogenetic but largely due to a more acceptable choice of the Ranales as a primitive order and the concept developed thereupon of the primitive flower.

A serious objection to this system has been due to the two evolutionary lines considered by Bessey. The Perigyny–epigyny line (Cotyloidae) particularly, cannot be assumed to constitute a single evolutionary line. Character correlations most strongly suggest that the features such as perigyny, epigyny, etc. have been evolved independently in several phyletic lines.

Hans Hallier of Hamburg, presented a phylogenetic system (1905) which resembles that of Bessey, although the two were developed independently. His classification was primarily based on the study of herbarium material and the literature together with the paleontological evidence. Hallier's classification has appeared in many of his papers, the most comprehensive being the one published in 1912.

He considered seed plants to comprise two phyla, each monophyletic and from an unknown and extinct tribe of cycads related to Bennettitales and showing affinities with Marattiales. Monocots were regarded as more advanced than dicots and to have been derived from extinct stocks ancestral to Lardizabalaceae.

The strobiloid type of flower was considered to be more primitive in the dicots as well as in the monocots. Similarly, the features such as polycarpy and the spiral arrangement of floral parts were regarded more primitive than the syncarpy and cyclic arrangement.

The dicots were derived through the orders of his Proterogenes and included 4 primary subdivisions and 29 orders. His treatment of monocotyledons was somewhat scrambled, but some of the significant features lie in the recognition of Amaryllidaceae as an unnatural taxon and consideration of Gramineae and Cyperaceae in distinct orders. It is mainly due to the realignment of genera and families, that the classification is regarded valuable. Nevertheless, in spite of certain advantages, this did not receive a wide following.

John Hutchinson from England, proposed a plan that in its basic principles, somewhat paralleled that of Bessey. He was mainly concerned with the classification of angiosperms. His phylogenetic system first appeared in a two-volume work *The Families of Flowering Plants* (1926,1934), and underwent several revisions. The final treatment appeared in 1973.

Angiosperms were considered monophyletic in origin from some hypothetical proangiosperms. In his initial subdivision, the angiosperms were regarded as evolved along two separate evolutionary lines, Herbaceae—including most of the predominantly herbaceous families derived from Ranales *sensu stricto*—and the Lignosae—including fundamentally woody representatives derived from Magnoliales. The monocotyledons were derived from the stocks ancestral to Ranales.

Lignosae were further grouped into 54 orders beginning with Magnoliales-Dilleniales-Rosales, etc. and ending in Bignoniales and Verbenales. Herbaceae were further grouped into 28 orders beginning with Ranales-Rhoeadales-Caryophyllales, etc. and ending in Boraginales and Lamiales.

In the first publication (1926), the dicotyledons included two subclasses, the Archichlamydeae (petals free or absent) and Metachlamydeae (pertals united). The former were further divided into 59 orders and 213 families while the latter were divided into 23 orders and 51 families.

The monocotyledons were divided into three distinct groups on the basis of the nature of the perianth—Calyciferae, Corolliferae and Glumiflorae. These were further divided into 29 orders and 104 families.

In the last revision (1973), little alteration was made in the system. Lythraceae have been moved or transferred from the Herbaceae to the Lignosae, in the order Myrtales. This alteration was also made in 1969. A number of minifamilies proposed by various authors have either been accepted or sometimes different points of view have been supplied. Little alteration has been made in the monocotyledons for this third revised edition.

Thus in this revision there are 83 orders and 349 families of the dicotyledons and 29 orders and 69 families of the monocotyledons.

Figure 7.2 gives the linear sequence of orders in Hutchinson's system as revised in 1973. Figures in parentheses indicate the number of families.

In the phylogenetic tree, Hutchinson did not derive one order directly from the other but from its ancestral stock. This is more safe and acceptable than

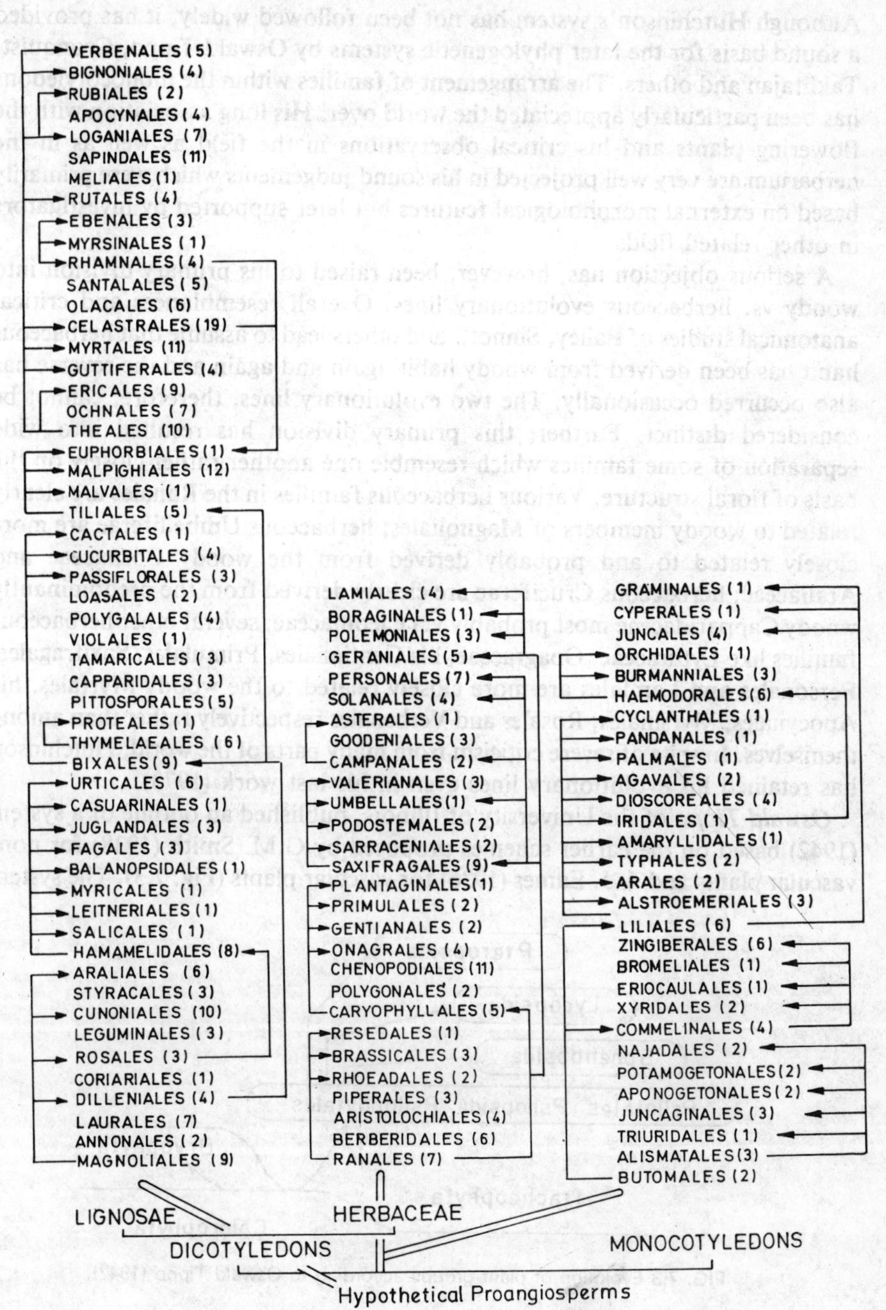

FIG. 7.2 Linear sequence of orders in Hutchinson's system (1973).

to believe any present-day order to be directly ancestral to any other. It is also evident from the number of families (originally 342 families, further split up into about 368 and finally as many as 418) that their delimitation was done very critically and therefore their relationships appear to be more natural.

Although Hutchinson's system has not been followed widely, it has provided a sound basis for the later phylogenetic systems by Oswald Tippo, Cronquist, Takhtajan and others. The arrangement of families within the monocotyledons has been particularly appreciated the world over. His long association with the flowering plants and his critical observations in the field as well as in the herbarium are very well projected in his sound judgements which were primarily based on external morphological features but later supported by investigators in other related fields.

A serious objection has, however, been raised to his primary division into woody vs. herbaceous evolutionary lines. Overall resemblances and critical anatomical studies of Bailey, Sinnott, and others lead to assume that herbaceous habit has been derived from woody habit again and again and the reverse has also occurred occasionally. The two evolutionary lines, therefore, cannot be considered distinct. Further, this primary division has resulted into wide separation of some families which resemble one another rather closely on the basis of floral structure. Various herbaceous families in the Ranales are clearly related to woody members of Magnoliales; herbaceous Umbelliferae are more closely related to and probably derived from the woody Cornaceae and Araliaceae; herbaceous Cruciferae are clearly derived from the predominantly woody Capparidaceae most probably via Cleomaceae; several other herbaceous families like Lythraceae, Onagraceae, his Gentianales, Primulales, Saxifragales, Personales and Lamiales are more closely related to the woody Myrtales, his Apocynales, Myrsinales, Rosales and Verbenales respectively rather than among themselves. In spite of severe criticism from many parts of the world, Hutchinson has retained his evolutionary lines even in his last work (1973).

Oswald Tippo of the University of Illinois, published an outline of a system (1942) based on the earlier schemes proposed by G.M. Smith (1938) for non-vascular plants and A.J. Eames (1936) for vascular plants (Fig. 7.3). The system

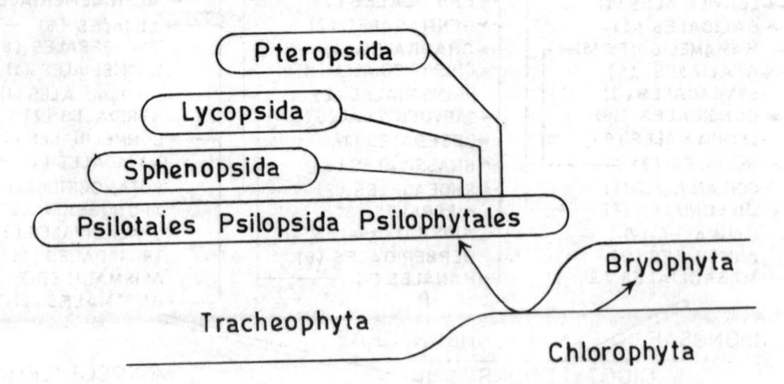

FIG. 7.3 Evolution of plant groups according to Oswald Tippo (1942).

was claimed to be phylogenetic and was adopted in the United States on a large scale. The system emphasises that the Pteridophyta is not a homogeneous group and that there is no distinct line of demarcation between pteridophytes and spermatophytes. The relationships indicated are derived from a sound study of palaeobotanical data and a comparison of these with the data obtained through study of living plants. Tippo considered Magnoliales to be very primitive order while the Amentiferae were taken to be advanced and recent. Following is the outline of this system:

Kingdom Plantae

Subkingdom Thallophyta

Phylum: Cyanophyta, Chlorophyta, Chrysophyta
Phylum: Pyrrophyta, Phaeophyta
Phylum: Rhodophyta, Schizophyta, Myxomycophyta
Phylum: Eumycophyta

Subkingdom Embryophyta

Phylum: Bryophyta (3 classes—Musci, Hepaticae, Anthocerotae)
Tracheophyta
Subphylum: Psilopsida
Lycopsida
Sphenopsida
Pteropsida
Class- Filicineae
Gymnospermae
Angiospermae

Karl Mez of the University of Koenigsberg published an outline of his classification (1926) based on serodiagnostic data and modified it in 1936. He established that relationships between larger groups of angiosperms could be determined by serodiagnosis, and arranged groups accordingly. The method consists of the study and analysis of protein reaction of plants of different families with the blood serum of experimental animals such as rabbits or guineapigs.

Although there has been less adoption of his system, the serodiagnostic method is now being widely used to determine relationships of plants of doubtful affinities. More about this will be discussed in Chapter 8.

G. Gunderson of the United States proposed a new system (1950) of classification of dicotyledons which is claimed to be phylogenetic. The data which served the basis of his classification was derived from cytology, anatomy, together with morphology. The dicotyledons have been divided into 10 groups such as Magnoliflorae, Cistiflorae, Theaflorae, Rosiflorae, etc., of which the first is considered to be the most primitive. These ten groups are further divided into 42 orders. Gunderson ignored the polypetalous and sympetalous characters of flowers.

Lyman Benson of Pomona College, California, developed not a new system of classification but rearranged the families of Engler, Prantl and Bessey's systems. This was presented in the form of a chart (1957) essentially considering the dynamic nature of plant families. Instead of proposing a phylogenetic tree like other authors, he presented a two-dimensional chart, thus developing an essentially horizontal arrangement.

Benson did not think any flowering plant order to have been derived from any other living order and believed that the related orders have evolved from pre-existing groups with some members similar to the species now composing the living taxa. The origin of angiosperms as a class was thought to be obscure.

The woody Ranales were regarded to have retained more primitive features than any other living group, and it was inferred that the ancestors of flowering plants had these characters in combination with other primitive characters, some of which have disappeared and others of which have persisted in other orders.

The position in the chart for any dicotyledonous or monocotyledonous order corresponds roughly to its degree of specialisation in any characters, often the degree of departure from the five floral features characteristic of primitive Ranales or Alismatales. This is expressed in rough proportion by the chart distance of each order from Ranales or Alismatales (Fig. 7.4). The size of figures representing each order is in rough proportion to the number of species composing it.

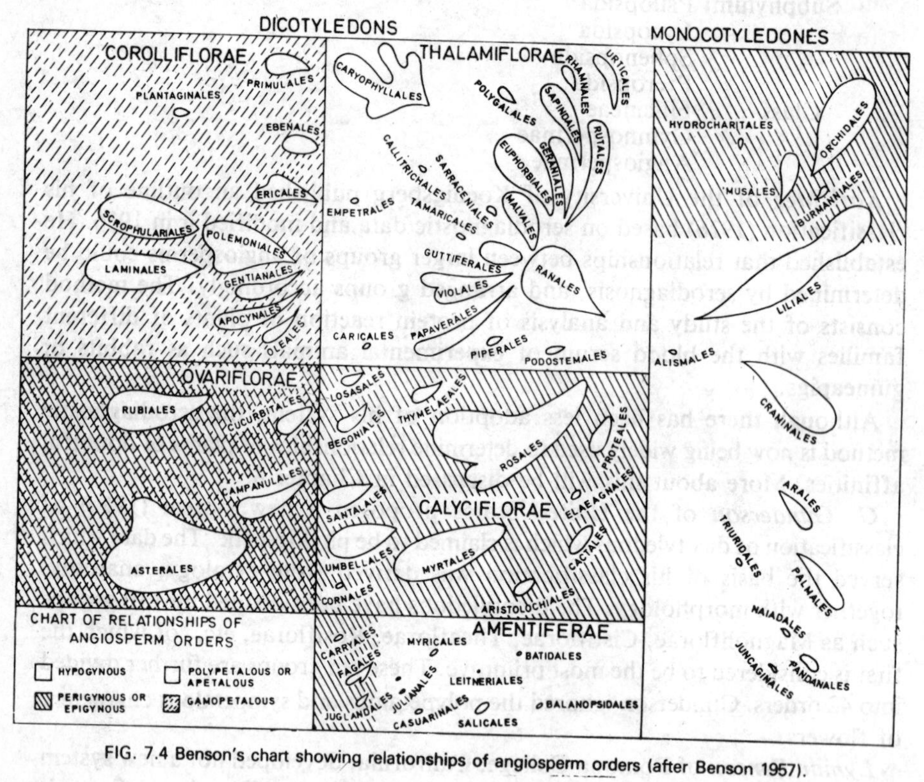

FIG. 7.4 Benson's chart showing relationships of angiosperm orders (after Benson 1957).

Although the system appears to be suitable for teaching purposes, it appears that primitive families under Ranales, in spite of their priority of position, lack uniformity and relationship. The division of sympetalous families into two distinct groups, as in Bessey's system, into Corolliflorae and Ovariflorae, is purely artificial. Similarly, placement of taxa such as Proteales, Elaeagnales, Cactales, etc. in a single division Calyciflorae is not a natural one.

The system, obviously, has not been widely followed, but the method of presentation has been appreciated by later authors.

Armen L. Takhtajan of Leningrad developed a preliminary phylogenetic diagram of the orders of higher plants (1942) in a paper on structural types of gynoecium and placentation. The actual system of classification based on phylogenetic principles (1953) was published in 1954 and translated into English in 1958. Later he traced the evolution of angiosperms (1959) and proposed a new system (1964) in Russian. He was especially inspired by Hallier's attempts (1905, 1908, 1912) to create a synthetic evolutionary classification of flowering plants based on Darwinian philosophy. According to Takhtajan (1980), the Hallier system was more synthetic and displayed a much deeper insight into the morphological evolution and phylogeny of flowering plants than any other contemporary classification, including the Bessey system.

In his system published in 1954, Takhtajan considered the order Magnoliales, *sensu lato*, as the most primitive and archaic group which gave rise to all other branches of angiosperms. He derived monocotyledons and Nymphaeales from a hypothetical common dicotyledonous ancestor with vesselless wood and monocolpate pollen. The amentiferous families were regarded by him to be derived from Hamamelidales, following Hallier and Hutchinson.

This system published in 1954 has later gone through a series of modifications and elaborations, but the nucleus of the system and the basic features of the branching pattern of phyletic diagram remain essentially the same.

The main innovation in the revision published in 1966 was the subdivision of both classes of Magnoliophyta (angiosperms) into subclasses which were proposed in 1964 and validated in 1966. Takhtajan retained the rank of superorder as a supplementary rank intercalated between subclass and order, deriving superordinate names from generic names and with an ending *-anae* (e.g. Magnolianae, Rafflesianae, Ranunculanae, etc.). He discarded the traditional ending *-florae* used by him in 1964.

Some more gradual modifications were made in the revisions (Takhtajan, 1969, 1973), and the most recent verdict appeared in 1980. These revisions obviously have incorporated the newer data as they went on accumulating. The most significant modification has been in the class Liliopsida, especially in the delimitation and arrangement of the families of the superorder Lilianae.

Magnoliophyta are regarded to be monophyletic in origin, most probably derived from Bennettitale-like ancestors or stocks ancestral to them. The Magnoliopsida (dicotyledons) are believed to be more primitive than the Liliopsida (monocotyledons) and the latter have been considered to be derived from the stocks ancestral to Nymphaeales.

Takhtajan (1980) recognised 2 classes of Magnoliophya consisting of 7 subclasses, 20 superorders, 71 orders and 333 families of Magnoliopsida and 3 subclasses, 8 superorders, 21 orders and 77 families of the Liliopsida.

Figure 7.5 shows the putative relationships among the classes, subclasses and orders of flowering plants.

Following is the synopsis of taxa in Takhtajan's (1980) classification system. (Figures in parentheses indicate number of families.)

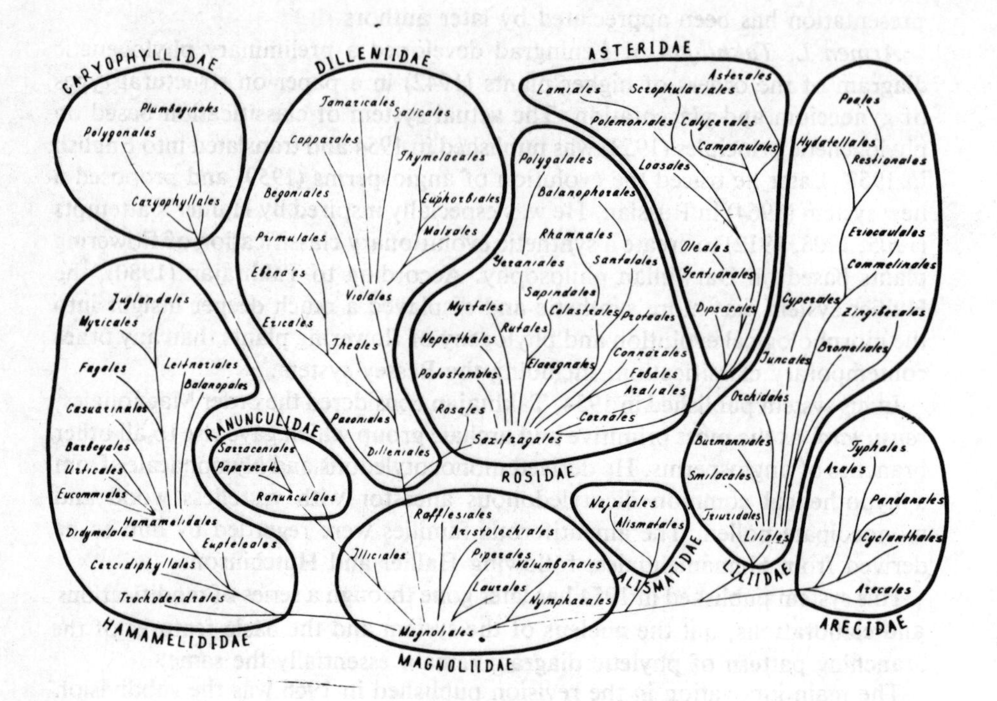

FIG. 7.5 Putative relationships among the classes, subclasses, and orders of flowering plants. (Reprinted from Takhtajan, 1980 by permission of the New York Botanical Garden, New York.)

Division: Magnoliophyta or Angiospermae (419)

Class: Magnoliopsida or Dicotyledones (342)

Subclass A. Magnoliidae (29)
Superorder I. Magnolianae (23)
Order: 1. Magnoliales (8)
2. Illiciales (2)
3. Laurales (10)
Suborder: Monimineae (6)
Chloranthineae (1)
Lactoridineae (1)
Laurineae (2)
Order: 4. Piperales (2)
5. Aristolochiales (1)
Superorder II. Rafflesianae (2)
Order: 6. Rafflesiales (2)
Superorder III. Nymphaeanae (4)
Order: 7. Nymphaeales (3)
Suborder: Nymphaeineae (2)
Ceratophyllineae (1)
Order: 8. Nelumbonales (1)

Subclass B.		Ranunculidae (9)
Superorder IV.		Ranunculanae (9)
Order:	9.	Ranunculalaes (7)
	10.	Papaverales (1)
	11.	Serraceniales (1)
Subclass C.		Hamamelididae (26)
Superorder V.		Hamamelidanae (23)
Order:	12.	Trochodendrales (2)
	13.	Cercidiphyllales (1)
	14.	Eupteleales (1)
	15.	Didymelales (1)
	16.	Hamamelidales (6)
Suborder:		Hamamelidineae (4)
		Buxineae (2)
Order:	17.	Eucommiales (1)
	18.	Urticales (5)
	19.	Barbeyales (1)
	20.	Casuarinales (1)
	21.	Fagales (2)
	22.	Balanopales (1)
	23.	Leitneriales (1)
Superorder VI.		Juglandanae (3)
Order:	24.	Myricales (1)
	25.	Juglandales (2)
Subclass D.		Caryophyllidae (16)
Superorder VII.		Caryophyllanae (15)
Order:	26.	Caryophyllales (14)
Suborder:		Phytolaccineae (10)
		Caryophyllineae (2)
		Chenopodiineae (2)
Order:	27.	Polygonales (1)
Superorder VIII.		Plumbaginanae (1)
Order:	28.	Plumbaginales (1)
Subclass E.		Dilleniidae (78)
Superorder IX.		Dillenianae (47)
Order:	29.	Dilleniales (2)
	30.	Paeoniales (1)
	31.	Theales (19)
	32.	Violales (14)
Suborder:		Violineae (13)
		Cucurbitineae (1)
Order:	33.	Begoniales (2)
	34.	Capparales (5)
Suborder:		Capparineae (3)
		Resedineae (1)
		Moringineae (1)
Order:	35.	Tamaricales (3)
Suborder:		Tamaricineae (2)
		Fonquierineae (1)
Order:	36.	Salicales (1)
Superorder		Ericanae (16)
Order:	37.	Ericales (8)
	38.	Ebenales (5)
	39.	Primulales (3)
Superorder XI		Malvanae (15)

Order:	40.	Malvales (10)
	41.	Euphorbiales (4)
	42.	Thymelaeales (1)
Subclass F.		Rosidae (137)
Superorder: XII.		Rosanae (41)
Order:	43.	Saxifragales (24)
Suborder		Cunoniineae (4)
		Pittosporineae (9)
		Saxifragineae (11)
Order:	44.	Rosales (3)
	45.	Fabales (1)
	46.	Connarales (1)
	47.	Podostemales (1)
	48.	Nepenthales (1)
Superorder XIII.		Myrtanae (14)
Order:	49.	Myrtales (14)
Suborder:		Myrtineae (11)
		Halorgineae (1)
		Rhizophorineae (1)
		Lecythidineae (1)
Superorder XIV.		Rutanae (42)
Order:	50	Rutales (15)
Suborder:		Rutaneae (14)
		Coriariineae (1)
Order:	51.	Sapindales (13)
	52.	Geraniales (8)
Suborder		Linineae (3)
		Geraniineae (2)
		Balsamininea (2)
		Limnanthineae (1)
Order:	53.	Polygalales (6)
Superorder XV.		Aralianae (12)
Order:	54.	Cornales (10)
	55.	Araliales (2)
Superorder XVI.		Celastranae (27)
Order:	56.	Celastrales (15)
Suborder:		Incacininea (7)
		Celastrineae (8)
Order:	57.	Santalales (6)
Suborder:		Santalineae (4)
		Loranthineae (2)
Order:	58.	Balanophorales (2)
	59.	Rhamnales (3)
	60.	Elaeagnales (1)
Superorder XVII		Proteanae (1)
Order:	61.	Proteales (1)
Subclass G.		Asteridae (47)
Superorder XVIII.		Gentiananae (15)
Order:	62.	Gentianales (8)
	63.	Oleales (1)
	64.	Dipsacales (5)
	65.	Loasales (1)
Superorder XIX.		Lamianae (26)
Order:	66.	Polemoniales (7)

Suborder:		Convolvulineae (2)
		Polemoniineae (1)
		Boraginineae (4)
Order:	67.	Lamiales (3)
	68.	Scrophulariales (16)
Suborder:		Solanineae (2)
		Scrophulariineae (13)
		Hippurineae (1)
Superorder XX.		Asteranae (6)
Order:	69.	Campanulales (4)
Suborder:		Campanulineae (3)
		Goodeniineae (1)
Order:	70.	Calycerales (1)
	71.	Asterales (1)
Class Liliopsida or Monocotyledones (77)		
Subclass A.		Alismatidae (14)
Superorder I.		Alismatanae(14)
Order:	1.	Alismatales (4)
Suborder:		Butomineae (1)
		Alismatineae (2)
		Hydrocharitineae (1)
Order	2.	Najadales (10)
Suborder:		Aponogetonineae (1)
		Scheuchzeriineae (1)
		Potamogetonineae (6)
		Zosterineae (1)
		Najadineae (1)
Subclass B.		Liliidae (57)
Superorder II.		Triuridanae (1)
Order	3.	Triuridales (1)
Superorder III.		Lilianae (33)
Order	4.	Liliales (23)
Suborder:		Liliineae (10)
		Asphodelineae (4)
		Asparagineae (2)
		Iridineae (2)
		Haemodorineae (3)
		Pontederiineae (1)
		Philydrineae (1)
Order:	5.	Smilacales (6)
	6.	Burmanniales (2)
	7.	Orchidales (1)
	8.	Bromeliales (1)
Superorder IV.		Juncanae (3)
Order:	9.	Juncales (2)
	10.	Cyperales (1)
Superorder V.		Commelinanae (12)
Order:	11.	Commelinales (4)
Suborder:		Xyridineae (2)
		Commelinineae (2)
Order:	12.	Eriocaulales (1)
	13.	Restionales (5)
	14.	Hydatellales (1)
	15.	Poales (1)

Superorder VI.		Zingiberanae (8)
Order:	16.	Zingiberales (8)
Subclass C.		Arecidae (6)
Superorder VII.		Arecanae (4)
Order:	17.	Arecales (1)
	18.	Cyclanthales (1)
	19.	Pandanales (1)
	20.	Typhales (1)
Superorder VIII.		Aranae (2)
Order:	21.	Arales (2)

Takhtajan's system, when it first appeared in 1954, was not much cared for, but since its publication in English, in the revised form, in 1969 it attracted the attention of the entire world. It was immediately followed in many parts of the world and was considered as one of the most satisfactory phylogenetic systems known at that time. His last revision in 1980 is particularly satisfactory in respect of his disposition of liliaceous families. This group of petaliferous monocotyledons was not considered in such details in the 1969 version.

The system is felt acceptable mainly due to its clearly defined evolutionary principles. Although it cannot claim to have made a final rearrangement of the families, particularly in his subclass Rosidae, the system has many plus points in its credit. It is now by the joint efforts of the limited number of botanists of various countries that the great progress in macrosystem of flowering plants has been achieved. As a result, modern systems, particularly those constructed during the last three decades, have much more in common. By now, most of the problems such as monophyly or polyphyly, interrelationships of dicots and monocots, primitive position of the Magnoliales, the secondary nature of the anemophilous families with reduced unisexual flowers, etc. have been satisfactorily settled. And here it should be emphasised that it was Takhtajan's system which paved the way for most of these later classifications.

The main objection to Takhtajan's system is his derivation of the monocotyledons from the stocks ancestral to the Nymphaeales. Stebbins (1974) is of the opinion that the similarities between these two groups are probably due to convergent evolution and the ancestors of both of them are completely obscured in the geological history.

Similarly, as pointed out in Chapter 5, there is objection to Takhtajan's idea of the cradle of angiosperms.

These objections, however, do not harm the phylogenetic system and the relationships of various groups are generally felt satisfactory.

Arthur Cronquist of the New York Botanical Gardens, presented a system for dicotyledons (1957) which was modified and published in collaboration with other two eminent botanists (1966) and the final modification appeared in 1968a. The treatment presented in his book *Evolution and Classification of Flowering Plants,* is a synthesis based on literature, personal observations and discussions with other botanists. This is an elaboration of Bessey's system and a refinement over Takhtajan's system (1964).

The traditional nomenclature of two main groups of angiosperms—Dicotyledons and Monocotyledons—was replaced by a new terminology—

Magnoliatae and Liliatae—respectively. These classes have been further divided into 10 subclasses, 6 of the Magnoliatae and 4 of the Liliatae.

The subclass Magnoliidae, which consists mainly of the families of the traditional Ranales, was regarded as the basal complex from which other angiosperms have been derived (Fig. 7.6a). The Hamamelidae were regarded as a group of wind-pollinated families with reduced, chiefly apetalous flowers that are often borne in catkins (the traditional Amentiferae). The Caryophyllidae

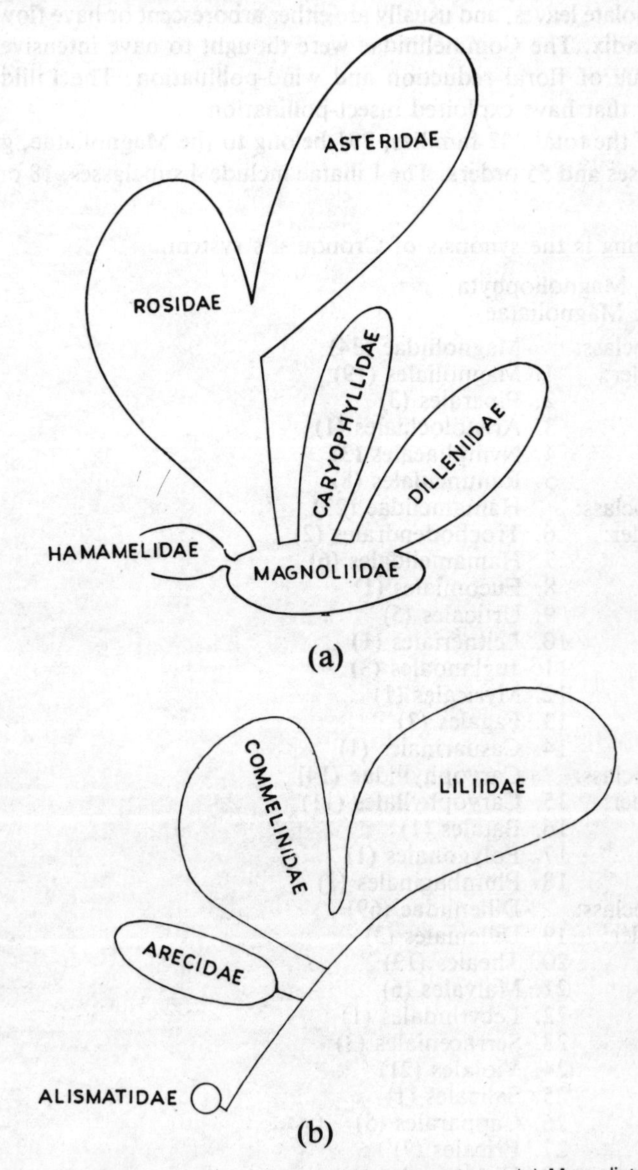

FIG. 7.6 Putative relationships of subclasses of flowering plants: (a) Magnoliatae, (b) Liliatae. (Redrawn from *Evolution and Classification of Flowering Plants* by A. Cronquist 1968, by permission of the author.)

show a strong tendency towards free-central placentation and many of them have betalains (nitrogenous anthocyanins and anthoxanthins). The Rosidae and Dilleniidae were considered to be parallel groups which are not well-distinguished morphologically. The Asteridae included the higher sympetalous families, mostly derived from the Rosidae.

In the Liliatae (Fig. 7.6b) the Alismatidae included chiefly aquatic members, whereas the other subclasses included those families which typically have large often petiolate leaves, and usually are either arborescent or have flowers crowded into a spadix. The Commelinidae were thought to have intensively exploited the avenue of floral reduction and wind-pollination. The Liliidae included members that have exploited insect-pollination.

Out of the total 352 families, 291 belong to the Magnoliatae, grouped into 6 subclasses and 55 orders. The Liliatae include 4 subclasses, 18 orders and 61 families.

Following is the synopsis of Cronquist's system.

Division: Magnoliophyta
A. Class: Magnoliatae

I. Subclass: Magnoliidae (34)
Order:
1. Magnoliales (19)
2. Piperales (3)
3. Aristolochiales (1)
4. Nymphaeales (3)
5. Ranunculales (8)

II. Subclass: Hamamelidae (23)
Order:
6. Trochodendrales (2)
7. Hamamelidales (6)
8. Eucomiales (1)
9. Urticales (5)
10. Leitneriales (1)
11. Juglandales (3)
12. Myricales (1)
13. Fagales (3)
14. Casuarinales (1)

III. Subclass: Caryophyllidae (14)
Order:
15. Caryophyllales (11)
16. Batales (1)
17. Polygonales (1)
18. Plumbaginales (1)

IV. Subclass: Dilleniidae (69)
Order:
19. Dilleniales (3)
20. Theales (13)
21. Malvales (6)
22. Lecythidales (1)
23. Serraceniales (3)
24. Violales (21)
25. Salicales (1)
26. Capparales (5)
27. Ericales (7)
28. Diapensiales (1)
29. Ebenales (5)
30. Primulales (3)

V. Subclass: Rosidae (108)
Order: 31. Rosales (17)
32. Podostemales (1)
33. Haloragales (4)
34. Myrtales (13)
35. Proteales (2)
36. Cornales (6)
37. Santalales (10)
38. Rafflesiales (3)
39. Celastrales (10)
40. Euphorbiales (5)
41. Rhamnales (3)
42. Sapindales (17)
43. Geraniales (5)
44. Linales (3)
45. Polygalales (7)
46. Umbellales (2)
VI. Subclass: Asteridae (43)
Order: 47. Gentianales (4)
48. Polemoniales (8)
49. Lamiales (5)
50. Plantaginales (1)
51. Scrophulariales (12)
52. Campanulales (6)
53. Rubiales (1)
54. Dipsacales (5)
55. Asterales (1)

B. Class: Liliatae
I. Subclass: Alismatidae (14)
Order: 1. Alismatales (3)
2. Hydrocharitales (1)
3. Najadales (8)
4. Triuridales (2)
II. Subclass: Commelinidae (25)
Order: 5. Commelinales (4)
6. Eriocaulales (1)
7. Restionales (5)
8. Juncales (2)
9. Cyperales (2)
10. Typhales (2)
11. Bromeliales (1)
12. Zingiberales (8)
III. Subclass: Arecidae (5)
Order: 13. Arecales (1)
14. Cyclanthales (1)
15. Pandanales (1)
16. Arales (2)
IV. Subclass: Liliidae (17)
Order: 17. Liliales (13)
18. Orchidales (4)

The treatment is synthetic. Vast literature has been quoted taking into account the significant contribution in different fields of science. Synoptical keys for each group up to the family level are very useful. In general, the system appears to be more natural and satisfactory. It has, therefore, been widely followed in America and some of the European countries in its original form or with slight modification.

At some levels, too much reliance on single characters (centrifugal stamens, free-central placentation, etc.) hampers the otherwise natural classification. The arrangement of families in Liliales, particularly with reference to submergence of Amaryllidaceae into Liliaceae, although tentative, has been severely criticised (Treub, 1974, 1975).

Recent Modifications

In addition to the main systems of angiosperm classification discussed above, there have appeared a vast number of modifications during the last decade or so. The underlying concept of floral evolution depicted in all these systems is greatly uniform, and the variations, if at all, are seen in the minor rearrangements and the status accorded to various taxa. *H.P. Banks,* for example, presented his views (1968) in a symposium on Evolution and Environment, wherein he proposed to include all the vascular plants in his division Tracheophyta. The latter was further divided into 7 subdivisions, namely, Rhyniophytina, Zosterophyllophytina, Psilophytina, Lycophytina, Sphenophytina, Trimerophytina and Pterophytina. The last name included the class Angiospermopsida among others. *D.W. Bierhorst,* in his book on morphology of vascular plants (1971), adopted a system very much similar to that presented by Banks and treated angiospermopsida as one of the 14 classes of the division Tracheophyta. *R.F. Thorne* proposed certain guiding principles of angiosperm phylogeny (1958, 1963) and later on presented a synopsis of his classification (1968). The detailed treatment of one of his superorders Annoniflorae appeared in 1974 and his comprehensive classification including 21 superorders, 50 orders, 74 suborders, 321 families and 432 subfamilies was published in 1976. The detailed realignments of the families in these superorders was presented in 1977. The class Angiospermae was named as Annonopsida.

Thorne considered his system to be considerably different from other systems, particularly those of Takhtajan (1969, 1973) and Cronquist (1968a), because he attempted to stress relationships more than differences. Further, he claimed his taxa to be more inclusive than those of others with more "disintegrative tendencies". According to him, the divergences of his system from other systems are "startling realignments that are new or at least different from standard treatments."

His superorders included Annoniflorae, Theiflorae, Malviflorae, Rutiflorae, Rosiflorae, Asteriflorae, Liliiflorae, Alismatiflorae, Commeliniflorae and others. In a phylogenetic shrub presented by him (1976), those superorders were placed towards the centre which were thought to retain the most primitive original features of the protoangiosperms, for example, Annoniflorae, Hamamelidiflorae and Rosiflorae. Radiating from the centre were the other taxa that deviate most from their presumed protoangiospermous ancestry. He accepted both, the subdivision Angiosperms as well as the two classes, Magnoliopsida and Liliopsida, as monophyletic taxa.

Thorne, like the other recent authors, also considered data from all available evidence. Although it is claimed by him that his system diverges in many respects from the contemporary systems, the main theme remained the same as proposed by Takhtajan (1969) and Cronquist (1968a). Again, while claiming various taxa to be more inclusive, Thorne enumerated 21 superorders instead of 13 by Takhtajan. Merxmuller (1977) stated, "This reminds me a little of the old Englerian times in which so many infra-specific categories like proles, subvariety, subforma and so have been in vogue. We should deliberate whether this superordinal inflation is not another fruitless trial of expressing quite doubtful phylogenetical contexts by box-in-box schemes." Further, he stated, "At all events this inflated classification is a perfect means for confusing nontaxonomists by a fashionable application of non-existing nomenclatural rules to these higher categories."

R.M.T. Dahlgren of Copenhagen presented a method of illustrating an angiosperm system as an imaginary phylogenetic shrub in transection, in a textbook of angiosperm taxonomy (Dahlgren *et al.,* 1974). A revised system, with a diagram, was presented in 1975 and a commentary on this presentation was provided in 1977. A complete revision again appeared in 1980 wherein the author states that the new classification is still provisional.

This new system of classification (Dahlgren, 1980), like that of Dahlgren (1975), is shown as a two-dimensional diagram of framework, but differs in numerous major and minor features. Here the angiosperms (Magnoliopsida) represent a class divisible into two subclasses, Magnoliidae and Liliidae, corresponding to the di- and monocotyledons. Magnoliidae are divided into 24 Superorders, 80 orders and 346 families while Liliidae are divided into 7 Superorders, 26 orders and 92 families.

In the construction of classification, an attempt has been made to take into consideration as much information as possible. The division of the class Magnoliopsida into two main subclasses, Magnoliidae and Liliidae has been considered somewhat arbitrary and would probably not stand a test according to cladistic methods. However, Liliidae stand out as a possibly monophyletic group by virtue of their single cotyledon and characteristic triangular protein bodies in the sieve tube plastids (Behnke, 1969), in addition to the less constant differences from Magnoliidae.

The phylogenetic shrub has been depicted to show placement of variously shaped figures representing the orders close to one another (See Fig.7.7) when members of the orders are similar in several characters that reflect presumably phylogenetic relationships. The size of these figures roughly corresponds to the number of species in the orders and the extensions of the figures to various directions indicate diversity of characters within them.

Dahlgren did not consider angiosperms to be polyphyletic in origin from different gymnosperms but believed that the combination of several very characteristic attributes (secondary endosperm, 8-nucleate embryosac, companion cells in the phloem, etc.) would hardly have evolved independently in different gymnospermous groups.

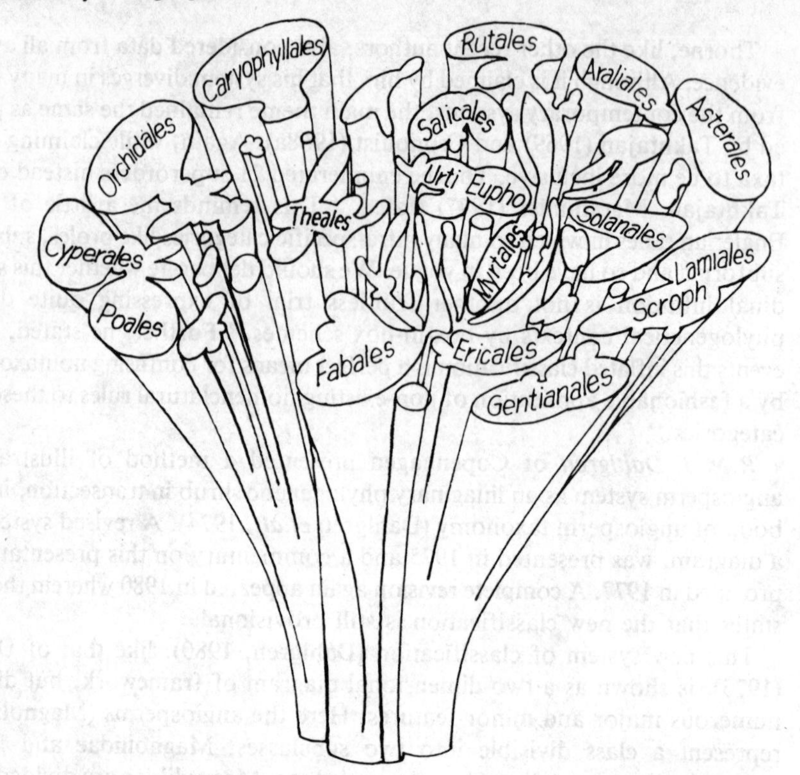

FIG. 7.7 Cross-section of Dahlgren's phylogenetic shrub. (Reproduced from *Plant Systematics and Evolution* ed. by K. Kubitzki 1977, by permission of Springer Verlag, New York.)

In accordance with Thorne (1968, 1976), the Superorders bear the termination *-florae* which takes precedence over *-anae* used by Takhtajan (1969) and Dahlgren (1975). With regard to Liliiflorae, a splitter's approach has been chosen at the family level.

Following is the synopsis of Dahlgren's system of classification as appeared in 1980. (Figures in parentheses indicate number of families.)

Class–Magnoliopsida
Subclass–Magnoliidae (346)

Superorder: Magnoliiflorae (24)
Order: Annonales (4)
Illiciales (2)
Laurales (8)
Nelumbonales (1)
Aristolochiales (1)
Refflesiales (2)
Magnoliales (6)

Superorder: Nymphaeaflorae (5)
Order: Nymphaeales (3)
Piperales (2)

Superorder: Ranunculiflorae (10)
Order: Papaverales (2)
Ranunculales (8)

Superorder: Caryophylliflorae (9)
  Order: Caryophyllales (9)
Superorder: Polygoniflorae (1)
  Order: Polygonales (1)
Superorder: Malviflorae (32)
  Order: Paeoniales (1)
  Elaeagnales (1)
  Dilleniales (1)
  Malvales (13)
  Plumbaginales (2)
  Thymelaeales (1)
  Urticales (6)
  Euphorbiales (6)
  Rhamnales (1)
Superorder: Violiflorae (14)
  Order: Violales (13)
  Salicales (1)
  Tamaricales (2)
  Capparales (7)
  Salvadorales (1)
Superorder: Theiflorae (2)
  Order: Theales (17)
  Droserales (3)
Superorder: Primuliflorae (9)
  Order: Ebenales (4)
  Primulales (5)

Superorder: Rosiflorae (39)
  Order: Trochodendrales (4)
  Hamamelidales (4)
  Fagales (3)
  Balanopales (1)
  Juglandales (2)
  Myricales (1)
  Casuarinales (1)
  Buxales (2)
  Cunoniales (8)
  Saxifragales (7)
  Gunnerales (1)
  Rosales (3)
  Malales (2)
Superorder: Podostemiflorae (1)
  Order: Podostemales (1)
Superorder: Fabiflorae (3)
  Order: Fabales (3)
Superorder: Proteiflorae (1)
  Order: Proteales (1)
Superorder: Myrtiflorae (14)
  Order: Myrtales (12)
  Haloragales (1)
  Rhizophorales (1)

Superorder: Rutiflorae (45)
Order: Rutales (6)
Sapindales (15)
Balsaminales (1)
Polygalales (5)
Geraniales (16)
Tropaeolales (2)
Superorder: Santaliflorae (13)
Order: Celastrales (5)
Vitidales (1)
Santalales (7)
Superorder: Balanoflorae (2)
Order: Balanophorales (2)
Superorder: Araliiflorae (6)
Order: Pittosporales (3)
Araliales (3)
Superorder: Asteriflorae (4)
Order: Campanulales (3)
Asterales (1)
Superorder: Solaniflorae (13)
Order: Solanales (7)
Boraginales (6)
Superorder: Corniflorae (49)
Order: Fouquieriales (1)
Serraceniales (1)
Ericales (10)
Eucomiales (1)
Cornales (29)
Dipsacales (7)
Superorder: Loasiflorae (1)
Order: Loasales (1)
Superorder: Gentianiflorae (8)
Order: Goodeniales (1)
Gentianales (6)
Oleales (1)
Superorder: Lamiflorae (23)
Order: Scrophulariales (18)
Hydrostachyales (1)
Hippuridales (1)
Lamiales (3)
Subclass: Liliidae (92)
Superorder: Alismatiflorae (12)
Order: Hydrocharitales (3)
Zosterales (8)
Alismatales (1)
Superorder: Triuridiflorae (1))
Order: Triuridales (1)
Superorder: Ariflorae (2)
Order: Arales (2)

Superorder: Liliiflorae (53)
  Order: Dioscoreales (5)
  Asparagales (31)
  Hydatellales (1)
  Liliales (8)
  Burmanniales (3)
  Philydrales (1)
  Orchidales (3)
  Velloziales (1)
  Bromeliales (1)
  Haemodorales (1)
  Pontederiales (1)
  Typhales (2)

Superorder: Zingiberiflorae (8)
  Order: Zingiberales (8)

Superorder: Commeliniflorae (13)
  Order: Commelinales (2)
  Eriocaulales (2)
  Juncales (1)
  Cyperales (1)
  Poales (5)

Superorder: Areciflorae (3)
  Order: Arecales (1)
  Cyclanthales (1)
  Pandanales (1)

This system, as can be seen, is yet another modification of Takhtajan's original plan taking into account additional data. The recent revision of both Takhtajan's and Dahlgren's systems are similar in many respects, which is bound to happen when two taxonomists are handling the same data.

Corner (1981), however, has criticised the system and holds that the classification includes un-natural orders and superorders. He has pointed out the basic factors of phylogenetic taxonomy and has firmly stated that the leptocauly leads to parallel evolution and specific multiplication. He has also criticised the nomenclature of various groups adopted by Dahlgren and has suggested the name "Pseudon" for a conjectural taxon.

Dahlgren (1981) has attempted to clarify most of the doubts and objections raised by Corner. It appears from the controversy that there will continue to be two distinct groups of investigators working with widely different areas in taxonomic research—those following the basic philosophy of *intensive* investigation in limited groups like Prof. Corner and those attempting *extensive* "general purpose" investigation. Their approaches being vastly different, there is bound to be controversial assessment of the results achieved by them.

A student of taxonomy must keep a record of both and try to find out the most useful data presented by them.

In concluding the discussion on the post-Darwinian systems of classification, it may be said that much has been thought about the evolutionary trends in flowering plants and the problem has not been settled to the entire satisfaction of all. This, in fact, is impossible, although disagreement may continue in respect of many minor aspects of a natural classification.

8

Taxonomy: A Synthetic Discipline

One of the principal aims of taxonomy is to provide a system of classification of living organisms based on evolutionary relationships. It is evident from the brief historical account of plant classification (Chapter 2) that at least some of the pre-Darwinian systems did aim at providing a natural classification using as many exomorphic characters as possible. However, since the evolution has taken a divergent course in different groups and the extent and speed of evolutionary changes in various characters of different groups of plants have been different, a comprehensive knowledge of the taxa from various aspects becomes very essential for the appropriate placement of taxa in the taxonomic systems. The morphological approach has certainly provided a workable system but the modern trend in taxonomy has involved sustained accumulation of data from several fields like anatomy, cytology, embryology, palynology, genetics, physiology, ecology, plant geography and various others. The study of herbarium specimens is being supported by the study of plant populations. The newer aspects of taxonomy like cyto-taxonomy, chemo-taxonomy, numerical taxonomy, biosystematics, etc. have greatly clarified confusions in the systems devised by classical taxonomy.

This chapter provides information on the applicability of data from various disciplines of science to the modern taxonomic procedures. Thus, taxonomy, which has become the most dynamic subject, particularly during the past 30 years, has not only provided the classifications based on synthetic theory but also revealed the mechanisms of evolution at various levels of taxonomic hierarchy.

External Morphology

Most of the taxonomic evidence is generally drawn from the external morphological features. This is so because, in general, there is a high degree of coincidence between the expressed phenotypic characters and the genotype of the taxon. Taxonomists still rely today to a very large extent on morphological characters chiefly because they are easily visible and can conveniently be employed in the classification. Such classifications, however, are not necessarily regarded by the taxonomists to be ideal but they are regarded as the most appropriate and most rapid for the purpose of expressing the pattern of diversity in organisms and are useful as a general reference system into which other kinds of information can be incorporated. In the following paragraphs the discussion is restricted around those characters of flowering plants which can be readily seen with the naked eye or with the aid of a 10× hand lens. Other microscopic external features such as the the epidermis and its outgrowth will be considered under anatomical characters for the sake of convenience.

It is argued by the investigators in other fields of botany that exomorphic features are less important than the endomorphic or other features. But this assumption does not hold good, at least for plants. Some of these features may be stable in certain groups and show considerable variation in others. Bailey (1951), for example, concluded that endomorphic characters such as anatomy are neither more nor less reliable than exomorphic features.

In recent years the traditional morphological features are being examined more carefully and interpreted by employing biometric and various graphic techniques. As a result, some of the neglected characters are being brought to light and their importance is being assessed fruitfully in taxonomic practices. Vegetative features such as habit, underground organs, leaves and their venation, stipules, etc. can be profitably used in identification of trees and shrubs as they are less variable in such groups. Klems (1960), for instance, has shown how adaptive radiation in *Aeonium* (Crassulaceae) is dependent upon the diversification of growth form in relation to different habitats. Underground parts are generally not carefully collected and preserved in the herbarium specimens. In some instances they have been shown to be highly reliable and useful in diagnostic keys. Burkill and Prain (1936) have used structure and morphology of root-tubers in the delineation of a large number of species of a tropical genus *Dioscorea* (Dioscoreaceae). Chouard (1931) has placed great emphasis on the bulb and other underground parts in the classification of Scilleae in Liliaceae. In *Chlorophytum* (Liliaceae) two species, viz. *C. glaucum* Dalz. and *C. glaucoides* Blatt. are not readily distinguishable from other morphological features, but in the former the root-fibres are thick and without terminal tubers while in the latter they are rather slender and end in ellipsoid tubers. Similarly, other two species, viz. *C. tuberosum* (Roxb.) Baker and *C. borivilianum* Sant. and Fern. can be readily distinguished by their root morphology. In the former the tubers are borne at the end of slender fibres while in the latter they are sessile.

Leaf characters are extensively employed for the recognition of species in many temperate genera such as *Ulmus* (Melville, 1951, 1955) *Betula* (Natho, 1959) and others. Species of *Dalbergia* (Papilionaceae), viz. *D. latifolia* Roxb., *D. sissoo* Roxb. and *D. sympathetica* Nimmo can be readily distinguished by their leaflet size, shape and arrangement on the rachis. Leaves of herbaceous species are more often variable and thus cannot be used reliably in distinguishing one species from the other. Stipule characters are much variable in groups of the Rosaceae but are fairly constant within a species. Leaf venation is more carefully studied by the palaeobotanists and used in the description of fossils.

Pant (1958) has described numerous patterns in the venation of *Glossopteris* leaves. Davis and Heywood (1963) have cited several examples where vegetative features can be useful in the delimitation of plant groups. They have also given an account of the ontogenetic characters used in taxonomy. According to these authors, the relationship between phylogeny and ontogeny is a subtle and complicated one which has been less studied in plants than in animals. It is interesting to note that embryos and young plants of related forms usually resemble one another more closely than the adult stages.

Floral characters such as the inflorescence, flowers and associated structures form the traditional basis for descriptive and taxonomic work and are so familiar to students of taxonomy that they need not be discussed here. An account of these may be found in Lawrence (1951) and some more neglected features have been pointed out by Davis and Heywood (1963).

Characters of fruits and seeds also have been largely useful in the construction of diagnostic keys especially at and above the generic level. Fruit morphology appears to be fairly constant within the genus whereas seed structure is often helpful in distinguishing one species from the other. In a large number of species, however, both fruit and seed characters are fairly constant and thus not useful in specific distinction. Aggregate fruits are generally common within the order Ranales (sensu lato) as most of the members of the group have apocarpous gynoecia. Different families of Rhoeadales can be readily distinguished on the basis of fruit characters while generic limits can be satisfactorily defined in the Moraceae on this basis.

Seeds have received a cursory attention in the past but are being used profitably at a specific level recently. Duke (1961), for example, has indicated that features of seed such as shape, sculpturing and colour provide a critical indication of the systematic positions of species in *Drymaria* (Caryophyllaceae). The only reliable distinction between the two genera *Chlorophytum* and *Anthericum* of the Liliaceae appears to be that of the number and shape of seeds (Obermeyer, 1962). Presence or absence of mucilage on testa of seeds distinguishes species of *Ocimum* (Labiatae) to some extent, and the genera *Sisymbrella* and *Nasturtium* (Cruciferae). Hairy outgrowths on the testa, their length and colour provide useful characters in the distinction of genera and/or species in the Malvaceae, Convolvulaceae, Asclepiadaceae and Acanthaceae. Seeds of the palm, *Lodoecia maldivica* (Gmel.) Pers., *Plantago exigua* (L.f.) Murr. (Plantaginaceae) and *Entada pursaetha* DC. (Mimosaceae) are so very characteristic that there is no parallel for them in the whole of the plant kingdom.

Microscopic Morphology and Anatomy

Epidermal Characters

In the normal taxonomic procedure where gross morphological characters suffice in the construction of groups or identification of taxa, the features such as hairs, trichomes, cell-types, nectaries, etc. are neglected. It is only when gross features are felt inadequate that the microscopic morphology is employed for taxonomic purposes. Linsbauer (1930) and later Metcalfe & Chalk (1950) have listed numerous features of epidermis that are now being used frequently in taxonomic studies.

Stomata

Stomata and associated epidermal cells are proving to be increasingly important sources of taxonomic characters. The presence or absence of stomata on the upper surface of a leaf is a good diagnostic feature in the separation of *Alnus subcordata* C.A. Mey and *A. orientalis* Decne. (Betulaceae) which are otherwise difficult to distinguish. Dumbbell-shaped guard cells are characteristic of grasses and sedges.

The mode of development of stomata and their spatial relation to neighbouring cells are considered with reference to classification and phylogeny. In gymnosperms, for instance, two main types, *haplocheilic* (guard cells and subsidiary cells both developed from the epidermal cells, i.e. they are perigene) and *syndetocheilic* (guard cells developing from epidermal cells while subsidiary cells develop from subepidermal cells, i.e. they are mesogene) are recognised. In angiosperms, four main types are known to occur in the dicotyledons. These are: (i) anomocytic (without subsidiary cells), (ii) anisocytic (with unequal subsidiary cells), (iii) paracytic (with two subsidiary cells lying parallel to the long axis of guard cells) and (iv) dicytic (with two subsidiary cells lying at right angles to the long axis of guard cells). In the monocotyledons, four other types are described (Stebbins & Khush, 1961). Here the stoma may have: (i) four or more subsidiary cells of equal size as in *Rhoeo* (Commelinaceae); (ii) only four subsidiary cells with two lateral cells larger than the two polar cells as in *Commelina*; (iii) two subsidiary cells which are parallel to the long axis of the guard cells as in many monocotyledons; or (iv) no subsidiary cells as in most of the Liliales. The third type may be further classified into: (a) stoma with beanshaped guard cells as in other monocotyledons and (b) stoma with dumbbell-shaped guard cells as in Gramineae. The evolutionary sequence in monocotyledons appears to be from 4-celled stomata to 2-celled, and the anomocytic type seems to be a highly evolved stomatal complex (Stebbins & Khush, 1961). In dicotyledons, the developmental studies made by Pant and Kidwai (1964) and a series of observations by Paliwal (1965, 1966, 1968, 1969 and 1970) and Paliwal & Kakkar (1971) indicate that occasional differences in the organisation of mature stomata in the different organs of the same plant or even on the same surface of a given organ do occur. According to Paliwal & Kakkar (1971), the variability in the organisation of mature stomata results from either of the following conditions: (i) difference in the number of subsidiary cells cut off from the meristemoid; (ii) divisions in the lateral and (iii) adjoining epidermal cells. Pant & Kidwai (1964), based on their observations on *Phyla nodiflora* (L.) Green (Verbenaceae), raised the doubt that prior to employing the stomatal character for taxonomic purposes, a survey of the variability for the taxa under consideration is desirable. Recently, the structure and taxonomic value of stomata of *Eugenia* (Myrtaceae) have been pointed out by Vau Wyk *et al.* (1982).

The structure of other epidermal cells also varies in certain groups of plants and has been used as a taxonomic character in recent years. Distribution of cell types expressed in a systematised way is termed as *dermogram,* and the dermograms may be indicated for each species as a dermotype (Prat, 1932). Dermotype studies have been employed with success in the taxonomy of *Eleocharis mamillata* (H. Lindb.) H. Lindb. (Cyperaceae) and allied species (Walters, 1953), species of *Puccinellia* (Gramineae) (Sorensen, 1953; Tutin, 1955); Mediterranean races of *Dactylis glomerata* (Gramineae) (Borill, 1961); *Agrostis* (Gramineae) and related genera (Bjorkman, 1960) and various others. Recently, Ramayya & Rajgopal (1968, 1971) have proposed even a generic key for the Indian members of Portulacaceae and Aizoaceae based on their dermotype studies of these families.

Trichomes

Epidermal outgrowths exhibit great diversity of form structure and function and thus are of much taxonomic value. Plant-hair types have been successfully used in the classification of genera and species and in the recognition of hybrids within certain groups. In Cruciferae, for example, Schulz (1936) used the type of hair as a major criterion in the subdivision of the family into tribes and genera. It is one of the features separating the closely related genera *Hutchinsia* and *Hornungia.* At the same time, it may be said that in some species of this family the presence of particular hair type varies in different parts of the plant. In the genus *Digitalis* (Scrophulariaceae), two groups of species have been recognised on the basis of presence or absence of glandular hairs. Martinez (1931) characterised various components of *D. purpurea* L. on this basis.

Rollins (1941) found the trichomes of *Arabis* (Cruciferae) to be unicellular and eglandular, but in some species they are simple while in others they are branched. The branches may arise like those of a tree (dendritic hairs) or be star-like. In some species of *Arabis* they are terete, in others flattened and in still others basally swollen. Rollin's study of the trichomes of two species of *Parthenium* (Compositae) and their natural hybrids is particularly interesting. In a series of observations (1944, 1945, 1946, 1949) he has shown that in *P. argentatum* the trichomes are T-shaped while in *P. incanum* they are whip-like with a long thread. Intermediate types of trichomes are observed in the hybrids between these species.

In *Rhododendron* (Ericaceae), Cowan (1950) has shown that the trichomes afford useful characters for taxonomic separation of infrageneric and specific levels. Similar studies also have been made on the genus by Seithe (1960).

The presence or absence of glandular hairs has been used for separation of species in various genera of Labiatae. Recent studies on the genus *Salvia* by Singh *et al.* (1974) are particularly interesting. They have shown that in *Salvia* the two species groups can be clearly defined on this basis.

Ramayya (1969) has provided a generic key for the Indian members of Compositae on the basis of his critical studies of trichomes in the family. Metcalfe (1968) brought out the importance of the form and structure of trichomes, especially those of the reproductive organs, in the taxonomy of Eriocaulaceae.

Other microscopic characters include minute organs, both vegetative as well as floral. In the families such as Compositae, Euphorbiaceae, Urticaceae, Moraceae, Eriocaulaceae, Cyperaceae and Gramineae the flowers are generally minute and therefore need microscopic observation. A new science of Synantherology has been proposed for the detailed microscopic studies of floral organs of the Compositae (King and Robinson, 1970). The flowers of *Euphorbia, Urtica, Pouzolzia* (Urticaceae), *Ficus* (Moraceae) are so minute that the variation in their floral parts easily escapes attention of a casual observer and inexperienced taxonomists. Similarly, great difficulties arise in the observation of floral parts in *Eriocaulon* and cyperaceous genera. Presence or absence of hairs on the receptacle, the number, size and form of sepals, the presence or absence of black glands on petals and the colour of anthers (black, dark-green, white or pale yellow) are some of the diagnostic characters for the separation of species of *Eriocaulon*. In Cyperaceae and Gramineae, where the floral parts are generally reduced, minute structures like rhachilla, glumes, hypogynous bristles, lemmas, paleas, lodicules and ornamentation of nuts play the main role in their taxonomy. Stebbins (1956) gave an excellent summary of the significance of minute structures in the classification of the grass family. Benson (1962) has pointed out the taxonomic significance of nectary scales in *Ranunculus* for the characterisation of subgenera and sections, in combination with other characters.

Anatomical Characters

Although the study of plant anatomy dates back to the works of the Italian, Marcello Malpighi and the Englishman Nehemiah Grew during the last quarter of the seventeenth century, it is only since the nineteenth century that the anatomical data have been used extensively as a taxonomic tool. It is now agreed by most of the taxonomists that the data concerning the histological structure of the vegetative as well as reproductive organs of flowering plants can be usually employed for taxonomic and phylogenetic purposes. It is useful not only at the higher levels but in certain instances, can be employed even at the specific level.

Auguste Mathiew was one of the pioneers, who used features of wood anatomy in the description of forest plants in *Florae forestiere* (1858). He was probably the first to propose the systematic value of wood structure. Later, in his classic book *Systematische Anatomie der Dicotyledonen* (1899), Solereder brought out the systematic value of anatomical structures in dicotyledons. This book was subsequently translated into English (1908) and has been greatly modified by Metcalfe and Chalk (1950) in their two-volume work, *Anatomy of the Dicotyledons*. The authors of this book suggested several anatomical features of taxonomic value, and these, together with certain others, will be considered in the following paragraphs.

Cell Structure

Isolated cells of peculiar morphology or performing some special function occur in certain plants. Their occurrence may be sporadic in the plant kingdom as a whole, but is more or less constant for a group of plants in which they occur, thus serving a taxonomic purpose. Motor cells, for example, are peculiar cells of the grass leaf epidermis and not known outside the group. Similarly, bulliform cells occur in the epidermis of many monocotyledons. The structure of cork and silica cells in the epidermis of grasses and sedges has been widely used in their taxonomy (Metcalfe, 1968).

Sclereids, i.e. cells with very thick lignified walls, are widely distributed in the plant body. They exhibit various shapes, size and characteristics of their walls. In general, two main types are recognised, viz. isomorphic and polymorphic types. Sclereid forms may be characteristic of species and may be of taxonomic value. They have been of some taxonomic significance in *Camellia* (Theaceae) (Foster, 1944; Barua and Dutta, 1959); *Mouriria* (Melastomataceae) (Foster, 1947); *Monstera* (Araceae) (Bloch, 1946); *Nymphaea* (Nyamphaeaceae) (Gaudet, 1960) and some Melastomataceae (Rao, 1957).

Laticifers are cells or a series of fused cells containing latex and are common features of many succulent plants and other plants of arid regions. They vary widely in their structure and the latex in their composition. Their presence or absence and when present, their structure has been of some taxonomic value. In Aroideae (De Bary, 1884), for example, certain species lack laticifers or any related structures while others have longitudinal rows of elongated, cylindrical, sac-like cells. Some authors consider that Fumariaceae which lack laticifers (Sperlich, 1939) should be considered distinct from the related family Papaveraceae having a well developed latex system. In the former family laticifers are replaced by idioblasts. It is one of the reasons for considering these two families as distinct from the rest of the families in Engler's Rhoeadales (Cruciferae, Capparidaceae, Resedaceae, Moringaceae and Tovariaceae, c.f. Cronquist, 1968a).

Recently, Treub (1975) reclassified the families and orders of Liliales *sensu lato* and considered *Allium* and related genera, possessing latex cells, as forming an order Alliales, distinct from the rest of the members.

Pate and Gunning (1972) described a highly specialised cellular adaptation in which ingrowths of cell wall material increase the surface area of a plasma membrane. Cells carrying this adaptation have been termed *transfer cells.* They are taken to represent a versatile apparatus facilitating transmembrane flux of solutes in a wide variety of anatomical situations in plants. Watson, Pate and Gunning (1977), based on their survey of A-type transfer cells (present in the vascular tissue) in the leaves of 118 species of Leguminosae-Papilionoideae, suggested that their presence or absence is taxonomically predictable both at the tribal level and in terms of major series of tribes. Members of "pulvinate" forms (tropical tribes) generally lack transfer cells, while "epulvinate" forms (temperate tribes) commonly possess them. This new data can certainly be extended to other plant groups as an additional character in their taxonomy.

Other Anatomical Characters

Metcalfe and Chalk (1950) suggested that the structure of petioles might provide characters of taxonomic value, and Howard (1963) published results of such investigations. He developed a system of petiole types based on such features as leaf position, presence or absence of stipules and their vascularisation, nodal structure, number of traces, etc. These have been shown to be useful in the identification of families, genera and even species in certain cases.

Leaf anatomy has been widely employed in taxonomically difficult groups such as Coniferae, Euphorbiaceae, Cyperaceae and Gramineae. Vidakovie (1957), for instance, used epidermal and hypodermal structure, breadth and height of needles, number of layers of the transfusion parenchyma as well as number of resin canals in the delimitation of various races of *Pinus nigra*. Webster (1967) considered leaf anatomical features such as chloroplast structure together with other morphological characters in the delimitation of the genus *Chamaesyce* from *Euphorbia*. Metcalfe (1968) has pointed out several leaf anatomical characters in Cyperaceae that are distinct from those of the grass family. Similarly, he has also pointed out that the distribution pattern of sclerenchyma in the leaves of certain Cyperaceae is of diagnostic value at the species level. Benson (1962) stated that the investigations of cross-sections of the leaves of a number of species of *Ranunculus* show considerable variation in the palisade layer and the spongy mesophyll tissue. In Gramineae, tissue arrangements are extremely diverse in the major taxonomic groups. The tissues that show the most differences are the endodermal sheath, parenchyma sheath and the mesophyll, particularly the arrangement of the cells outside the parenchyma sheath. This was clearly demonstrated in Brown's survey (1958) of grass taxa based on a study of 72 genera. On the basis of their tissue arrangement, six main types are recognised in the grasses. They cannot, however, be segregated into the two traditional subfamilies, Pooideae and Panicoideae.

Stem anatomy has been particularly studied in the herbaceous members where it has proved to be of some diagnostic value. In the stem of *Ranunculus repens*, a species common in Europe and North America, there is relatively little strengthening tissue and is correlated with the creeping habit of the plant, while in the closely related species, *R. acris*, interfascicular tissue is sclerified and therefore an erect habit is possible (c.f. Benson, 1962). Carlquist (1957) has used anatomical features of the genus *Fitchia* (Compositae) in the classification of various species.

On the basis of stem anatomy, Stant (1952) considered the Oleaceous genus *Nyctanthes* to show more relatedness with Verbenaceae and Shaw (1952) actually transferred it to the latter family. This, however, has not been accepted by all, and subsequently, on the basis of their comparative study of certain genera of Oleaceae as well as of Verbenaceae, Kundu and Anima (1968) arrived at a different conclusion. They proposed a separate family Nyctanthaceae, for the genus and considered it to be related to neither of the earlier families.

Stace (1970) has shown that in the subgenus *Genuini* of *Juncus*, anatomical characters of stem and foliar bract can be used to distinguish most British species. Further, it is also possible to identify parents of several hybrids on anatomical grounds.

There is considerable variety in the anatomy of stems of *Dioscorea* and can be successfully employed in the delimitation of species that are not easily separable on exomorphic grounds. Ayensu (1970, 1970a) has stressed these facts and stated that the taxonomic study of the genus should take into account the diagnostically useful characters of the stem.

Systematic position of the saprophytic genus *Petrosavia* has been recently established by Stant (1970). Her investigations of this group have revealed a striking identity between the anatomical structures of the stem, root and leaf of the Triuridaceae and Petrosaviaceae. The resemblance, according to Stant, is so complete that she would have no hesitation in placing *Petrosavia* in the family Triuridaceae on the basis of anatomical evidence.

The most important anatomical features that have been used in taxonomy and phylogeny are those of the secondary wood. This is because of their conservative nature. Wood anatomy can be used at all taxonomic levels. At and above the family level it has been successfully used along with other lines of evidence to establish the systematic position of the primitive vesselless angiospermic families Winteraceae, Trochodendraceae, Tetracentraceae and Amborellaceae (all included under the Magnoliales). Similarly, it has been agreed by all phylogenists that the Englerian group of primitive angiosperms, namely, Amentiferae (including families like the Salicaceae, Betulaceae, Fagaceae, Juglandaceae, etc.) cannot be considered primitive since they have specialised wood (Tippo, 1938). Anatomical evidence also supports the case for considering the remarkable genera *Paeonia* and *Austrobaileya* as the types of independent families (Bailey and Swamy, 1949).

Recently, Gottwald (1977) investigated about 700 species belonging to 32 families of the order Magnoliales *sensu lato* together with other taxa exhibiting primitive wood anatomical features. He constructed six structural groups on this basis which show a marked gradation from primitive to advanced stages. The wood structure of Magnoliales *sensu lato* moderately derived while the most primitively structured heteroxylous taxa belong to the "Dillenial-Hamamelidal" and "Theal" group respectively. Accordingly, there is no compelling evidence to support phylogenetic schemes in which Magnoliales are placed as the only common based for all recent dicotyledons. Gottwald, for this reason, has discussed a new phylogenetic model assuming an early separation of angiosperms into at least two branches, namely, the "Magnolial-Annonal-Myristical-Laural" block and the "Theal-Dillenial-Hamamelidal" block. It is evident from these wood anatomical studies that within the span of evolution that can be deduced from the living plants, no family of the latter block has proceeded from the former or vice versa. Monimiaceae can be seen as a possible bridge or a "branching off family" originally connecting the two main structural blocks at a very early undetermined state of phylogeny.

In terms of further evolutionary development, the following lines, based on anatomical evidence, have also been suggested: from the "Annonal" group towards Ebenaceae; from the "Magnolial" group towards Rutaceae; from the "Dillenial-Hamamelidal" group towards Rosaceae (in part); and from the "Laural" group towards Leguminosae (in part) and Boraginaceae. The most primitive status accorded to the Dillenial complex also finds support from the studies on floral structure. Stebbins (1974), for example, has shown that the flowers of *Paenoia* (Paeoniaceae, now considered under the Dillenial group) and certain Winteraceae are more primitive than those of Magnoliaceae.

At and below the generic level, the most useful contribution of wood anatomy is to provide evidence for placing of taxa of uncertain affinity. In *Quercus* (Fagaceae), different subgenera and sections can be delimited with the help of anatomical evidence. The placement of the genus *Myristica* and the related genera close to Lauraceae is supported by the evidence of wood structure (Eames, 1961), while on the same basis Myristicaceae are considered unrelated to Annonaceae and Eupomatiaceae. Similarly, placing of Calycanthacee in or near Rosales or Myrtales is not supported by wood structure. The relationship and possible derivation of *Casuarina* from Hamamelidaceae is supported by the comparative study of wood anatomy. A number of revisions of North African genera include keys based on anatomical as well as traditional morphological characters. These include keys for *Phyllyrea* (Sebastian, 1956); *Frankenia* (Negre, 1960); *Marrubium* (Marmey, 1958); *Euphorbiai* Vindt, 1960) and such others.

Recent investigations in the vegetative and floral anatomical structures of some Indian and tropical African species of *Chlorophytum* (Liliaceae) have been shown to be of great taxonomic significance. Naik and Nirgude (1981a, 1981b) have not only pointed out their applications in specific delimitation but have shown a close correlation between anatomical and other features such as chromosome number, duration of aerial shoot and ecology. There appear to be two distinct groups of species of *Chlorophytum;* one is characterised by species distributed in semi-arid situations that are diploids with basic chromosome number $x = 8$ and have short-lived aerial shoots and metaxylem vessel elements with spiral or slightly scalariform thickening of their lateral walls. The other group consists of species mostly inhabiting high altitudes with moist and cool climate that are polyploids with basic chromosome number $x = 7$ and have long-lived aerial shoots and metaxylem vessel elements with scalariform to pitted thickening of their lateral walls.

Ultrastructural Systematics

Morphology and taxonomy have benefitted greatly in recent years from information obtained by using advanced technology in microscopy, particularly Scanning Electron Microscopy (SEM) and Transmission Electron Microscopy (TEM). Heywood (1967, 1968, 1969) and Heywood and Dakhshini (1971) have demonstrated and reviewed the benefits of scanning electron microscopy to plant systematics and have suggested that this ultrastructural device represents one of the most powerful taxonomic tools now available for systematic research. Blair and Turner (1972) pointed out that a subdiscipline of taxonomy, termed "ultrastructural systematics" has been established and "it is clear that data obtained by electron microscopy can be used at almost any hierarchical level, proving especially instructive in the choice of alternatives for the phyletic position of a taxon." Cole and Behnke (1975), recently reviewed the vast data obtained by using modern techniques of electron microscopy and their rôle in plant systematics. TEM and SEM techniques have been particularly useful in the study of pollen surface structures (Echlin, 1968; Straka, 1971), surface relief of leaf waxes (Eglington and Hamilton, 1967; Hallam and Chambers, 1970), structure of sieve element plastids (Behnke, 1972), surface structure of seeds and fruits

(Chuang and Heckard, 1972; Whiffin and Tomb, 1972), leaf surface structures (Amelunxen *et al.*, 1967; Bocher, 1972; Schill *et al.* 1973a, b), structure of xylem vessels and pits (Scurfield *et al.*, 1970; Butterfield and Meylan, 1972; Meylan and Butterfield, 1972), structure of pappus in Compositae (Lundgren, 1972), structure of thorns in Euphortbiaceae (Schill *et al.*, 1973b) and many other similar structures of taxonomic importance.

It is beyond the scope of this work to review all the investigations carried out in this new field and assess their application to taxonomic problems. A brief mention, however, is made of the exhaustive search made by Behnke (1965, 1967, 1969a, 1969b, 1972, 1975a, 1975b) in respect of sieve-element plastids and its application in the classification of higher taxa of angiosperms.

Behnke made use of two characters observed under TEM. They are:

1. Dilated cisternae of endoplasmic reticulum in root cap cells and bundle parenchyma cells; and
2. micromorphological differences identified within sieve-element plastids.

The first character mentioned above is a characteristic feature of members of Capparales. The term "dilated cisternae" (DC) was first used by Bonnett & Newcomb (1965) for dilated sections of endoplasmic reticulum in root cells of *Raphanus sativus* L. Similar structures containing tubular protein were found in the phloem parenchyma of leaf vein of *Brassica chinensis* L. by Favali and Gerola (1968). Iversen (1970) initiated the first systematic overlook on the occurrence of DC in Cruciferae. According to Behnke (1977), these organelles are typical of Cruciferae and Capparidaceae.

The second character of sieve-element plastid has a more wider application in plant classification. Behnke, in a series of observations since about a decade, has demonstrated ultrastructural details of sieve-element plastids which can be used to characterise plant taxa. They were first detected in Dioscoreaceae (Behnke, 1965, 1967) and subsequently in 21 other families of monocotyledons (Behnke, 1969a). The present knowledge of the distribution of sieve-element plastids is due to Behnke's continued research (1969b, 1972, 1975a, 1975b) based on 690 species from about 190 families.

The ultrastructural features of sieve-element plastids which are of systematic value are associated with the accumulation of protein and starch. The protein accumulations are used as the main discriminating features in the classification of types and subtypes. P-type, for example, indicates presence while S-type indicates absence of protein accumulations. Their morphology and combinations define subtypes.

Specific subtype characterise monocotyledons (P II) and Centrospermae (P III), Magnoliales/Laurales (P I) and Fabales (P IV) contain distinct subtypes in some of their families and genera, while others have only S-type. Behnke is of the opinion that classification and delimitation of higher taxa in flowering plants can be aided by utilising the different types of sieve-element plastids. An analysis of investigated species indicates a distribution of 35 per cent P-type and 65 per cent S-type. P-type are considered to be ancestral and on multiple occasions the S-type has been thought to be derived by loss of protein. P I subtype is held to be the most primitive among P-subtypes of flowering plants.

Floral Anatomy

Since the reproductive organs show great conservatism, they have been widely used in the classifications. It is also quite likely that the vascular supply to these floral organs is also conservative and thus more reliable in taxonomic and phylogenetic interpretations.

The flower is conceived by the majority of botanists as a determinate stem tip or a receptacle bearing sporophylls and other appendages that are sterile. The sterile appendages are typically of two kinds: *sepals,* which together form the *calyx* and *petals* which make up the *corolla.* Sepals and petals commonly differ in form and size and other characters. In some families they may be closely alike, as in most of the petaliferous monocotyledons, and may be termed *tepals* or *perianth.* Commonly, sepals are more or less leaf-like or bract-like in form and structure and generally possess three vascular strands. Petals, on the other hand, are typically laminar and larger than sepals. They exhibit great range in form, size and structure. In many families they represent sterile stamens but in some primitive families, they are probably modified leaves, like the sepals. They are generally provided with a single vascular trace.

The fertile appendages are of two types: *microsporophylls* or stamens which bear microsporangia and *megasporophylls* or carpels bearing megasporangia. Stamens are commonly provided with a single vascular strand while carpels are typically 3-traced.

The type of flower now generally recognised as morphologically simple is one that shows the least change from the originally primitive flower. It is now agreed by majority of the morphologists that the ancestral flower was bisexual, with numerous stamens and carpels, with or without a bract-like perianth. All the appendages were spirally arranged and the flower was symmetrical and without fusion among its parts. The major principles of evolutionary modification have been as follows (after Eames, 1961):

1. From any parts, indefinite in number to few, definite in number.
2. From 3 to 4 sets of appendages to one.
3. From spiral to whorled arrangement of appendages.
4. From free floral parts to fusion, connation and adnation.
5. From radial symmetry (actinomorphy) to bilateral symmetry (zygomorphy).

The application of floral anatomy to taxonomy is clearly more limited than that of the other branches of anatomy in view of the technical and interpretative difficulties involved. Most results of such studies have been applied to the field of phylogenetic systematics. Puri (1951) has brought out the significant role played by the floral anatomy in the solution of morphological problems. According to Eames (1953), the floral anatomical characters of families and genera are generally well marked and even specific characters may be quite clear in some cases.

Embryology in Relation to Taxonomy

As early as the second and third quarter of the nineteenth century, Hofmeister and Strasberger indicated the possibility of using embryological characters in taxonomy, but it is only after about 90 years, i.e. by the second quarter of the present century, that the data has been actually used in taxonomy. Excellent detailed treatments have been published by Johansen (1950), Maheshwari (1950), Cave (1962), Kapil (1962), Johri (1963, 1967), Davis (1966) and a few others. Although in a strict sense, embryology is confined to a study of the embryo, Maheshwari supported those authors who include under it other events which lead to fertilisation. Cave (1959, 1962) adopted a similar broad view in outlining those embryological features that are of taxonomic value. According to Maheshwari, there can be numerous such features, the more common ones are:

1. *Anther tapetum*—whether glandular or amoeboid.
2. *Quadripartition of microspore mother cells*—whether it takes place by furrowing or by the formation of cell plates, whether the mode of division is simultaneous or successive, arrangement of microspores whether tetrahedral, isobilateral, linear, T-shaped or otherwise.
3. *Mature pollen grain*—number and position of germ pores, exine stratification, number of cells at the time of anthesis, etc.
4. *Development and structure of the ovule*—number of integuments in a developing and mature ovule, vasculature of integuments, characteristics of micropyle, obturator, etc.
5. *Form and extent of the nucellus*—whether it is broad and massive (crassinucellate ovules) or ephemeral (tenuinucellate), presence or absence of hypostase, persistence or gradual disappearance of nucellus.
6. *Nature of archesporium in the ovule*— one-celled or many-celled, presence or absence of wall layers, type of division of nucellar epidermal cells.
7. *Megasporogenesis and development of the embryo sac*—arrangement of megaspores, position of the functioning megaspore, whether embryo sac is mono-, bi- or tetrasporic, number of divisions required for differentiation of mature egg.
8. *Form and organisation of mature embryo sac*—number and distribution of its nuclei, formation of embryo sac haustoria.
9. *Fertilisation*
10. *Endosperm*—nuclear, cellular or helobial type, endosperm haustoria, nature of food reserves, persistence or gradual disappearance in the mature seed.
11. *Embryo*—form and organisation of mature embryo, suspensor haustoria.
12. *Abnormalities*—parthenogenesis, apomixis, polyembryony, etc.

Davis and Heywood (1963) are of the opinion that the data contributed by embryology to taxonomy are rather scarce and generally not well known. Corner (1951) also commented that the different types of embryo sacs, endosperm and embryogenesis seem to have little or no taxonomic significance and that they are either examples of polyphyletic convergence from diverse families or the classifications are not critical.

In spite of these remarks it seems quite reasonable to accept the significant contributions made by Johansen (1950), Maheshwari (1950), Cave (1953, 1959, 1962), Murgai (1962), Rau (1962), Johri (1963), Arekal (1963), Davis (1966), Sporne (1969), Bhandari (1971), Rembert (1971), Philipson (1974, 1977) and many others in solving taxonomic problems with the help of embryological data. Maheshwari (1950) and Johri (1963) have provided lists of such families, tribes, etc. where embryology has either supported earlier classifications or has proposed a new systematic position for the taxon concerned. It is, however, not possible, in a limited scope of the present book, to review the vast amount of literature on this subject published in the last 30 years, but the following few examples are discussed in order to evaluate the importance of the various embryological characters in the taxonomy of angiosperms.

Application of Embryological Data in Taxonomy

1. Above the Family Level

It should be noted in the first instance that the delimitation of angiosperms as a whole largely depends on embryological characters. Enclosed ovules that are mostly anatropous, polygonum type of embryo sac in majority of flowering plants, double fertilisation and triple fusion, and post-fertilisation development of polyploid endosperm are some of the embryological features which not only characterise the whole group of angiosperms but also support its probable monophyletic origin. Further, the most primary classification of the subdivision Angiospermae into two classes, namely, Monocotyledonae and Dictoyledonae is based on the characteristics of embryo, which are almost constant for the group. The exceptions, however, only prove the rule.

Quite a few orders of angiosperms are morphologically well defined and also exhibit a set of uniform embryological features. Caryophyllales or more widely known as Centrospermae are embryologically very distinctive. They characteristically have trinucleate pollen, campylotropous or amphitropous, bitegmic crassinucellate ovules, commonly with the inner integument longer than the outer and very often with a space between the integuments toward the chalazal end. The seed has a curved, peripheral embryo, more or less surrounding the food storage tissue which consists mainly of perisperm, with little or no endosperm. According to Cronquist (1968a), no plants outside the order are known to present this combination of characters.

Two orders, Polygonales and Plumbaginales, which are considered to be related to each other, are also clearly related to Caryophyllales and exhibit similar embryological features to a great extent.

Ericales are a homogeneous group of sympetalous families in wnich most of the members share a long series of embryological features in common, including, notably, the production of pollen in tetrads.

The order Lecythidales, once considered to be related to Myrtales, differs from the latter in alternate leaves of its members, centrifugal stamens, lack of internal phloem and a series of embryological features (Mauritzon, 1939). Gentianales differ from other sympetalous orders in having mostly simple and opposite leaves, well developed internal phloem and the lack of integumentary tapetum. They also have a nuclear endosperm. Some of the families like Buddlejaceae, Menyanthaceae and Oleaceae treated under Gentianales. are now removed from them since they possess integumentary tapetum and have a cellular endosperm.

The monocotyledonous order Helobiae *(sensu* Engler) is characterised by the helobial type of endosperm. Although recent systems have raised the order to the level of subclass, the relationships of the constituent orders is scarcely disputed. Similarly, Farinosae of Engler, the members of which are now regarded under the sub-class Commelinidae, usually have a mealy or starchy endosperm and the embryo lies alongside the endosperm rather than being surrounded by it. The highly evolved order Orchidales is characterised by undifferentiated embryo and very little or no endosperm.

2. At and Below the Family Level

Certain families and genera once regarded to have a doubtful systematic position, have now been ascribed their proper placements with supporting embryological evidence. The situation in some of the families with doubtful affinities has been discussed by Maheshwari (1950) and certain broad aspects of them together with some other families and genera will be presented here.

Empetraceae were considered by Don (1827) to be closely related to Euphorbiaceae and Celastraceae. However, Bentham and Hooker (1880) treated them as an anomalous family under Monochlamydeae. Later, several taxonomists thought that they are related to Ericaceae on the basis of several morphological features. This latter view has been supported by Samuelsson (1913) on the basis of embryological data.

Lennoaceae were at one time included in Ericales, but more recent studies have shown that they lack the embryological peculiarities of Ericales and are wholly out of place there. They are now considered to be related to Hydrophyllaceae and Boraginaceae, and Cronquist (1968) has placed them in Polemoniales somewhere near the point of origin of Lamiales.

Members of the family Cactaceae present a large number of variable characters and thus were treated variously by different authors. Wettstein (1935) regarded them under Centrospermae but others assigned them either an ordinal rank or placed them near Passiflorales. That Wettstein's opinion is more acceptable has been now supported embryologically (Mauritzon, 1934; Newmann, 1935) as well as on the basis of phytochemistry (Mabry, 1966).

The systematic position of Garryaceae has been disputed for a long time. They have been referred to Amentiferae by Engler and Gilg (1924) and Engler and Diels (1936). Bentham and Hooker (1880) and Wangerin (1910) included them high up in the polypetalous families near Cornaceae. That this latter placement is more natural, has been confirmed by Hallock's (1930) work on morphology and embryology. Comparative morphological and phylogenetic studies of the family (Mosely and Beeks, 1955) also support the view of their inclusion in the Cornales.

The family Onagraceae is characterised by the peculiar monosporic four-nucleate embryo sac in all its genera except *Trapa.* This genus has been placed variously by different systematists, (i) under Onagraceae, (ii) as an isolated member of Haloragaceae, and (iii) as the only genus of the monotypic family Trapaceae. Embryological evidence strongly favours the last view. In addition to its eight-nucleate embryo sac, *Trapa* has a well developed suspensor haustorium, both these features being unknown in any other member of Onagraceae. Further, in Onagraceae, the ovary is inferior and tetralocular with numerous ovules on axile placentae and fruit is generally a loculicidal capsule. In *Trapa,* on the other hand, the ovary is semi-inferior, bilocular with one ovule in each locule and the fruit is a large one-seeded drupe.

Highly reduced members of the genus *Callitriche* are included in Callitrichaceae. The systematic position of the family had been considered doubtful. It was thought by some to be related to Haloragaceae, by others under Caryophyllaceae and still others placed it under Euphorbiaceae. Embryological studies by Jorgensen (1923, 1925) have revealed a combination of characters which suggest the close affinity of the family with the members of the Lamiales (c.f. Cronquist, 1968a).

There has also been a rearrangement of the tribes, and subfamilies within the Liliaceae. A large number of genera also have been assigned their positions on morphological as well as embryological grounds. Similarly, Reeder (1957) has confirmed the earlier report of van Tieghem of the embryos in grasses. Two basic types, festucoid and panicoid, occur in the grass family and support the erection of the two subfamilies Festucoideae and Panicoideae on morphological grounds.

Individual genera and subgenera may also be characterised by certain embryological features, and these may be used in deciding on taxonomic delimitation and natural affinities. Harling (1951), for example, found great variation in the embryo sac development in the genus *Chrysanthemum* (Compositae) as circumscribed by Hoffman. Similarly, the troublesome classification of allied genera such as *Leucanthemum-Pyrethrum-Tanacetum* can be possible when embryological features are used in support of the other criteria. Embryological features also support the recognition of *Chrysanthemum balsamita* as a type of a separate genus, as was proposed by Desfontaines (1792).

The genus *Paeonia* has greatly attracted the attention of morphologists, anatomists and others with a view to determine its systematic position. Yakovlev and Yoffe (1959) reported a coenocytic phase in the embryogenesis of *Paeonia.* This phase although common in the gymnosperms, is unknown elsewhere within the angiosperms.

The need for caution in the interpretation of embryological data is pointed out by Mohan Ram (1959). Further, the taxonomic identification of material used for embryological studies is vital, as it is for any other systematic studies. In the absence of voucher specimens, it is exceedingly difficult to recheck the earlier reports, in the same way that many of the earlier chromosome reports have had to be rejected.

Use of Palynological Data in Taxonomy

Pollen morphological characters were fully appreciated by authors such as Lindley, von Mohl and Fritzsche as early as 1830-1840. But generally, these characters are overlooked by taxonomists due to lack of sufficient data. Recently, however, considerable attention is being paid to pollen morphology, and the science of palynology (study of spores and pollen grains) has entered into current taxonomic thinking.

The first comprehensive book on palynology was written by Wodehouse (1935) and subsequently Erdtman contributed a treatise on pollen analysis (1943). The first manual, *Pollen Morphology and Plant Taxonomy,* appeared in 1952 which deals with angiosperms (Erdtman, 1952). This book provided a summary of pollen morphological characteristics of all angiosperm families. As a result of the work of these early authors there has recently been a great increase in the comparative analytical studies of pollen morphology and wall structure. Results of considerable systematic and phylogenetic value have been obtained and the conclusions drawn from such studies are generally in agreement with those drawn from other fields of study.

Characters of Pollen and their Role in Taxonomy

The main characters of taxonomic value in pollen grains are, number and position of furrows, number, position and complexity of apertures and the form of sculpturing of the exine. Variation is also shown in size and general type.

Most angiospermous pollen grains fall into only two general types, *uniaperturate* and *triaperturate,* from which some less common types have been derived. Uniaperturate pollen grains have a single germinal furrow or pore situated at the proximal or distal position. The proximal form of aperatures is always found in Pteridophyta but in Pteridosperms, the position is reported to be either proximal or distal (Potonie, 1967). The proximal aperture is sometimes found in primitive angiosperms (Nair, 1968), but the distal position is predominant in flowering plants. Uniaperturate pollen grains are characteristic of the monocotyledons and some members of Magnoliidae.

Triaperturate pollen grains have three germinal furrows, either radiating like the lines of a trilete mark from a common point or forming a triangle at the distal position. Various other number of furrows and other type of apertures are situated along the equatorial line (zonal position) or distributed over the entire surface (global distribution). The triaperturate or triaperturate-derived pollen grains occur in the bulk of dicotyledons and are unknown elsewhere. Thus, along with the zonal and global position of apertures, evolved the many aperturate condition also.

Each of these two main types appears to have given rise to multiaperturate and nonaperturate types which are found in both monocotyledons and dicotyledons. The multiaperturate type results from cross-partitioning of one germinal furrow into several. The biaperturate type found in certain monocotyledons also reflects cross-partitioning. The non-aperturate type results from progressive shortening and eventual elimination of the furrow.

Erdtman (1952) and, subsequently, Nair (1970) have developed an elaborate terminology according to the position, number and shape of apertures. Accordingly, the polar apertures are either monopolar or bipolar. Monopolar apertures are further classified as proximalipolar (germinal furrow at the proximal end) or distalipolar (germinal furrow at the distal end). Monolete spores have one laesura, *trilete* spores are devoid of laesurae. In *hilate* spores the laesura(e) is/are reduced to a more or less circular, indistinctly delimited aperture.

The distalipolar aperture is termed *furrow* or *sulcus*. A sulcus always reaches or passes across the distal pole. Sulcate grains are either monosulcate, trisulcate, trichotomosulcate or very rarely tetrachotomosulcate. A more or less circular distal aperture is termed *ulcus* and may be derived from a sulcus or a sulcoid aperture. The ulcus has either a smooth (psilate) or rather ragged margin. A bisulcate grain has two furrows parallel to each other with the distal pole in the centre between the furrows. In trisulcate grains the furrows form a triangle around the pole.

Equatorial elongate apertures with one of their axes crossing the equator at right angles are termed *colpi* (singular colpus), while circular apertures are known as *pores*. Pollen grains with such apertures are termed *colpate* or *porate* respectively. In some plants both types of apertures occur as one superimposed above the other and the grains having these are termed *colporate*. Global apertures are known as *rugae* if they are elongate and *foraminae* if they are circular. Grains having these are then termed *rugate* or *forate* respectively (Fig. 8.1).

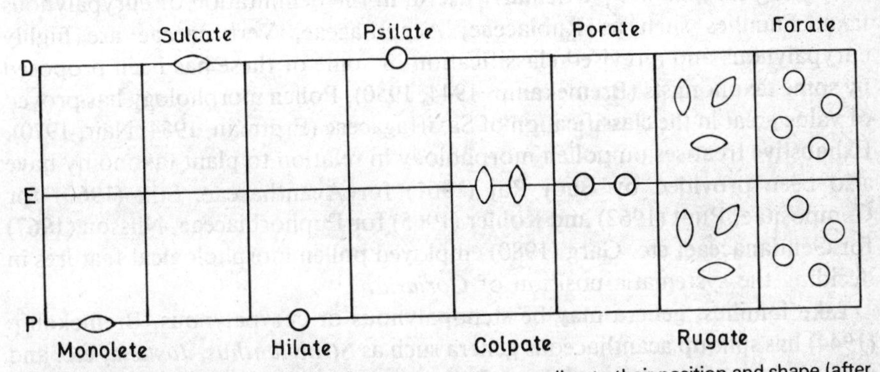

FIG. 8.1 Diagrammatic representation of aperture types according to their position and shape (after Erdtman, 1952).

The consensus is that the evolutionary progression is from colpate to colporate to porate, but there are many grades, refinements and special conditions.

The sculpturing of the external substance (exine) of pollen grains presents a remarkable series of microscopic characters and may vary from family to family. Commonly, the family and often the genus may be identified by the pollen grains. Elaboration of the exine is characteristically found in insect- and bird distributed pollen while in anemophilous groups it has become smooth and thin. Erdtman (1952) has developed an exhaustive and rather intricate terminology for describing various exine sculptures and has used it in his systematic treatment. In recent years the pollen wall structure has become the subject of very detailed and critical study, employing phase contrast and ultraviolet microscopy as well as the more conventional light microscopy

(Erdtman, 1954, 1956, 1959). Ultrafine sections of grains have also been studied under the electron microscope (Fernandez-Moran and Dahl, 1952; Muhlethaler, 1953). With the improvement of techniques (Afzelius, 1954, 1956) it has been possible to demonstrate fine details of the structure of the walls (sporoderms) and their stratification.

In most angiosperms the pollen grain has two nuclei at the time it is shed from the anther. The generative nucleus divides later to produce two sperm nuclei. In a number of taxa, however, the grains are trinucleate. The early division of generative nucleus apparently represents one more step in the progressive compression of the gametophyte (Brewbaker, 1967).

The taxonomic and evolutionary importance of pollen morphology may be at specific, generic or higher levels. In many cases the type of pollen of a taxon is characteristic and constant. Such a taxon is termed *stenopalynous* or *unipalynous* (c.f. Nair, 1970), and may be exclusive of that group, e.g. thick walled grains of the Gyrostemonaceae of Australia. In other cases, the types of pollen may vary considerably in size, aperture, stratification of exine, etc. Such taxa are termed *eurypalynous* or *multipalynous*. Stenopalynous taxa are generally considered to be very natural. Asclepiadaceae, Cruciferae, Gramineae, Labiatae, etc. are some of the stenopalynous families. Eurypalynous taxa, on the other hand, are taken to be heterogeneous, at least in certain instances. Palynological data are particularly useful in the delimitation of eurypalynous taxa. Families such as Rubiaceae, Acanthaceae, Verbenaceae are highly eurypalynous and a revised classification of some of these has been proposed by some taxonomists (Bremekamp, 1944, 1950). Pollen morphology has proved of value great in the classification of Saxifragaceae (Erdtman, 1954; Nair, 1970). Exhaustive treatises on pollen morphology in relation to plant taxonomy have also been provided by Bhoj Raj (1961) for Acanthaceae, Stix (1960) for Compositae, Punt (1962) and Kohler (1965) for Euphorbiaceae, Nilsson (1967) for Gentianaceae, etc. Garg (1980) employed pollen morphological features in deciding the systematic position of *Coriaria*.

Like families, genera may be stenopalynous or eurypalynous. Bremekamp (1944) has split up acanthaceous genera such as *Strobilanthus, Justicia,* etc. and proposed more natural groupings. Pollen morphology has been used in certain cases to provide pollen keys for the identification of plants of a given region (Faegri and Iversen, 1950, 1964; Nair, 1965). Some regions have been exhaustively investigated for their pollen types and as a result pollen floras have been compiled. Some of them include those by Selling (1947) for Hawaii, Bakker (1953) for South Africa, Ikuse (1956) for Japan, Erdtman and Praglowskii (1963) for Scandinavia, Nair (1965) for Western Himalaya, etc.

Pollen Evolution in Early Angiosperms

The presumed primitive taxa of the present-day angiosperms exhibit two forms, namely, monocolpate and tricolpate or trichotomocolpate. According to Nair (1970), there appear to be two clear phylogenetic stocks among these primitive members. Further, monocotyledons are considered closely related to magnolian dicotyledons, since both these groups have characteristic monocolpate pollen grains, and herbaceous dicotyledons such as Ranunculaceae which are characterised by the trichotomocolpate pollen grains apparently should be regarded as not related to monocotyledons. It is concluded, following Campbell (1930), that the 'monocot stock', 'magnolian stock' and the 'ranalian stock' might represent three independent phylogenetic lines with their phyletic roots in protangiosperms.

It is further supposed that angiosperms originated possibly in the preangiospermous pteridosperms which are characterised by trichotomosulcate pollen grains, as the other lower vascular plants including ferns. Accordingly, the earliest angiosperms must have possessed trichotomocolpate pollen grains alone. From such a primitive taxon, the monocolpate *'monocot-magnolian dicot complex'* stock on the one hand and the *ranalian dicot* stock on the other, originated and evolved.

Hickey and Doyle (1977), however, have firmly stated that the fossil evidence makes all theories of angiosperm evolution implausible which regard groups with exclusively tricolpate or derived pollen types as primitive including Dilleniaceae as proposed by Stebbins (1974). They further stated, "the fact that the early angiosperm record is consistent with a coherent radiation from an initial monosulcate stock with simple low rank leaves, is just the sort of data taken elsewhere in the paleontology as evidence for monophylesis and leaves little room for theories that the angiosperms are markedly polyphyletic."

Cytotaxonomy

Cytotaxonomy is the utilisation of cytological characters and phenomena for the elucidation of taxonomic problems. However, as has been rightly indicated by Solbrig (1968), most cytotaxonomic studies have largely made use of only two nuclear aspects: (i) number, shape and size of chromosomes and (ii) the behaviour of chromosomes during meiosis, and to a lesser extent, their behaviour during mitosis.

During the last seven or eight decades, data provided by the chromosome cytologists have gained the widest currency and there is now an extensive literature pertaining to the taxonomic role of chromosome studies. Recently, Ehrendorfer (1964) has reviewed the previous work in this discipline. Here the two aspects of nuclear studies mentioned above will be dealt with in some details.

Karyotype

Levitsky (1924) defined karyotype as "the phenotypic appearance of the somatic chromosomes." Although, the term 'idiogram' is also used in a somewhat similar sense, the term 'karyotype' is the one which has been established by general usage, and the term idiogram is now applied to the diagrammatic representation of the karyotype. Thus, as defined above, the karyotype will be dealt in the following paragraphs to include number, size and gross structure of chromosomes as seen at mitotic metaphase. These different aspects of the karyotype will be discussed in turn.

Chromosome Number

All individuals within a species usually have the same chromosome number, although there are exceptions. It is during the divisions that several changes occur in chromosomes including the gene sequence, their number and even the loss of chromosomes themselves. The process, however, is slow but when it is perpetuated, new chromosomal races evolve.

Chromosome numbers recorded for vascular plants show a wide range from four in somatic cells of *Haplopappus gracilis* (Compositae) to 530 in those of *Poa litorosa* (Gramineae), 500-520 in species of *Kalanchoe* and *Echeveria* (both Crassulaceae), 308 in *Morus nigra* (Moraceae) and about 1240 in *Ophioglossum* species.

This great diversity of chromosome numbers and their relative constancy within populations and species provide an important character for taxonomic groupings of large number of plants.

There are three broad classes of chromosome number relationship with taxonomic groups. These are:

1. *Constant number.* Certain groups of vascular plants possess a constant number of chromosomes in all their constituent members and can be of restricted taxonomic utility. Genera such as *Pinus* and *Quercus* have $n = 12$ chromosomes in all the known species and can be delimited from other related genera on the basis of chromosome number.

2. *Euploidy.* When chromosome numbers in various members of a taxon are in the proportion of exact multiples, the series is described as euploidy. Several such examples can be found in flowering plants and the ferns. In Malvaceae, for instance, the somatic numbers in various species range from 10, 15, 20, 25, ...40; from 12, 18, 24 to 30; from 14, 28, 42, 56 to 84 and so on. In the genus *Taraxacum* (Compositae), there are species with $2n = 16$, 24, 32, 40 and 48 chromosomes. Various members of such an euploid series may be unified by a *basic number* or x which is the gametic number of a diploid species and other species can be described as triploids ($3x$), tetraploids ($4x$), hexaploids ($6x$) ... polyploids (nx). Thus one of series in Malvaceae has $x = 5$ while the others have $x = 6, 7$, etc. In *Taraxacum* the basic number is $x = 8$. In the groups where the diploid species are unknown, the basic number is inferred and the accuracy of the inference obviously depends upon the chromosome data available for the group.

The basic number is very frequently constant for a genus or higher taxa and has proved useful in supraspecific studies. In many instances more than one basic number can be present in a group. In the absence of living diploid members, the inferred base numbers ranging between 2 and 13 may be conveniently referred to as the *primary basic numbers* while the remainder are termed *secondary basic numbers.* In the living species of *Chlorophytum* (Liliaceae), for example, the chromosome numbers vary from 14 to 28, 42, 56, 84, etc. and also from 16 to 32. This means that *Chlorophytum* has two basic numbers $x = 7$ and 8. However, from the detailed analysis of the meiotic behaviour of chromosomes in one of the species, *C. laxum,* the present author (Naik, 1976a) has shown that the two base numbers 7 and 8 can be considered as secondary, most probably derived from the primary basic number $x=4$.

In certain groups, the closely related species are cytologically distinct, one being a diploid and the other a tetraploid. Such clearly related pairs are termed polyploid pairs. These have been shown experimentally in *Nasturtium officinale* ($2n=32$) and *N. macrophyllum* ($2n=64$); *Cardamine hirsuta* ($2n=16$) and *C. flexuosa* ($2n = 32$) of the Cruciferae and *Saxifraga hyperborea* ($2n = 26$) and *S. rivularis* ($2n=52$) of the Saxifragaceae.

The role of hybridisation in evolution has been well known and certain authors have assigned a dominant role to this process. In the broadest sense, hybridisation involves crossing of any two genetically unlike individuals and they may have different base numbers of chromosomes. In nature, it has been observed, that such hybrids undergo polyploidy and since each chromosome is doubled the pairing at meiosis is restored. This polyploidy, resulting from the hybridisation of two genetically dissimilar organisms (and also having different basic chromosome numbers), is termed *dibasic polyploidy*. It has been well documented in a number of instances. In Cruciferae, for example, *Brassica oleracea* ($2n = 18$) and *B. rapa* ($2n = 20$) have been shown to hybridise in nature to give rise to *B. napus* ($2n = 38$) after polyploidy. A well known example of *Raphanobrassica,* a hybrid between *Brassica oleracea* ($2n = 18$) and *Raphanus sativus* ($2n = 20$), has $2n = 38$ chromosomes and was artificially synthesised by Karpechenko (1927, 1928). Several such examples have been listed by Stebbins (1950), Davis and Heywood (1963) and Wagner (1968).

3. *Aneuploidy.* If the chromosome numbers found within a group bear no simple numerical relationship to each other, then the series is termed as an aneuploid series or simply *aneuploidy*. Here, two distinct phenomena occur: (i) increase or decrease in the number of chromosomes whereby the same genetic material becomes distributed in a different number leading to a change in the basic number; (ii) the basic number is unaltered but the genetic material present is changed through the addition or loss of chromosomes.

The first phenomenon is more important from the taxonomic and evolutionary point of view where new variations and recombinations lead to the evolution of new varieties and ultimately to new species. But in the second phenomenon, the genetic make-up of a taxon becomes imbalanced due to loss or addition, and an unstable condition prevails. It obviously cannot be perpetuated and cannot give rise to well differentiated novelties. It is thus, much less important from the evolutionary point of view.

In nature, a large number of plant groups are known to exhibit aneuploidy. Various species of *Carex* (Cyperaceae) show a wide range of chromosome numbers from $n = 6$ to 112 with multiples of 5, 6, 7, and 8.

Changes in the basic number of chromosomes are brought about by various mechanisms. Some of the more common mechanisms are being discussed here.

The commonest type of change in chromosome number takes place by polyploidy. This, however, does not disturb the basic number. However, since the polyploids have increased sets of genes some of them can afford to lose one or two chromosomes and get stabilised in nature with this new chromosome number evolved through, what is termed as, *secondary polyploidy*. This naturally brings about a different basic number. Most of the species of *Dahlia* (Compositae), for instance, have $x = 8$, but *D. merckii* with $n = 18$ is regarded as a secondary polyploid by addition of two pairs of chromosomes.

Loss of chromosome/s, fragmentation or misdivision of centromere can take place as irregularities during the cell division even in the diploid species. Darlington (1937) has shown how conditions favouring the loss or gain of chromosome can be produced by means of unequal translocations. Such aneuploid alteration of the basic number has been carefully studied in *Crepis* (Compositae) and its relatives (Babcock and Cameron, 1934; Babcock, Stebbins and Jenkins, 1937; Babcock, 1942, 1947). Several other examples showing loss of chromosomes have been documented in the literature and reviewed by Stebbins (1950). It should, however, be noted that progressive increase in the basic chromosome number is much less common in plants. Darlington (1936) has suggested that in *Fritillaria pudica* (Liliaceae), $x = 13$ has probably been derived from $x = 12$, the common basic number for other related species. Levan (1932, 1935) has shown similar increase from $x = 7$ to $x = 8$ in *Allium* (Alliaceae).

Increase in the basic number is brought about by a process known as *polysomaty* wherein there is a duplication of one or a pair of chromosomes. This means that any one pair may undergo polyploidy. Plants containing such extra chromosomes are known as *trisomics* ($2n + 1$, with one extra chromosome), *tetrasomics* ($2n + 2$, with two extra chromosomes) and so on, while those with loss of one or two chromosomes are known as *monosomics* ($2n - 1$) or *nullisomics* ($2n - 2$). Polysomics have been detected in *Nicotiana* (Goodspeed and Avery, 1939), *Datura* (Blakeslee and Belling, 1924) and Maize (McClintock, 1929). They are usually unstable and since they are not isolated genetically from their relatives under natural conditions, they would lose their identity through crossing with normal plants followed by selection for more viable, genetically balanced normal disomic types.

The complements of some plant and animal species contain, in addition to normal chromosomes, one or more *accessory* or supernumerary chromosomes. They have been detected in a large number of plants (Darlington, 1937; Hakansson, 1945; Fernandez, 1946 and many others). In higher plants they have been termed B-*chromosomes*. They are generally of a much smaller size than the other members of the chromosome complement. In plants, they are of unknown origin. Their function also appears to be not clearly known. Nevertheless, it has been detected that they perpetuate in certain natural populations and may have some evolutionary significance. In *Dipcadi* (Liliaceae), there appears to be some correlation between the edaphic conditions and number of B-chromosomes (Naik, 1974). In certain natural populations, they might as well have been established as normal members of the complement.

Chromosome Size and Structure

Although chromosome volume, expressed as a function of DNA content (Rees, 1963), can occasionally be used to characterise the size of the karyotype, it is customary to use chromosome length for this purpose. In most plants chromosome length varies from 0.5-30 μ (Warmke, 1941).

In many genera and families of flowering plants, conspicuous differences in appearances of the karyotype have been found in species having the same chromosome number. In some instances these differences follow definite trends associated with trends of morphological specialisation. In the primitive genus *Helleborus* (Ranunculaceae), for example, the chromosomes in the karyotype differ little from each other in size and most of them are V-shaped with median or submedian centromeres. Karyotypes of this nature are the most common ones. Levitzky (1931) considered them as generalised types. Various specialised types have been considered to have been derived from these. Thus, the chromosomes with uniform length may gradually differ in size and shape from V-shaped (metacentric) to L-shaped (submetacentric) to J-shaped (acrocentric) and ultimately to rod-shaped or i-shaped (telocentric) and become asymmetrical. In the advanced genera *Aconitum* and *Delphinium* (Ranunculaceae), for example, the flowers are zygomorphic with the largest number of J-shaped chromosomes.

Less commonly, the reverse trends of specialisation, i.e. from telocentric chromosomes to metacentric ones have been demonstrated in certain members of the Commelinaceae (Jones, 1970).

A karyotype consisting of chromosomes all essentially similar to each other in size and with median or submedian centromeres may be termed as a *symmetrical* one. *Asymmetrical* karyotypes possess many chromosomes with subterminal centromeres, or great differences in size between the largest and the smallest chromosomes, or both (Stebbins, 1950). It may be stated from a general review of karyotypes in about 20,000 species of angiosperms that plants with asymmetrical karyotypes are usually specialised morphologically. On the other hand, while symmetrical karyotypes are most often found in plants which are morphologically more or less generalised, they also occur in relatively specialised species or genera.

In addition to the size and position of the centromere, the karyotypes can be differentiated on the basis of *secondary constrictions* and *satellites*. The satellites (small bead-like appendages), which in many species occur at the ends of one or more pairs of chromosomes, are separated from the rest of the chromosome by a secondary constriction which corresponds with the nucleolar organising region of the chromosomes. Very little is known about the evolutionary changes in the satellites and nucleoli. The wide distribution of these structures throughout the plant kingdom shows that they are a valuable, if not essential, part of the chromosomal complement. Furthermore, a nucleolar organiser with its accompanying satellite may be either lost or gained during evolution.

Behaviour of Chromosomes During Meiosis

The theory of evolution introduced the concept of hereditary continuity in time and hence genetic relationship between species and other taxa derived from a common origin. This means that all the members of a species have to be interfertile and members of different species are genetically isolated. This formed the basis for the *biological species concept* of modern taxonomy. Genetic experimentation, however, has shown that the taxonomic species are not always genetically isolated from each other, nor necessarily interfertile within themselves. In nature, various intermediate conditions are observed and often it becomes difficult to delimit such taxa on morphological grounds alone. Their relationships, either close or distant, is often detected by studying the behaviour of their chromosomes at meiosis.

In vascular plants, natural hybrids, both between closely related as well as distantly related taxa, are quite different. This situation was considered by the early cytologists as an ideal one to provide an explanation by artificial hybridisation of the relationship and stage of speciation of two taxa. Abnormal meiotic behaviour in hybrids due to chromosomal aberrations can usually be interpreted rather easily. Consequently it is usually possible to interpret the causes of hybrid sterility when they are solely or largely due to chromosomal differences between parents. This type of sterility or chromosomal sterility (Solbrig, 1968) is the most frequent kind of sterility observed in plants and is apparent at the time of spore formation. Stebbins (1950, 1958a), Solbrig (1968), Wagner (1968) and others have described numerous examples of this kind.

In short, it may be said that, meiotic abnormalities such as non-pairing, crossing over and subsequent change in chromosome size, translocations or unequal interchanges, lagging chromosomes, bridge formation, non-disjunction and several others (c.f. Darlington, 1937) can be easily detected and interpreted. These are generally observed during microsporogenesis. Various meiotic abnormalities and their interpretations have been provided by Swanson (1957) and other cytologists.

Use of Cytological Studies in Taxonomy

Cytological studies, or more particularly, the karyotype data, have been shown to be useful in táxonomy at all levels up to that of the family and even above, but most involve species and groups of species.

Above the Genus Level

There are few examples of the use of karyotype studies for differentiating families. Warburg (1938), for example, concluded that while Geraniaceae, Oxalidaceae and Tropaeolaceae are cytologically close to each other, Limnanthaceae differ markedly in chromosome size, number and behaviour. Balsaminaceae, which Warburg found to be cytologically intermediate between the above two groups, are now placed in Sapindales (Cronquist, 1968a).

Raven and Kyhos (1965) have shown karyotype affinities for the closely related Magnoliaceae, Himantendraceae and Degeneriaceae and also for Schisandraceae and Illiciaceae while there is a marked difference in chromosome numbers of the Lauraceae ($x = 12$) and Hernandiaceae ($n = 20, 40$). Recently, Wiens (1975) has provided cytological evidence for separation of Viscaceae from

Loranthaceae. Various members of Loranthaceae are unified by a single basic chromosome number $x=9$ while Viscaceae are characterised by a series of aneuploid numbers ranging from 10 to 14.

The number and size of chromosomes have provided a valuable confirmatory evidence for the delimitation of boundaries between the subfamilies and tribes of a large number of families. Avdulov (1931) and Hubbard (1948), for example, have attempted to rearrange tribes in Gramineae. Avdulov found that if grasses are classified on the basis of the number and size of their chromosomes, a system that is stri ingly similar to that based on other features is developed. Stebbins (1958b) provided information on the evolution of grasses on the basis of cytogenetics. In Compositae, chromosome numbers have proved to be of great value in the delimitation of tribes. Raven *et al.* (1960); Raven and Kyhos (1961), Hair (1962), Ornduff *et al.* (1963, 1967), Payne *et al.* (1964) and Solbrig *et al.* (1964) have indicated that cytologically, the tribe Helenieae (Compositae) is a diverse group of various affinities. Similarly, out of the total 22 genera in Onagraceae, 18 are known cytologically. Kurabayashi *et al.* (1962) recognised three modally distinct groups of tribes which differ in karyotype uniformity, chromosome size and intrachromosomal contraction cycles between interphase and mitotic metaphase.

At and Below the Genus Level

The taxonomic value of chromosome studies is generally greater at these levels than at the family level. Numerous such examples have been described by Stebbins (1950), Benson (1962), Davis and Heywood (1963), Ehrendorfer (1964), Grant (1963), Larsen (1963), Lewis (1967) and various other authors. Here, only a brief mention of some of them will be attempted.

The classical example of the use of chromosomal characters in the delimitation of genera can be seen in *Crepis, Cymboseris* and *Youngia* of the Compositae (Babcock, 1947). In *Crepis,* various species have $x=7$, 6, 5, 4 or 3 chromosomes, while the basic numbers of other related genera are either $x=8$ or $x=9$. In *Clarkia* (Onagraceae), lines of evolution from species to species have been traced (Lewis, 1951-1958). After thorough cytological and genetic study, Lewis and his students have submerged the genus *Godetia* in *Clarkia.* On the other hand, Lewis and Raven (1961) brought out significant differences in chromosome numbers and other cytological features between two closely related genera, *Hauya* and *Xylonagra* of Onagraceae.

In certain genera such as *Eucalyptus* (Myrtaceae), *Ribes* (Saxifragaceae), *Pinus* (Pinaceae), *Quercus* (Fagaceae), etc., the chromosome number does not vary from species to species. In such taxa, although the chromosome study is unlikely to help intrageneric groupings, it is possible to delimit the number of species included in them.

At the species level, the karyotype data appears to be extremely useful and instances can be seen in the studies of *Clarkia* (Lewis and his students, 1951-1958), *Gossypium* (Hutchinson and Stephens, 1947), *Nicotiana* (Goodspeed, 1945, 1947), *Viola* (Pettet, 1964), *Gilia* (Grant *et al.*, 1950-1954, 1960, 1964), *Potentilla, Achillea* (Clausen, 1951 and Clausen, Keck and Heisey,

1939-1958) and a host of others. Recently, cytological data has been shown to be useful in the taxonomy of *Chlorophytum* (Liliaceae) by the present author (Naik, 1977a), Three species, namely, *C. bharuchae, C. glaucum* and *C. glaucoides,* are morphologically rather difficult to distinguish from one another but C. bharuchae has $2n = 16$ chromosomes while the other two have $2n = 42$. Further, species with $2n = 42$ differ in their karyomorphology.

Present Status of Karyotype Studies

It is clear from the examples quoted above and many others, that karyotype data can support conclusions based on other data at all levels of taxonomic hierarchy. However, it has also been noted that karyotype variation or variation in the number of chromosomes are sometimes not correlated with morphological features. This is particularly so in the case of autopolyploids and their related diploids (c.f. Naik, 1976b). Taxonomic status of such taxa is rather disputable. Extreme views are held by those who believe in biological and typological species concepts.

There are various limitations in using karyotype data in taxonomy. Although there are several lists compiled for the chromosome numbers up to date, the ones published uptil the 1950s have been shown to be not very reliable. In Magnoliaceae, for example, Raven and Kyhos (1965) observed, "it is worth pointing out that not a single one of the chromosome numbers summarized by Darlington and Wylie for this family is accurate." Further, in the absence of voucher specimens, it is often difficult to recheck the records and a great care is needed while utilising the data published by casual cytologists. In many instances, experienced cytologists do not give much attention to taxonomy of the group investigated. Similarly, field taxonomists sometimes attempt to record chromosome numbers in certain plants based on their observations of a single squash. Both may lead to wrong conclusions. In order to overcome this and similar difficulties, it is becoming customary to deposit herbarium and cytological voucher specimens and to accompany published records by good photographs. Further, as remarked by Moore (1968), it is more usual now to find the combination of cytologists and taxonomists, whether in a single person or in a closely knit group, so that collaboration between the two approaches should be more and more fruitful. He has further expressed the need for more careful and exhaustive work in the tropical plant groups, which is meagre at present. This is amply evidenced by a single example of a tropical genus *Chlorophytum* in which out of about 150 species, the chromosome data is available for hardly 20 species. It is hoped that this unfortunate situation will soon be altered through sustained cytotaxonomic investigations in the rich tropical floras.

Phytochemistry and Taxonomy

Taxonomy—a theory and practice of classification—when incorporated with the data from chemical constituents, form a hybrid discipline of *chemo-*

taxonomy. Data from chemistry of plant products is termed *phytochemistry*. *Chemical systematics* is the study of chemical variation in various organisms and their relationships. The following paragraphs are presented here in order to introduce the ways in which chemical data may be used in plant taxonomy.

The principles, procedures and results of investigations into chemical variation of plant groups are applied mainly for two purposes: first, to provide taxonomic characters which may improve existing plant classification, i.e. a strict taxonomic purpose, and second, to add to the knowledge of phylogeny or evolutionary relationship.

Place of Chemistry in Taxonomy

Studies of chemical variation have been suggested to be one of the principal growing points in the field of taxonomy. At the same time, like various other disciplines, it must not be thought of as a replacement of other taxonomic characters but at best a major source of new characters and information. All other sources of taxonomic evidence still exist and are still producing new ideas and facts which cannot be ignored. As a contributory discipline in taxonomic and evolutionary studies, chemotaxonomy has gained an important status in recent years.

It should be noted that not all kinds of chemical substances present in plants reveal information useful to the taxonomists. Assessment of the taxonomic value of various chemical substances is reviewed in later paragraphs. All chemical materials synthesised by an organism reflect the information in DNA, RNA and various amino-acids in the form of proteins. These latter molecules have been termed as *semantides* (Zuckerkandl and Pauling, 1965). Semantides, thus contain useful information for taxonomy and phylogeny.

Chemical evidence is of particular significance in the simplest organisms—the bacteria—and it has been used effectively in all more complex groups from the fungi to the most highly specialised angiosperms.

Chemical characters may have a particularly high taxonomic value when they can be shown to be stable, unambiguous and not easily, if at all, changeable. Probably, the smaller and more cryptic the character, the more important it is for indicating relationship. It is not always proper to consider chemical characters as more indicative of relationship than other characters such as external morphology, anatomy, cytology, etc. They are considered more important, as in case of other characters, only when they show a high degree of correlation with other features.

Historical Account

Use of chemical evidence in plant classification has a long history. In fact, the chief importance of botany to early man was that it generated knowledge about edible or medical properties of plants. Both these properties depend on chemical contents, which are hence the basis for classification. Smith (1976) stated, "Early man, with an interest in chemotaxonomy, must have paid a high price for knowledge of the edibility of wild plants." Further, "Primitive chemotaxonomy was thus an applied science, with extremely practical aims and benefits. Plants with similar chemical properties would have been grouped together...." Such a classification was gradually elaborated through subsequent human social evolution (Gibbs, 1963). The famous herbals, depicting illustrations of medicinal plants, evolved sometime in the sixteenth and seventeenth centuries.

Gardens were established for the presentation and dissemination of valuable plants. Nehemia Grew (1673), James Petiver (1899), William Withering (1785), and A.P. De Candolle (1804) may be regarded as the pioneers who employed chemical data in plant classification. Eykman (1888) and Greshoff (1891) have summarised the early works on comparative chemistry in plant taxonomy. Abbott (1886) published a paper on chemical constituents of plants which, according to Smith (1976), can be taken as the beginning of the modern phase of chemotaxonomy. Subsequently, the most important phenomena of "precipitin test" was discovered through the efforts of Ehlrich (1891), Krause (1897), Kowarski (1901) and Nuttall (1901).

Plant serology developed fastest in Germany at Koenigsberg through the efforts of Gohlke, Mez and Ziegenspeck, who were the pioneers. Another school at Berlin, headed by Gilg and Schuroff, however, refuted most the findings of the Koenigsberg school. The techniques of serology were considerably developed during the 1920s and 1940s by workers like Boyden (1942) in America and Moritz (1934) in Germany.

McNair (1917 to 1945) published a series of papers to apply comparative chemistry to taxonomy. According to him (1945), in the seed, chemical ontogeny is often from carbohydrate to saturated oil to unsaturated oil. This may represent recapitulation, and carbohydrate storage may be taken to be primitive, while oil storage an advanced character. Further, according to this author, the monocotyledons are more primitive than the dicotyledons and that the sympetalae are the most advanced of the dicotyledons.

The Institut fur Pharmakognosie of the University of Kiel, Germany, has long been the centre of research in applications of chemistry to taxonomy.

The recent growth of chemotaxonomy as a popular field of research is largely due to the development of rapid analytical techniques such as chromatography and electrophoresis. The most recent development in the technology involves automatic protein "sequenators" which compares amino-acids in the given protein relatively quickly.

Stages in Chemotaxonomic Investigation

Following are the principal stages to be followed in chemotaxonomic investigation:

1. *Taxonomic survey.* In traditional manner, on the basis of morphological features, a taxonomy of the desired group should be established. All possible variations in a group must be predetermined and then only samples can be chosen for further investigation.

2. *Chemical techniques and pilot surveys.* A suitable technique for chemical survey should be chosen depending upon the groups to be investigated. Similarly, a choice of chemical constituent to be detected should be determined since certain constituents may be constant for a group or may be variable within the group. Then the distribution of the chemical material must be established in various individuals and their parts.

3. *Detailed analysis.* This should be taken in respect of all the material available for investigation.

4. *Comparative study and interpretation.* A critical comparative account of the data collected may then lead to some acceptable and sensible interpretation.

5. *Taxonomic changes.* Chemotaxonomic studies must then be considered along with other available information for regrouping of the taxa, if necessary. The chemical data may either support existing classification or may not do so. But at no time regrouping or a taxonomic change should be recommended on the basis of a single character or feature.

6. *Phylogenetic interpretation.* Chemical data may have some bearing on the phylogeny of the group. This should be properly assessed.

Use of Chemical Criteria in Plant Taxonomy

Of the large number of chemical constituents known till date, only a few important ones have been discussed in the following paragraphs. It should, however, be noted that there exists vast literature on the use of chemical data in taxonomy at all levels and to review the subject in its totality is beyond the scope of this text.

Chemical characters may be considered under three categories, namely, (i) directly visible characters (ii) chemical test characters and (iii) proteins.

Directly Visible Characters

These are rather restricted in number and have attracted the attention of anatomists since long (c.f. Solereder, 1908), and their distribution is well known.

Starch grains develop in the plastids and these may be simple or compound, concentric or eccentric and may possess various shapes in different groups. Reichert (1913) listed as many as 350 species which show differentiation and specificity of various kinds of starch grains. Tateoka (1962), has reviewed the use of starch grains in the determination of certain tribes in the grass family. In the tribe Hordeae, for example, the typical members have compound grains, while ***Nardus, Lolium*** and ***Parapholis,*** having simple grains appear to be out of place in that tribe.

Raphides are bundles of needle shaped crystals of calcium oxalate and occur in special sacs. General occurrence of raphides in orchids was noted as a feature of taxonomic importance as early as 1833 by Robert Brown.

Gulliver (1866) reported that only three families, namely, Balsaminaceae, Onagraceae and Rubiaceae can be characterised as raphide bearers. Gibbs (1963) confirmed this report being true for Rubiaceae at least for Britain. Similarly, since *Trapa* and *Montinia* included earlier in the Onagraceae, lack raphides, they should be placed elsewhere. Further, all members of Saxifragaceae have raphides, while *Hydrangea* which is devoid of them, is better placed in a separate family Hydrangeaceae.

Tomlinson (1962) suggested 8 families within Scitamineae to fall into four natural groups: (i) Heliconiaceae, Musaceae and Strelitziaceae having raphide sacs and symmetrical guard cells; (ii) Costaceae, Marantaceae and Zingiberaceae having asymmetrical guard cells and lacking raphide sacs; (iii) Cannaceae lacking raphide sacs and with symmetrical guard cells and (iv) Lowiaceae having raphide sacs and asymmetrical guard cells. He further considered the presence of raphide sacs to be a primitive feature being absent in more specialised families.

Crystals of calcium oxalate of different shapes, other than raphides were found useful in the taxonomy of *Allium* (Jaccard and Frey, 1928; Kharchenko, 1928).

Lapachol, a yellowish powder, is recognised as 2-hydroxy-3-1, 4-naphthoquinone. Masses of it can be seen in the cells of wood of a number of bignoniaceous plants. Outside Bignoniaceae, lapachol is known from *Avicennia* (Verbenaceae) and *Bassia* (Sapotaceae).

Silica occurs in a large number of dicotyledonous families. In the Gramineae, it is prominent in the epidermis of the leaves. Twenty different forms have been recognised and are useful in taxonomy of grasses. Silica cells also occur in Palmae (Tomlinson, 1961).

Gypsum, in the form of crystals of $CaSO_4$, $2H_2O$, occurs in some plants. Brunswick (1920) found them in every member of Tamaricaceae but did not find them in the nearly related(?) Frankaniaceae and Fouqueriaceae which have crystals of calcium oxalate instead.

Chemical Test Characters or Plant Products

Many of these products are formed as metabolic by-products. These may not be essential, as it appears, for the functioning of plants and thus can be regarded important in taxonomy. Following are some of the best known plant products which are reliable taxonomic features.

Phenolics and betalains. These have been proved to be of the greatest taxonomic value. They can be extracted from plants relatively quickly and readily separated by paper chromatography. Plant phenolics are so numerous that detailed information monographs on the chemistry of these compounds have been compiled (Harborne, 1964, 1967; Ribereau-Gayon, 1972).

The phenolic molecules most often studied in chemotaxonomy fall into a general class known as the flavonoids. They are the largest group of naturally occurring phenols. These are further classified into *flavones, flavanones, isoflavones* and *isoflavonoids, flavanols, anthocyanidins,* etc. These are known from leaves, flowers and fruits. Differences in the phenolic contents of different plant organs have often been reported. Similarly, they vary in response to light and growth (Galston, 1969). In general, extracts of vegetative tissues are more reliable and convenient in chemotaxonomy. The flower pigments, which are usually anthocyanins and anthoxanthins, vary greatly and have been shown to be under genetic control (Moncrieff, 1931). But at the same time, all variation in pigment production is not genetic in origin. Commonly, anthocyanin production increases with the defficiency in nutrients such as nitrogen and phosphorus.

Bate-Smith (1948, 1958, 1962) has reviewed the early application of evidence from phenolics to taxonomic problems. According to him, leuco-anthocyanins are generally present in woody plants. The herbaceous Primulaceae, however, are exceptionally rich in leuco-anthocyanins, and some of the woody members of Oleaceae and Scrophulariaceae lack them completely. Phenolic characters have been used by Bate-Smith (1958) in the rearrangement of the species of *Iris*. Williams (1982) pointed out chemical evidence from the flavonoides in the classification of *Malus* species.

Betalains are different from the rest of the phenolic compounds owing to the presence of nitrogen in them. They are red (betacyanins) and yellow (betaxanthins) pigments and occur only in ten families of angiosperms, which are traditionally included in a single order Centrospermae. The structure of betalains is quite unlike that of anthocyanidins—they are not flavonoids either. The discovery of these unique pigments in Centrospermae supports the delimitation of the order based on other features. Cactaceae were not regarded here by earlier authors. However, since they have betalain pigments, they seem well established as members of Centrospermae. On the other hand, Caryophyllaceae and Molluginaceae which lack betalains, have been retained in this order on other grounds.

Oils, Fats and Waxes. Lipids, together with the proteins and carbohydrates, form the bulk of the organic matter of plant tissue and therefore, are a potential source of taxonomic evidence. They are somewhat heterogenous group and are completely or partially soluble in organic solvents such as ethanol, ether or chloroform. Fats are distinguished from oils by their physical state at normal temperatures—fats are solids while oils are liquids.

Simple lipids contain only carbon, hydrogen and oxygen and are esters of fatty acids with glycerol, a trihydric alcohol. Natural fats and oils are complex mixtures of many such esters and do not have a constant composition. The greater the proportion of saturated fatty acids in a lipid, the higher is the melting point. Saturation is usually measured by the *iodine number,* i.e. the number of grams of iodine absorbed by a hundred grams of fat, oil or fatty acid. Some lipids contain nitrogen and/or phosphorus in addition to carbon, hydrogen and oxygen. These are called *phospholipids*.

Lipids are found in all parts of plants but occur in the highest concentration in the storage organs, seeds and fruits. They form droplets suspended in the cytoplasm. Plant waxes occur in cuticular layers. Cutin itself is a natural polyester of fatty and hydroxy fatty acids.

McNair (1929), for the first time, assessed the taxonomic significance of lipids. He believed that the iodine number of lipids was higher (i.e. lipids are more saturated) in more advanced plant groups. However, it has been shown that the iodine number is a rather unstable character and must be used carefully.

The major fatty acids occur in several families and the unusual fatty acids only can be considered to have some taxonomic value. Bacterial lipids, for example, contain fatty acids which are not found in other plants. In flowering plants certain fatty acids such as chaulmoogric acid and some related acids have restricted distribution (e.g. in members of Flacourtiaceae). Other such examples are erucic acid (Cruciferae), petroselinic acid (Umbelliferae), xymenynic acid (Santalaceae and Olacaceae), etc.

Alkaloids. During the nineteenth century, chemists tried to identify the plant products which have striking properties of affecting the nervous system of animals. Many of such products were found to be basic and became known as alkaloids. Alkaloids are unexpectedly widely distributed in flowering plants and ferns. Manske (1950) suggested that there are about 38 to 39 families that can be regarded as alkaloid-containing families. According to Hegnauer (1963), none of the larger families is free from them.

No satisfactory definition of alkaloids exists even today (Smith, 1976) because they do not constitute a natural group of materials in terms of source, structure or properties. They are organic, nitrogen-containing bases, usually with a heterocyclic ring of some kind. They are by-products of plant metabolism and are synthesised from amino acids or their derivatives. They are considered to be non-essential for plant growth.

Three main categories of alkaloids are distinguished, namely, *true alkaloids* having a nitrogen-containing heterocyclic nucleus derived from a biogenetic amine; *protoalkaloids* derived from amino acids but lacking any heterocyclic ring and *pseudoalkaloids* which are biogenetically unrelated to amino acids, and are derived from terpenes, sterols, aliphatic acids, nicotinic acids or purines. The following discussion excludes the last category.

Alkaloids are not universally accumulated by plants. Some families are especially rich in alkaloidal species, such as Berberidaceae, Leguminosae, Ranunculaceae and Solanaceae. Alkaloids characterising species of a particular taxon are frequently of the same chemical or biogenetic group. Thus Papaveraceae contain isoquinoline alkaloids always including protopine. Many Leguminosae have lupin alkaloids, while Solanaceae have tropane derivatives. Gramineae and Compositae, on the other hand, produce many different types of alkaloids (Hegnauer, 1966). Sometimes, the specialised alkaloids, such as morphine (*Papaver, somniferum*), coniine (few Umbelliferae), strychnine (some species of *Strychnos*, Loganiaceae), etc. show a very narrow distribution.

Hegnauer (1963) reviewed the use of alkaloids in taxonomy as follows:

Colchicine Group: Santavy (1956) demonstrated that many of the results on the distribution of colchicine given by Klein and Pollauf (1929) were incorrect. Santavy and his co-workers could detect colchicine and related alkaloids only in *Gloriosa, Littonia, Ornithoglossum, Iphigenia, Colchicum, Androcymbium, Didipax* and *Anguillaria,* all of the Liliaceae.

If the distribution of colchicine in Liliaceae is compared with the systems proposed by Krause (1930), Hutchinson (1959) and Buxbaum (1925, 1927, 1936), it is apparent that the last named shows the best correlation.

Amaryllidaceae: Rearrangement by Hutchinson (1959), particularly the segregation of Agavoideae, undoubtedly fits better with the Dracaenoideae. Similarly, segregation of Alloideae into a separate order Alliales by Treub (1975) can be said to be justified since they do not have alkaloids.

Polycarpicae: Thirteen of the 25 families placed by Wettstein in Polycarpicae are considered to be free from alkaloids. These are mainly monotypic or oligotypic families of uncertain position. Chemically, two clusters are recognised: (i) Annonaceae, Aristolochiaceae, Berberidaceae, Magnoliaceae, Menispermaceae and Ranunculaceae having magnoflorine and berberine and (ii) Hernandiaceae, Lauraceae, Monimiaceae and Nymphaeaceae having only the latter compound. On the basis of distribution of benzylisoquinoline alkaloids, Cronquist (1968a), Kubitzki (1969) and, later on, several other taxonomists (Takhtajan, 1969; Thorne, 1968, 1976; Dahlgren, 1975) rearranged families with apocarpous gynoecia in their Magnoliidae (Magnolianae).

Rhoeadales: Engler and Diels (1936) considered seven families in this order including Papaveraceae, Capparidaceae, Cruciferae, Tovariaceae, Resedaceae, Moringaceae and Breschneideraceae. However, the true alkaloids occur only in the Papaveraceae and hence most of the later taxonomists (Hutchinson, 1959; Melchior, 1964; Cronquist, 1968a; Takhtajan, 1969, 1973, 1980; Dahlgren, 1975, 1977, 1980; Thorne, 1976) consider this family to be closely related to certain families within Magnoliidae (e.g. Ranunculaceae, Berberidaceae) while the rest of the families have affinity with Dilleniidae. Thus, the relationship of this family with Berberidaceae, as suggested by Hallier (1905) may be considered more natural.

Mears and Mabry (1971) have given several interesting examples of alkaloid restriction and its possible taxonomic value in Leguminosae.

Some alkaloids, however, are scattered in distribution, occurring in plants which are thought to be only distantly related on other criteria. These alkaloids may not be synthesised in the same way in the different species and cannot be considered to have a general taxonomic significance. Nicotine, for example, is present either in large or small quantities in a number of taxa including *Nicotiana, Duboisia* and *Salpiglossis* of Solanaceae; *Zinnia* and *Eclipta* of Compositae; *Equisetum* (Equisetaceae), *Sedum* (Crassulaceae) *Mucuna* (Leguminosae), *Asclepias* (Asclepiadaceae), *Herpestes* (Scrophulariaceae) and others. Berberine is another similar alkaloid with random distribution in many species.

Cyanogenic compounds. Hegnauer (1977) defined the term *cyanogenesis* as the ability of certain plants to release hydrocyanic acid after injury of cells. Usually cyanophoric plants contain one or several cyanogenic glycosides. Since 1801, when Bohm first detected HCN and amygdalin (the first plant glycoside) in seeds of *Prunus amygdalus* (Rosaceae), many rosaceous and other plants have been shown to be cyanophoric.

There are five main biosynthetic groups of cyanophoric compounds recognised in vascular plants. The greatest number of presently known cyanogenic glycosides belongs to the two aromatic groups. Till date about 2,056 species of vascular plants are known to be cyanophoric. In angiosperms they occur erratically. Cyanogenic taxa are relatively frequent in Araceae, Juncaceae, Juncaginaceae, Gramineae and Scheuchzeriaceae among the monocotyledons and several dicotyledonous families.

The facts known today suggest that more than one biosynthetic group of cyanophoric compounds occur only in very large genera or families belonging to Dilleniidae, Rosidae and Asteridae. In these taxa, accumulation of cyanogenic compounds is taxonomically significant at the infra-familiar level. Linamarin, for example, is a character of many *Loteae, Trifolieae* and *Phaseolae* in Fabaceae and *Calenduleae* in Asteraceae.

Terpenoids and steroids. These materials resemble alkaloids and glucosides. In a narrow sense, terpenoids are regarded as the components of essential oils. This large group of compounds has movalonic acid as a precursor (Goodwin, 1970). Over a hundred monoterpenoids are known as components of essential oils. True steroids are mostly alcohols or esters. Terpenoids can be compared by quick spot tests in chromatography.

The most noted example of the use of terpenoids in plant taxonomy is the classical work of Mirov (1961) on gum terpentines of *Pinus*.

Iridoid compounds. Bate-Smith and Swain (1966) indicated the possible value of the monoterpenoid cyclopentanoid lactones, known as *iridoids,* to taxonomists. Several taxonomic changes have been made or suggested on the basis of iridoid distribution. *Buddleia,* which contains aucubin, has been transferred from Loganiaceae to Buddleiaceae, near Scrophulariaceae in the 12th edition of Engler's *Syllabus*. Hegnauer suggested minor modification of Takhtajan's system of classification to bring all iridoid-containing orders into one group, with a possible common origin. Jensen, Nielsen and Dahlgren (1975) brought out systematic importance of iridoid compounds in angiosperms. Their results were incorporated by Dahlgren (1975) in his system which has recently gained popularity.

Cronquist (1977) has put forward the speculative interpretation that changes in the major groups of chemical repellants had an important role in the rise of major new groups of dicotyledons. Each set of repellants tends to lose its effectiveness as insects and other predators become resistant to it. A new kind of repellant gives the plant a competitive advantage and permits the evolutionary expansion of a new group. Thus, the isoquinoline alkaloids of Magnoliidae gave way to the tannins of Hamamelidae, Rosidae and Dilleniidae and these in turn, gave way to the iridoid compounds that were most effectively exploited by Asteridae. Within Asteridae, the rise of the relatively recent family Asteraceae may relate to a shift to polyacetylenes and sesquiterpene lactones in place of already less effective iridoids.

Proteins

There are several reasons for the importance of proteins in chemotaxonomy. First, they are large, complex molecules which might show little qualitative variation in response to changing environmental factors. Secondly, proteins are universally distributed. Thirdly, they are often present in quantity and many of them are relatively simple to extract and handle. Lastly, numerous cheap, simple and rapid methods of protein analysis and comparison are now available for the taxonomists. Electrophoresis has been a particularly important method of protein separation for taxonomic purposes.

In order to avoid any confusion due to variability of proteins, it is essential to base taxonomic interpretations on comparisons of proteins from homologous organs of the same age. Protein variation also occurs between plants in different populations of the same species. At the level of species and genus, considerable differences in protein complements have been recorded. These form evidence upon which taxonomic systems may be founded, tested or demolished.

Several examples of protein analysis and comparison in plant taxonomy are available. However, only a few important works are cited in the following paragraphs.

Desborough and Peloquin (1969), for example, separated the soluble tuber proteins of species of *Solanum* by disc electrophoresis. Certain bands which were consistently present in all the 16 species tested by the authors are of potential taxonomic value. Johnson and Hall (1965) demonstrated phylogenetic affinities in Triticinae by protein electrophoresis. Similarly, in *Magnolia* (Pickering and Fairbrothers, 1967) and in *Brassica* (Vaughn, 1968), electrophoresis seems to have been very successful when combined with serological methods. In the tribe Vicieae of the legumes the tryptic peptides of *Vicia* and *Lathyrus* are similar suggesting the close relationship of these genera (Jackson *et al.,* 1967). Further, *Lens,* and *Pisum* preparations showed differences from the *Vicia-Lathyrus* pattern while *Cicer* was rather distinct.

Serology and Taxonomy

Boyden (1964) defined serology as that portion of Biology which is concerned with the nature and interactions of *antigenic* material and *antibodies,* while Smith (1976) defined it as "the study of the origins and properties of antisera." Antigens or agglutinogens occur in red blood cells and antibodies or agglutinins originate in the serum of blood. Both these substances cause clumping of blood. Extracts of some plant proteins can haemolyse (destroy) the red blood cells. When such protein extracts of plants are injected into bodies of animals such as rabbits or mice, they bring about haemolysis in the beginning but later on the animal blood produces antibodies in the serum which are capable of inhibiting normal haemolysis. Serum from such immunised blood can be used as a reagent to identify similar or identical antigens. Serological reactions between antibodies and antigenic material results in the formation of a precipitate. This is called *precipitin reaction.* Kraus (1897) showed that this reaction indicates similarity of antigens. Kowarski (1901), Bertarelli (1902) and Magnus (1908) were the first notable serologists. They compared proteins from various grass and legume species, showing similarities and differences. Later, serotaxonomy developed and became popular in Germany. The Koenigsberg school headed by Gohlke was founded in 1914. Mez and Ziegenspeck (1926) produced a "Stammbaum" or "family tree" for the whole plant kingdom based largely on serological results. Another school that of Gilg and Schurhoff, in Berlin disagreed with the results of the Koenigsberg school, and as a result of their conflict there was a decline of serology in Germany. Other early workers to have made significant contribution to the application of serology to systematics include Rives (1923), Nelson and Biskeland (1928) and Moritz (1933) to name a few.The school of serology at Rutgers University, New Jersey, headed by Boyden made important contributions to the theory and technical progress of serotaxonomy in recent years.

Jensen (1968) compared the proteins of mature seeds of 20 ranunculacean genera and improved their classification. Genera such as *Trollis, Delphinium, Actaea, Aquilegia, Ranunculus* and *Eranthis* are regarded serologically similar to *Adonis*. Similarly, he showed that the genus *Hydrastis* (Berberidaceae) shows closer serological similarity to Ranunculaceae.

Gell, Hawkes and Wight (1960) and later Hawkes and Lester (1966, 1968) compared potato species on the basis of double diffusion tests and showed that Mexican species fell in three groups and *Solanum morelliforme* is only distantly related to other tuber-bearing solanums.

A lot of research has also been done into the application of serological methods to the taxonomy of legumes (Kloz, 1971). Fairbrothers and his co-workers have developed Boyden's school at New Jersey. Their contribution to serotaxonomic researches in various plant groups has provided solutions to many problems in taxonomy. Particular mention may be made of their work on grasses (Fairbrothers and Johnson, 1961), Cornaceae and Nyssaceae (Fairbrothers and Johnson, 1964), *Typha* (Lee and Fairbrothers, 1967), *Magnolia* (Pickering and Fairbrothers, 1967). Smith (1968a, b; 1969a, b; 1972) has applied modern serological techniques to critical groups of grasses such as *Bromus*. Lee and Fairbrothers (1978) have recently used these techniques to the systematics of Rubiaceae and related families. According to them, the quantitative data emphasised the similarity of Rubiaceae to Cornaceae and Caprifoliaceae and the presaturation tests revealed similarity with Apocynaceae, Asclepiadaceae and Gentianaceae. Similarly, two rubiaceous genera *Asperula* and *Galium* were found to be serologically similar to each other while being the most dissimilar from all other genera of the family.

In addition to these reports, there are several exhaustive phytochemical investigations that have appeared in the last 20 years. Harborne, Boulter and Turner (1971), for example, have given a detailed account of chemotaxonomy of Leguminosae, whereas Haywood, Harborne and Turner (1977) have provided phytochemistry of Compositae. Carbonnier and Cauwet-Marc (1981) made comparative phytochemical investigation of the genus *Bupleurum* (Umbelliferae).

Phytogeography, Ecology and Genetics

Although there are signs of flowering plants possibly from the Triassic (about 200 million years ago; Axelrod, 1970), their rise to dominance occurred only during the Cretaceous period some 125 million years ago. Within this short period of about 80 million years, they occupied almost all the surface of land where life was possible. Just how they have spread so rapidly is, as Darwin said, "an abominable mystery". Whatever our views may be about the actual origin of new species, angiosperms, when they first arose, must have occupied an extremely limited area, perhaps no more than the space covered by a single individual, and their attainment of any appreciable range must be a matter of actual movement of individual plants (Good, 1974). Further, the evidence suggests that the earlier flowering plants were mostly woody plants and the herbaceous species of today have obviously evolved later on reaching areas with extreme climatic conditions such as lack of water and severe cold.

Phytogeography and Speciation

It is generally accepted today that the later Cretaceous and major part of the Tertiary period were a time of relatively constant climates, characterised by genial, moist conditions varying little with the passage of time and associated with a minimum of relief on the world's surface. Angiosperms, then, may be pictured as originating and slowly diversifying for millions of years. It was an age of natural evolution by the inherent process of change with time. During this period the distribution of flowering plants was also far more generalised then it is today. Temperature and other climatic gradients were everywhere more gradual. Mountains were lower and their climatic effects less pronounce. It is also believed that the land surfaces of the globe were less scattered. The continents are believed to have drifted away from one another in the later period causing separation or isolation of plant and animal populations. This geographical isolation has reached its maximum today and resulted in local speciation by the effects of segregated and isolated evolution. This, according to Good (1974), was probably the first kind of specialisation superimposed on the earlier generalised distribution of flowering plants.

Towards the end of the Tertiary era, the picture changed in almost every respect. At that time there were periodical catestrophies which consisted of a drastic and sudden alteration of temperature. This brought all kinds of minor and secondary variations which culminated in the Ice Age. It is possible that equatorial temperature values were but little affected and thus the gentler gradient from the equator to poles was replaced by a steep gradient culminating at higher altitudes in arctic and antarctic conditions.

The climatic change mentioned above was anticipated by a period of intense mountain building, particularly in the Meiocene period (about 30 million years ago). Their effect on the climate also was immense. The appreciable areas of the earth's crust raised into cooler layers of the atmosphere, the newly elevated mountain ranges intercepted the moisture leaden winds from the oceans and condemned many interior parts to aridity and in general these changes brought alterations in all sorts of climatic aspects and every kind of external condition which modified plant life. The effect of all this on flowering plants was profound. The factors of distribution took on new roles and values. The potentiality of dispersal became less significant, while the range of tolerance increased in importance. Changes of climate not only enforced migration but also determined the direction of plant evolution. The world today, thus, does not have a uniform flora but there are several floristic regions, characterised in their own way by a peculiar association of plant types.

The floristic regions of the world are determined on the basis of geographical distribution of plant genera. These are mapped individually, and from a comparison of distributions a number of natural units emerge which are distinctively characteristic of peculiar regions.

Three main sources of evidence of biogeographical theories have been suggested (Collinson, 1977). They are evidence of: (i) autecology, (ii) fossil record and (iii) climatic change. Evidence generated by autecological studies may throw light on the conditions which might limit the spread of a particular species. The fossil record provides evidence of past distribution and the climatic changes that might have directed the evolution.

Adaptations for Survival

The evolutionary success and the potentiality for further diversification depend upon the adaptation of a species or a taxon to: (i) survival of the seedling and adult plant under a variety of environmental conditions, (ii) cross-pollination and (iii) development and dispersal of seeds and establishment of seedlings (Stebbins, 1974).

The adaptations for survival may be accomplished by environmental modifications of the phenotypes. This is what is known as the ecotypic differentiation. The local populations which are made up of individuals with similar environmental tolerances are specialised to meet local environmental conditions and may be termed ***ecological races*** or ***ecotypes***. Their existence has been demonstrated in many woody and herbaceous species in relation to geographical variation of light, heat, moisture, soil chemistry and so on. It is through such ecotypes that the species can occupy wide ranges. Why some plants should have this ability while others are poorly fitted for wide dispersal is not well understood. Most probably, the environmental modifications, when incorporated into the genetic make-up, become permanent and bring about further differentiation within the populations and their ecotypes. Some species appear to be genetically conservative and cannot adapt to new environments. For most adaptive changes alteration of genotypes is required.

Adaptation to cross-pollination involves adaptive syndromes of characters which favour pollination by the most effective pollinator. These originate as mere modifications due to environment but are quickly incorporated into the genotypes.

The third adaptation involves much complexity and diversity. The three separate conditions demand somewhat conflicting requirements for seed development, seed dispersal and seedling establishment. Selection for increased seed number, for example, may bring about profound changes of the gynoecium while adaptation for protection of developing seeds may involve changes in the structure of flowers and their surrounding bracts. These and similar other adaptations have lead to the evolution of major categories of flowering plants. Adaptations for protection against insects and other predators consist mostly of repellent chemical substances but also include symbiotic relations with animals. These have been only recently recognised (Janzen, 1966, 1967).

Ecological Variations

It can be said that all these variations in plants mentioned above are the result of the plastic response of the individual to factors of the environment involving (i) climatic, (ii) edaphic and (iii) biotic factors. These ecological factors have two-fold effects upon individual—the direct effects upon the phenotype and the indirect effects on the genotype. Thus, individuals are the result of: (i) their genetic constitution and of (ii) environmental influences during their development.

Characters that are greatly modified by environmental conditions have been regarded traditionally as "bad" taxonomic characters. However, it is now apparent that any distinction between genetic and environmental influences upon phenotype is artificial and rather meaningless (Dobzhansky, 1970). The capacity of phenotypes, for example, to respond to environmental influences is itself under genetic control (Bradshaw, 1965), and there is some evidence that environmental modifications may become genetically "fixed" (Waddington, 1953).

Physiological studies of environmental modification (Bjorkman and Holmgren, 1963; Whitehead, 1963) indicate that it is not random or biologically insignificant but is frequently adaptive and of evolutionary and ecological importance (Heslop-Harrison, 1964; Bradshaw, 1965; Cook, 1968). Turesson (1922), for example, has shown that two species of *Lysimachia* (Primulaceae) respond differently to light intensity; one showing phenotypic response while the other showing genotypic differentiation—i.e., both altered genotypes and phenotypes may occur mixed in a single population (Nelson, 1965). The balance of the two mechanisms may vary between populations and also between species (Marshall and Jain, 1968; Jain 1969). In view of these considerations, Wells (1969) has made a detailed criticism of the "misleading distinction between environmentally induced phenotypic modification and genetically fixed ecological races."

As a result of recent studies in ecology, physiology and genetics, it is now apparent that phenotypic variation is of considerable ecological and evolutionary importance. This may therefore be an opportune time to reconsider the taxonomic status of phenotypic variation (Snaydon, 1973). Environmentally variable characters have so far been rejected in taxonomic consideration and more stable floral characters have been given greater attention. But according to Snaydon (1973), the vegetative characters, although much variable in response to environmental conditions, should be adequately studied and used in keys. Further, he questions the aim of taxonomy to classify abstract genotypes instead of concrete phenotypes. Indeed, it is often not possible to classify genotypes. Taxonomists have so far used only environmentally stable characters because phenotype closely reflects genotype.

Genetic variation within populations is apparently determined by complex interactions between genetic and ecological factors, where the environmental factors also partly determine the genetic factors, such as breeding system, mutation rate and dominance. The effect of ecological factors, both environmental and biotic, upon genetic variation within populations is probably greater than what had previously been assumed.

Genetic variation within populations has usually been studied at the morphological levels, but it may also be studied at the physiological and biochemical levels (Fairbrothers, 1968; Scandalios, 1969; Turner, 1970). Much of the genetic variation is of adaptive significance and should be recognised in taxonomy.

In general, the ecological information about various plant groups is not large and taxonomic delimitation between plant genera, families, etc. does not generally reflect differences in ecological behaviour. However, in certain groups there appears to be a good correlation between taxonomic limits and ecological behaviour. Plants, animals, fungi and bacteria, for example, are broadly equivalent to producers, consumers and decomposers respectively, in ecosystems. Within each of these groups there are also broadly equivalent taxonomic and ecological groupings; the taxonomic grouping into algae, bryophytes and angiosperms, for example, broadly corresponds to ecological differences. Many plant families are ecologically quite homogeneous, e.g. Chenopodiaceae, Salicaceae, Ericaceae, Plumbaginaceae, Orobanchaceae, Lentibulariaceae and Potamogetonaceae. Species are the highest taxonomic level that is of appreciable ecological value.

Genetic Variation

Apart from the environmental or ecological variations mentioned above, populations normally contain variation by random gene mutation. This variation is shuffled from generation to generation by gene segregation and recombination.

Gene Mutation

Mayr (1942) has defined mutation as "a discontinuous chromosomal change with a genetic effect". Such a mutation may occur at the gene level or at the chromosome or even genome level. Gene mutations primarily alter developmental processes and thus have specific effects on individual phenotypes. Chromosomal and genomic mutations alter the whole series of processes or affect the relationship between them and are primarily responsible for the origin of "biological species" (Stebbins, 1959a).

Effects of gene mutations on the organism are many and are of immediate concern to the taxonomists. They may bring about changes in the phenotypes such as zygomorphic corolla of *Antirrhinum* (Scrophulariaceae) to actinomorphic one, the gamosepalous calyx of *Silene* (Caryophyllaceae) to polysepalous one, or the spurred corolla of *Aquilegia* (Ranunculaceae) to spurless one. Other single gene effects are changes in phenotypic expression produced by environment, change of habit from annual to biennial, etc.

All these effects can be favoured by natural selection and thus contribute to evolutionary change. However, most mutations are probably disadvantages to the plant.

Polymorphism is the most common genetic variation in populations. In this, usually sharply distinct genetic variants occur side by side in a population. The polymorphic characters may involve flower colour forms, heterostylous forms *(Oxalis, Biophytum, Oldenlandia),* chemical forms *(Eucalyptus)* and various others. Such features may be uniform or cryptic, discontinuous or more rarely continuous, adaptive or not. Their genetic basis may be genic, chromosomal-segmental (inversions or translocations) or chromosomal.

Pleiotropic Gene Action: Many mutations, possibly the majority of them, affect several characteristics of the adult phenotype. This phenomenon is known as *pleiotropy*. Pleiotropic genes may produce different but related effects on different organs. In *Nicotiana,* for instance, the gene which produces long petioles also produces more acuminate leaf-tips, longer calyces with narrower sepal lobes, corollas with more acuminate lobes, longer anthers and more attenuated capsules (Stebbins, 1959a).

Recombination

Gene recombination is as important as mutation in the production of adaptive variation in higher plants. The recombination of genetic variability is largely determined by the breeding system. A whole series of mechanisms promoting cross-fertilisation and genetic system for self-incompatibility have evolved which have their selective advantage in promoting gene recombination. Self-fertilisation and apomixis are always secondary and have been derived from flexible cross-fertilised systems. It therefore becomes necessary for a taxonomist to have full knowledge of the breeding behaviour of populations.

Apomixis

In certain plant groups sexual reproduction is replaced by a non-sexual method. The plant populations may be wholly apomictic or may exhibit sexuality and apomixis at the same time. Many grasses show transition between complete sexuality and complete apomixis. Such cases are known as *facultative apomicts* while those plants in which no sexual phase is known are termed *obligate apomicts*.

The apomictic phenomenon can be divided into two main classes: (i) vegetative reproduction and (ii) agamospermy. In the first class, structures such as bulbils, tubers, rhizomes, stolons, etc. take over the whole reproduction. In nature there are several examples of this. All the individuals produced by these processes have the same genotype and consequently belong to the same biotype. There is formation of no new genotype and variation.

In the second type, agamospermy, seeds and embryos are formed but no sexual process is involved. Meiosis and fertilisation are avoided so that the resultant embryo is genotypically identical with the maternal plant.

Amphimixis

Plants which reproduce sexually may be either self- or cross-fertilised, each of them has certain advantages and disadvantages. "Pure lines" are developed through self-fertilisation (or endogamy, autogamy, inbreeding, etc.), while exogamy or cross-fertilisation (or heterogamy, outbreeding) increases heterozygosity.

Breeding Systems and Taxonomy

The breeding systems mentioned above have been treated variously in taxonomy, and the following paragraphs will be devoted to review them.

Inbreeders

Habitual inbreeders, in course of time, segregate into several pure lines or genetically homozygous populations. If the genetic differences are also reflected in their phenotypic characters, each line will be clearly distinguishable. The pure lines contain little capacity for evolution in response to environmental changes, and on hybridisation, these give rise to hybrids which on segregation, produce new lines. This aspect has been used in selection of crop plants for uniformity in certain morphological characters. All such inbreedings, however, are not recognised as distinct species since many of them lack constancy owing to their occasional outbreeding and large number. The same arguments are used against the taxonomic recognition of apomicts as species. At the same time, there are no hard and fast rules in dealing with the recognition of species in inbreeding groups. The recognition of inbreeding helps taxonomists to understand the variation pattern in these groups. According to Sharsmith (1961), the species boundaries, to a large extent are arbitrary, and units should be so circumscribed that will indicate biological relationships within them. The decision of naming these groups is a matter of experience depending on the knowledge available in respect of distribution, ecology, population size, etc. Roughly it can be said that the inbreeding populations which appear to be constant and occupy a considerable area should be recognised taxonomically (Davis and Heywood, 1963).

Cryptic speciation may take place between morphologically similar inbreeding populations as has been described in *Urginea indica* of the Liliaceae (Naik, 1976b), which lack genetic variability. But owing to genetic differences (such as polyploidy), they may be isolated from each other giving rise to "biological" species. Baker (1959) suggested that such inbreeding populations may have cryptic genetically isolated species as above or may evolve taxonomic microspecies without genetic isolation.

Outbreeders

The taxonomic separation of outbreeders is often difficult owing to their continuous pattern of morphological difference. In such cases, taxonomist seeks for a discontinuity and circumscribes a taxon accordingly. If however, he fails to do so, he prefers to keep them under one name (Baker, 1959).

In nature, inbreeding (self-compatibility) and outbreeding (self-incompatibility) does not exist in the same species. If such a case is met with, it is better to recognise the two races as distinct species. Several such examples are known, e.g. in *Primula* (Primulaceae), *Armeria* (Compositae), etc. (Baker, 1959, 1961).

Apomicts

The problems involved in classification of apomicts have been treated by many taxonomists (Valentine and Love, 1958; Clausen, 1960; Valentine, 1960; Wycherly, 1953; Love and Love, 1956; Hedberg, 1958; Kawano, 1963, etc.), but the subject still remains controversial. Apomicts, as has been described earlier, neither form populations nor do they exchange genes between their biotypes. Each of the biotypes builds up its own population by self-duplication. Thus the population may contain many biotypes. Different biotypes may mature at different times. Valentine (1960) is of the opinion that it may be difficult, except to a specialist, to recognise differences between the biotypes. But since each biotype is "true breeding", a finer discrimination may be possible in them than in amphimictic groups. As a result, a very large number of species may be described, but the actual number will depend on the nature of the apomictic mechanism involved and on the amount of attention that taxonomists have given to the group in question.

Facultative apomicts may show such a degree of variation that no useful classification of their variation is practicable. Examples of such groups in active state of evolution can be found in *Rubus fruticosus* (Gustafsson, 1946, 1947a, b); *Poa alpina* (Muntzing, 1954) and other species of *Poa* (Nygren, 1954). Largely obligate apomicts on the other hand, such as are found in *Ranunculus auricomus, Taraxacum* and *Alchemilla,* allow recognition of taxa of greater stability.

Biosystematics

The numerous disciplines of science thus reviewed produce a mass of data about given plants. This is not only sufficient for its own sake but often is very pertinent for a systematic investigation. The field of taxonomy, thus epitomises the research in various branches of biology centred on the organism itself and brings the varied factual information from them to bear on the problems of interrelationships, classification and evolution.

One of the most dynamic aspects of taxonomy, however, is the study of populations of living plants to establish the variation patterns present. This type of study, as stated by Rollins (1958), provides a rich source of understanding of a given taxon and when these patterns are properly evaluated, in terms of their repetition and geographical spread, they are at the base of a taxon's proper definition. Thus variation patterns arising from genetic sources within and between populations set the stage for the development of discontinuities upon which taxonomic systems may be founded. The development of taxonomy in relation to population sampling has lead to a new discipline of biology which has been termed variously as *Biosystematics, Experimental taxonomy, Genenomy, Genecology, Modern taxonomy, New systematics* and so on. The first one has been widely used.

The aims of biosystematics were first stated by Camp & Gily (1943); they are: (i) to delimit the natural biotic units and (ii) to apply to these units a system of nomenclature adequate to the task of conveying precise information regarding their defined limits, relationships, variability and dynamic structure. Clausen, Keck and Hiesey (1945) regarded genetics, cytology, comparative morphology and ecology as furnishing the critical data which together when applied to the organic evolution make up biosystematics.

The Population Concept

In general, there appears to be more reliance on genetics of organisms and various concepts of species consider them as groups of populations which interbreed with each other actually or potentially. If it is accepted that the species is a fundamental unit of nomenclatural systems, then the basis of taxonomy can be said to be reproducibility. In other words, the description of a taxon permits further samples to be accommodated in it. But in most cases, later collections necessitate a modification of the original description until a point is reached where all variations, all deviations from the original description have been included. This gives the complete range of reproducibility of the named taxon. In modern population taxonomy, instead of regarding the species as the basic unit, it is the local breeding population that is taken to be the starting point—the evolutionary unit.

Thus it can be understood that populations defined by biosystematists have different significance from those defined by taxonomists. Species and subspecies having definite geographic distribution are considered as populations by taxonomists. But when a taxon is known to represent a population, its characters have to be considered in relation to the individual members and in relation to the population as a whole. This means that there are *individual* characters possessed by some individuals and *population* characters shared by majority of the individuals within the population.

Local breeding population or "Mendelian population", as it is often termed, has been defined by Dobzhansky (1950) as *a reproductive community of sexual and cross-fertilising individuals which share in a common gene pool.* The largest and most inclusive Mendelian population is the "biological species". Other definitions of population have been given by Sirks (1951), Mather (1946) and others.

In broad terms it appears that biosystematics is taken to cover, on the one hand, a revivified systematics which takes into account the genetic and evolutionary nature of groups, and on the other hand, a separate discipline concerned with microevolutionary phenomena. It uses the group concepts based upon reproductive isolation and genetic structure but does not attempt to name these groups in the formal taxonomic units. Thus, biosystematics is better regarded as the extension of a classical taxonomy. It still retains the descriptive phase of taxonomy for morphological delimitation of the taxa but incorporates evidence from other kinds as well.

Steps of Biosystematic Studies

Biosystematic studies are generally carried out in three successive steps.

The *first step* involves thorough sampling of the taxon and its populations. It includes collection of a large number of samples from populations distributed throughout the geographical range of the taxon, as far as possible. Their cultivation for detailed later studies including cytology, anatomy, palynology, chemistry, physiology, etc. Cytological studies are extended to the detection of chromosome numbers, their morphology and behaviour at meiosis which usually indicate genetic differences, if any, of taxonomic significance, between the populations.

Before the development of the theory of evolution, one full specimen was considered adequate to represent each "specially created species". But as we know today, a single specimen represents only imperfectly, the natural population of which it was a part, for it depicts only one of many character combinations. As the complexity of species has become better understood, the necessity for many specimens become apparent. The ideal herbarium normally represents the complete range of geographical, ecological and other forms within each species in order to reveal either the constancy or the instability of the characters thought to distinguish taxa from each other. A preliminary knowledge about the range of variation within a species can be obtained from the herbarium study, and additional collection to fill the gaps may be made. This procedure facilitates the detection of discontinuities in population samples. The information drawn from herbarium study may then be correlated with data from study of other fields. Benson (1962) has documented such procedures, particularly exemplified by studies of genera such as *Ranunculus, Quercus, Prunus* and many others.

Field observations reveal genetic phenotypes which may be confirmed by further studies. The phenotypes reflect both the genetic variability within each species and the phenomenon of *intergradation* between, as well as within the species. Intergradation usually is explained by *hybridization* and formation of hybrid swarms derived by the crossing of two species followed by free interbreeding of the offsprings within each other and by back crosses to the parental types.

The discontinuities, as referred to earlier, indicate genetic isolation and thus help in the delimitation of taxa. These observations, however, have to be supported by experimental studies. The distant populations may not undergo hybridization due to long geographical distances and barriers between them but may or may not hybridize when grown together. This has to be confirmed by observations and experimentation.

Environmental factors such as water, temperature, soil type, etc. may determine phenotypic characters and lead to *ecological isolation* or intergradation of species. Sometimes in local ecological situations certain gene combinations derived through hybridization may be preserved, while others are eliminated. This may result in segregation of a local variety or of a local species.

The *second step* includes the determination of the ability of different populations to hybridize and a study of the vigour and fertility of the hybrids. This discloses the presence or absence of breeding barriers between groups and is of taxonomic importance as indicating the natural limits of the taxa of various levels or orders. The classical example of such studies in revealing the underlying reasons for the existence of natural populations and of the problem of classifying them is the artificial synthesis of *Galeopsis tetrahit* (Muntzing, 1930, 1932) of Labiatae.

The genus *Galeopsis* includes three species, namely, *G. pubescens* ($n = 8$), *G. speciosa* ($n = 8$) *G. tetrahit* ($n = 16$). The first two do not cross frequently in nature, and even in artificial hybridization, do not yield fertile hybrids. However, in one experiment a hybrid could be obtained which resembled *G. tetrahit,* a natural species. It crossed with natural species and produced fertile hybrids. Thus the equivalent of a natural species was synthesised from two others and a probable mode of origin of the species was established. At least some of the species in nature might have arisen in this manner. Many other instances in which natural hybridization has occurred are well documented in the literature. Some of the more familiar examples are found in *Parthenium* (Compositae, Rollins, 1944, 1945, 1946, 1949), *Ranunculus* (Coonen, 1939), *Crepis* (Compositae, Babcock, 1947), *Clarkia* (Onagraceae, Lewis, 1951, 1953a, 1953b; Lewis and Lewis, 1955; Lewis and Roberts, 1956; Lewis and Raven, 1958), *Glandularia* (Verbenaceae, Solbrig, 1968; Schnack and Covas, 1945a, 1945b; Schnack and Solbrig, 1953), *Gilia* (Polemoniaceae, Grant, 1965, 1966, 1971; Grant and Grant, 1960) and a number of others. (See Stebbins, 1950, 1959b, 1974; Anderson, 1949, 1953; Anderson and Stebbins, 1954; Clausen, 1951; Goodspeed, 1954; Davis and Heywood, 1963; Lewis, 1966 and Ehrendorfer, 1968 for additional examples.)

The *third step* involves study of the homology of chromosomes in the hybrids as determined at meiosis.

Information obtained from these three steps is compared with the data from comparative morphology and geographical distribution.

Biosystematic Categories

In order to arrive at a better understanding of the natural relationships of plant species, the traditional categories recognised in classical taxonomy are felt inadequate and as is reviewed earlier, the basic unit, viz. species, has not been satisfactorily defined so far. Biosystematists, therefore, have developed a classification for experimentally investigated natural taxa, based on the data from various fields of science. These categories, however, are not intended to be substitutes for those used in practice and naturally are not governed by different rules of nomenclature—they are taken to be the most convenient units representing evolutionary nodes. Many populations occupy positions intermediate between these nodes. These categories are steps or levels in the evolutionary scale of differentiation from local populations to higher category such as a genus.

The most widely accepted categories, in order of ascending phyletic value, are *ecotype, ecospecies, cenospecies* and *comparium*.

Ecotype is the basic unit in biosystematics, adapted to a particular environment but capable of producing fully fertile hybrids with other ecotypes. Thus, ecotypes of the same species are not isolated by genetic barrier. It is somewhat parallel with but not necessarily identical to the geographic, variety or *subspecies* of taxonomists. The term ecotype was first proposed by Turesson (1922a) for an "ecological unit to cover the product arising as a result of genotypical response of an ecospecies to a particular habitat." Turesson later redefined the ecotype; in 1929 he emphasised the genetic crossability between ecotypes. Later workers such as Gregor (1931) and Clausen, Keck and Hiesey (1939, 1945), narrowed the concept still further, and Gregor *et al.* (1936) gave a more satisfactory definition as "*a population distinguished by morphological and physiological characters, most frequently of quantitative nature, interfertile with other ecotypes of the ecospecies, but prevented from freely exchanging genes by ecological barriers.*" Different kinds of ecotypes are recognised as *edaphic, climatic* and *biotic*.

Ecospecies was first defined by Turesson as a group of plants comprising one or more ecotypes within the cenospecies, whose members are able to interchange their genes without detriment to the offspring. Related ecospecies are usually separated by incomplete genetic barriers, which, in addition to ecological barriers, are adequate to preclude free interchange of genes with any other ecospecies. Generally they inhabit different but often contiguous ecological or geographical areas. In general, the ecospecies roughly correspond to the taxonomic species or Linnean species, as some authors refer to them.

Cenospecies is a group of plants representing one or more ecospecies "of common evolutionary origin, so far as morphological, cytological and experimental facts indicate." Cenospecies of the same comparium are separated by genetic barriers and all the hybrids between them are sterile. Cenospecies thus, parallel the taxonomic sections or subsections of the genus.

Comparium is often comparable to taxonomic genus. It is composed of one or more cenospecies that are not able to intercross. Complete genetic barrier exists between distinct comparia.

Biosystematic categories also involve the use of genotype, biotype and phenotype. Stebbins (1950) explained *genotype* as sum total of all the genes present in the individual; the *biotype* consists of all the individuals having the same genotype. The *phenotype* is the form or appearance of an individual and represents the result of external factors on its genotype.

Methods in Biosystematic Studies

The techniques of experimental taxonomy comprise methods of testing to determine to which of the above described categories a population belongs. These methods include those of orthodox taxonomy as well as those of cytology and genetics combined with cultivation in uniform and in varied environments (better known as the *transplant* method).

This latter technique, although practiced by many nineteenth century taxonomists, has a systematic beginning in the twentieth century. The most extensive and systematic trials were made by Alexis Jordan (1846) on species of the French flora. He showed that many species (Linnean species) consist of local populations whose members are interfertile yet maintain themselves as recognisable units, often growing in separate ecological conditions. Many of the species redefined by Jordan are currently accepted after detailed taxonomic and biosystematic analyses of groups. Later on, Darwin (1859) brought out the significance of natural selection and its effects on survival. Gregor Mendel (1865) discovered, basic principles governing inheritance and Wilhem Johannsen (1903-1911) showed that two kinds of variation occurred within a species: (i) hereditary and (ii) environmental and thus inheritable. These studies were much expanded later by Turesson (1922-1931) and since then have been employed by Hall (1926, 1932), Gregor (1939), Clausen, Keck and Hiesey, (1939, 1945, 1948), Marsden-Jones and Turrill (1930-1945), Babcock (1947), Clausen and Hiesey (1958) and many others. Some of the recent publications that deal with the modern trends in plant taxonomy and/or biosystematic methods are by Hesiop-Harrison (1964b), Jones and Luchsinger (1979), Nair (1980), Solbrig (1966, 1970) and Stace (1980).

The principle methods are: (i) growth in uniform environment, (ii) growth in varied environments and (iii) cytogenetic analysis.

Growth in Uniform Environment

It provides a means of studying the variability in heredity. Population samples of the taxonomic category (e.g. species, subspecies) are procured from different environments and are grown in a common experimental plot or under uniform environmental conditions. This permits comparison of behaviour of plants of unlike heredity in the uniform condition, thereby distinguishing between hereditary variation and environmental modification.

Growth in Varied Environments

This as afforded by a series of field stations, helps in the detection of the interplay between heredity and environment. Conclusions obtained by growing clones of the same individual in varied environmental conditions help in the detection of a range of environmental tolerances of individuals, races and species.

Cytogenetic Analysis

This includes: (i) detection of chromosome number in various populations and correlation, if any, between chromosome number and external morphology and geographic distribution within the species complex, (ii) hybridization of selected forms for understanding sterility in hybrid progeny and analysis of genotypes of related ecotypes and ecospecies and (iii) study of chromosomal homology as detected at meiosis in hybrids.

Turesson's Experiments

Turesson was mainly concerned with the differentiation of populations in different ecological conditions and the genetic, morphological and physiological nature of this differentiation. He made a series of population samples from various parts of the species area and grew them in uniform conditions in his experimental garden at Akarp in Sweden. He noted the reactions of plants in cultivation over the years in terms of habit, height, flowering time, etc. and found that in some cases the differences noted in the field disappeared, in other cases the differences showed intergradations, but in most instances they persisted. These persistent differences, therefore, appeared to be due to genetic differences. He was also able to show that the genetically different races were often correlated with habitat differences and that similar selective forces in the habitat appeared to produce similar kinds of adaptations in different species. The term ecotype was applied to these products of reaction between the genotype and the habitat. As mentioned earlier, this concept of ecotype was modified by later studies by Gregor *et al. (1936).*

Clausen, Keck and Hiesey's Experiments

In California, H.M. Hall introduced a new era in taxonomy of plants. He believed evolution to be based upon the physiological adjustment of the organism expressed in morphological and histological adaptations. Accordingly he adapted ecological methods in taxonomic research. Hall's ideas were later developed by Clausen, Keck and Hiesey who published several research articles and books between 1940 and 1950.

Their famous transect experiment consists of the genecological studies of populations of various species including *Potentilla glandulosa* (Rosaceae) and *Achillea millefolium* (Compositae). A transect was taken across central California, about 200 miles long, covering extensive mountain systems with climatic differences. Experimental gardens were established at varying altitudes from about 30 metres (Stanford) to 500 metres (Mather) and 3,300 metres (Timberline), and were maintained free from weeds and invading vegetation. Their work extended for more than 30 years indicating the scope of the investigation.

Populations of the species mentioned above were grown at various altitudes and their response to climatic conditions was noted. There was a superficial resemblance or say parallelism in morphological as well as physiological features in the ecotypes adapted to similar climatic conditions. Hybrids between the ecotypes were shown to be fully fertile and could produce new genotypes with new adaptive features.

In both these experiments, namely by Turesson and Clausen, Keck and Hiesey, it is clearly indicated that interaction between habitat and genotype could apparently produce a recognisable unit or ecotype.

Gregor's Experiments

Similar investigations were undertaken by Gregor and his collaborators at the Scottish Society for Research and Plant Breeding. They called these investigations *experimental taxonomy*. The principles of experimental taxonomy and its practical procedures were stated by Gregor, Davey and Lang (1936) who regarded orthodox and experimental taxonomy as complementary. They emphasised the growing of races under uniform environmental conditions in the experimental garden so that the variation shown by races could be studied unaffected by the irregularities of their natural habitat. They worked on the races of *Plantago maritima* (Plantaginaceae) and concluded that the pattern of ecotype variation was more frequently continuous than discontinuous, corresponding to gradients shown by the habitats.

Gregor's views on continuity of ecotype variation gained support from work done on *Plantago lanceolata* by Bocher (1943) and by various other investigators who recognised these variants as ecoclines (e.g. Barber, 1955; Barber and Jackson, 1957; Bradshaw, 1959).

Russian School

A school of genecological studies developed in Russia under Dr. Sinskaja, who published the results of their work in three different books (1948, 1958 and 1960). This approach differs slightly from the other schools, and zonal variability of populations has been studied in great details.

Ecotypic Variation and Taxonomy

The conventional taxonomic units, especially the species, subspecies and variety, have been regarded by many ecologists as unsatisfactory for their work, but at the same time there are quite a number of others who are not seriously handicapped in practice by handling the species erected by taxonomists. Guinochet (1973) and Heywood (1973) appear to consider that for general physiological work, conventional taxonomic species should be employed while recognising at the same time that within them ecological races, ecotypes and other kinds of differentiated local populations occur in particular ecological conditions. Further, taxonomic species are models which have been set up on the basis of field samples which are considered to represent populations. The use of special categories to accommodate particular kinds of variation as a substitute for the formal categories of taxonomy is of only limited practical value. The more specialised the category, the less general value it possesses.

Hanelt (1972), for example, rejected the use of very detailed morphological classification of infraspecific variation and of special categories. He proposes instead a system in which one or few subspecies together with a large number of geographical races are recognised which are not given formal Latin names.

Taxonomy and Biosystematics

Taxonomists arrive at divergent views on the relationships of species within a large genus. Some believe the genus to be largely consisting of unrelated species or a large number of polymorphic species. Others consider the species to be showing continuous or overlapping variations and thus the genus is taken to be composed of several sections or subsections, while still others take it to be a polyphyletic group. Disputes of this type are generally settled more or less satisfactorily with the help of cytogenetic or cytotaxonomic studies. During the past few decades biologists have been able to comprehend to an increasing extent some of the ways in which small-scale evolution of plants and animals takes place.

This rather new discipline, appears to be modifying the procedure in taxonomy, thus building the latter into a synthetic science. Biosystematics, in general, has been of tremendous help in (i) delimiting the natural biotic units and (ii) the application of formal nomenclature to these units conveying precise information regarding their defined limits, relationships, variability and dynamic structure (Camp and Gilly, 1943). Thus, biosystematics is essentially an expansion of classical taxonomy (Davis and Heywood, 1963). It still employs comparative morphology as a primary means of describing, delimiting and defining taxa. Other kinds of evidence is then incorporated. In the genus *Nicotiana,* for example, about 60 species have been studied in great details by Goodspeed (1945) and others who correlated the findings of distributional patterns and morphological differences with studies of chromosome counts and breeding behaviour. Similar studies have been made by Cleland on *Oenothera,* by Babcock and Jenkins on *Crepis,* by Manton on Cruciferae and various others.

Limitations and Future Scope of Biosystematics

By about 1970 it was increasingly felt by botanists in general that the biosystematic procedure, although highly satisfactory so far as the results are concerned, as compared to the orthodox taxonomy is *painfully slow* and *needs team work.* This limitation cannot be overcome. But the biosystematic investigation of a particular genus may be undertaken only subsequent to the floristic exploration of a given region. It is only after such a preliminary survey that the problematic genera could be taken up for detailed studies. In India, where the vast tracts of natural vegetation are still more or less unexplored or underexplored, biosystematic studies may prove to be greatly handicapped due to lack of basic data.

Secondly, *formal nomenclature* of most of the biosystematic categories is unattainable, if not impossible. Much criticism has been faced by the taxonomists from their fellow investigators in the field of ecology.

These two limitations ultimately lead to the third one, i.e. the construction of phylogenetic classification, which is one of the aims of taxonomy.

Further, at least up to the end of 1970, biosystematic studies have been applied to the categories mostly below the generic level. Infrageneric and infraspecific categories have been classified to a greater satisfaction than before. But very little attempts have been possible at the higher levels. It is only through recent symposia that there is an awakening for natural classification of higher categories. Recent books by Stebbins (1974), Beck (1976), Kubitzki (1977) and others and a large number of research papers indicate attempts towards detection of evolution above the generic level and construction of their natural classification.

Again, the reliability of cytogenetic or biochemical data largely depends on the formal identification of the material based on external morphology. Large number of examples have been cited, for example, by Raven and Kyhos (1965), where chromosome numbers have been published without proper identity of the plants involved. Same is the case in respect of other disciplines, which are supposed to strengthen taxonomy.

While discussing the present status of biosystematics, Bocher (1970) stated that "Biosystematics should not develop into a superior synthetic science, it should deliver material for modern taxonomic synthesis". At the same time he also thought that it should not act as a supporting branch of science but should keep its own face stamped by experimental work.

Wagner (1970) warned us against the evolutionary noise and stated that the populations of normal, diploid, sexual and outbreeding species are the main pillars of evolution. He further said that we can expect to find and study all sorts of deviations such as polyploidy, hybridization, apomixis, etc. but the most significant research should be focussed on normal divergent species.

Numerical Taxonomy

Organisms are classified on the evidence obtained from their characters, therefore, it becomes necessary to employ all the characters for the ideal or a natural classification. But since each individual may possess thousands of characters, it becomes impracticable to use all characters and as Mayr has remarked, the number is limited by the patience of the investigator. This naturally leads to the problem of selection of suitable characters.

Taxonomists such as Bentham and Hooker, Engler and Prantl, Tippo, Hutchinson and others have employed morphological and anatomic characters as their major source of evidence while more recent workers including Takhtajan, Cronquist, Thorne, Dahlgren and others have based their classifications on relatively large number of attributes. It is for this reason that most of these later classifications have gained a wider acceptance. They are more natural.

The use of as many characters as possible, or ideally, all the characters for classification was proposed by Adanson (1763), and such classifications are called *Adansonian classifications*. The two important postulates are: (i) in constructing the classification each attribute selected is of equal weight and (ii) taxa are based on correlations between these attributes.

The Adansonian principles have received great support since the 1960s and have developed new methods in taxonomy included under a general term *numerical taxonomy*. It involves the numerical evaluation of the affinity or similarity between taxonomic units and the ordering of these units into taxa on the basis of their affinities. This is essentially an extension of the Adansonian classification using mathematical procedure with the primary aims of repeatability and objectivity (Davis and Heywood, 1963). There are two aspects of such procedures—the construction of taxonomic groups and discrimination.

Construction of Taxonomic Groups

In the past, taxonomic groups were constructed using characters by some form of weighting—physiological importance of characters in the pre-Adansonian taxonomy and phylogenetic importance in the post-Darwinian period or intuitive correlation weighting. In angiosperms, due to the absence of reliable fossil evidence, phylogenetic weighting becomes largely negative. Phenetic classification, on the other hand, is based on overall affinity as judged by using as many characters or as much evidence as is available. In practice it employs correlation weighting by mechanical methods of comparison. Various techniques are involved and newer ones are being incorporated (Sokal and Sneath, 1963; Estabrook and Rogers, 1966; Rohlf, 1965; Rohlf and Sokal, 1965; Bonner, 1964; Crawford and Wishart, 1967 and many others). The successive steps recognised by Sneath (1962) are:

1. Operational Taxonomic Units (OTUs)

The fundamental unit that can logically be classified by numerical methods is the individual organism. But generally it is not possible to use numerous individuals of the same species of each of several taxonomic groups to compute a classification. Further, such a study would reveal resemblances at the intraspecific level and usually would not offer much scope for higher levels. It is, therefore, customary to employ species as a unit for this purpose. Since the taxonomic units employed in numerical methods are not always comparable to formal taxonomic units, they are termed as *operational taxonomic units* (OTUs).

If a numerical taxonomic study of higher categories is to be undertaken, a higher taxon which represents a cluster of various polymorphic taxa should be employed as the OTU. Another solution is to use only a single representative of the polymorphic group.

2. Unit Characters

A unit character has been defined as *a taxonomic character of two or more states, which within the study at hand cannot be subdivided logically, except for subdivision brought about by changes in the method of coding* (Sokal and Sneath, 1963). Further, only the phenotypic characters are used for this basic information. Thus, the presence or absence of an awn in a grass spikelet may be a unit character. The organisational level of unit characters may differ from character to character. But as a rule, each character state should contribute one new item of information.

The proper selection of characters is a critical point in the application of numerical taxonomy, as it is in other disciplines of taxonomy. Certain characters are clearly disqualified for numerical taxonomy and these are listed by Sokal and Sneath (1963) as *inadmissible characters.* According to these authors, it is undesirable to use: (i) attributes which are not a reflection of the genotypes of the organisms themselves; (ii) any property which is a logical consequence of another, either partly or wholly; and (iii) characters which do not vary within the entire sample of organisms.

A large number of characters, at least more than 50, must be selected. Several hundreds will be more significant but too few characters are not reliable. These characters have then to be coded or given some symbol or mark.

(a) *Two-state coding:* This is the simplest form of coding where characters are divided into + and − or as 1 and 0. The positive characters are recorded as + or as 1 and negative characters as − or as 0. In case the organ possessing a given character is missing in an organism, the character must be scored NC. In other words, the symbol NC means "no comparison".

In samples of plant specimens, for example, the petals may be present (+) in some, absent (−) in others, while the flower itself may be lacking (NC) in still others.

(b) *Multi-state coding:* The multi-state characters may be either quantitative or qualitative. Quantitative characters can each be expressed by a single numerical value, e.g. amount of pubescence on a leaf. Such characters can be coded into number of states (1, 2, 3 ...) corresponding to their range of variation. Qualitative multi-state characters cannot be arranged in some order, and no reliable sequence can be established. In such cases, qualitative characters are conveniently converted into some new characters. Many a times, it is convenient to convert multi-state characters into two-state characters. In *additive coding,* for example, multiple characters with four states could be coded as:

		Two state characters	
	1	2	3
Multiple states	0 −	−	−
	1 +	−	−
	2 +	+	−
	3 +	+	+

In this way, a multistate character of n states is turned into $n - 1$ two-state characters. The data obtained by scoring the characters in OTUs are then arranged in a table in a matrix form as above and compared.

3. Measurement of Resemblance

There have been three methods devised so far for estimating phenetic resemblance between the taxonomic groups, namely (i) coefficients of association; (ii) coefficients of correlation; and (iii) measures of taxonomic distance using the convention of multidimensional space with one dimension for each character.

A. Cluster Analysis

A taxonomic system can be constructed from the resemblances among the OTUs. To form taxa different OTUs are grouped together on the basis of affinities found by measurement of resemblances. These groups of OTUs are termed clusters.

Clustering is achieved in two ways: (i) by employing the attributes one at a time—monothetic systems, or (ii) according to all their attributes considered simultaneously. The monothetic method obviously leads to artificial clustering while the second method gives a natural grouping. One cluster or a group is separated from the other by the dividing line which indicates a distinct gap between the two. It is often easy to separate categories of higher rank, i.e. above the genus level, clearly. In case of intraspecific clusters, there are often few discontinuities.

There are several techniques to describe structure in matrices of similarity coefficients. One of the common techniques is the *differential shading of the similarity matrix.* In this method, similarity coefficients are grouped into five to ten evenly spaced classes. Each of these classes are represented by different degrees of shading in the squares of half matrix. The highest value is generally shown darkest and the lowest value lightest, as in Fig. 8.2a. Then the half matrix can be seen as a pattern to different shades, limited by a diagonal of squares with the darkest shade (Fig. 8.2b). Thus, on rearrangement of the sequence of OTUs, clusters can be more sharply defined, as in Fig. 8.2c.

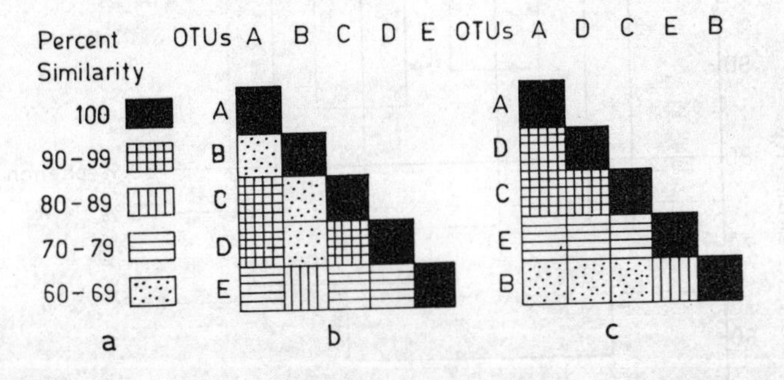

FIG. 8.2 Shaded similarity matrices: (a) percentage similarity, (b) with the OTU's arranged haphazardly, (c) after rearrangement of OTU's.

The groups of related OTUs based on high similarity coefficients can be analysed by a large number of numerical techniques such as *elementary cluster analysis, clustering by single, complete or average linkage, central or nodal clustering* and so on.

The groups of similar organisms recognised in this manner are termed *phenons.* The clusters of phenons are then rearranged in a dendrogram which summarises the main features of the cluster analysis.

5. Phenons and Rank

The groups or clusters established by numerical methods may be equivalent with those of classical taxonomic methods, i.e. usual rank categories such as genus, tribe or family. But these terms have evolutionary and nomenclatural background. If this is to be avoided, Sokal and Sneath (1962) have provided a new expression—*phenons.* Their level of affinity is indicated by prefacing them with a number. A group affiliated at 80 and above in the similarity scale may thus be termed 80-phenon. In Figs. 8.2b and c, clusters with different shade indicate 60 to 90 phenons. These terms are intended to cover the groups produced by any form of cluster analysis or from any form of similarity coefficients. Although phenons may be equivalent to various taxonomic groups, the term "phenon" is not synonymous with "taxon"

The delimitation of phenons is done by drawing a horizontal line across the dendrogram (Fig. 8.3) at a similarity value. A line at 75%, for example, creates five 75-phenons 1; 7; 3, 5, 6; 4, 9, 10; and 2, 8; while that at 80% creates six 80-phenons. Such a dendrogram will have a reference to a given taxon and cannot be transferred to any other study. In the above dendrogram, if OTUs 1 to 10 had been species, an 80-phenon line could indicate 6 subgenera and a 65-phenon line two genera. It should however be remembered that phenons are arbitrary and relative groups.

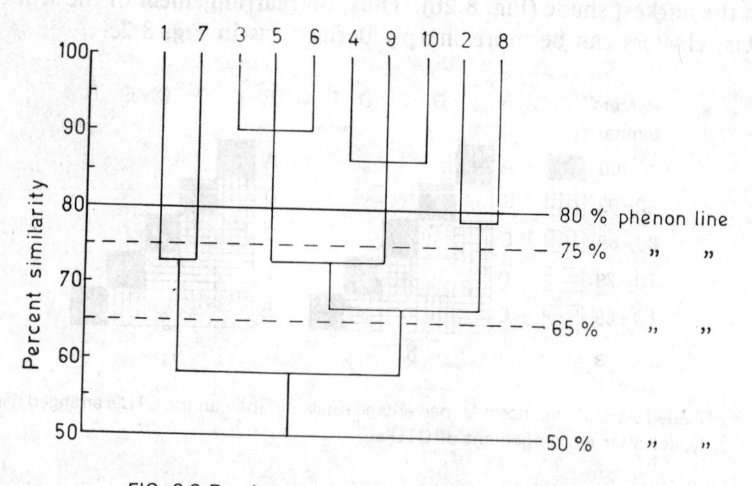

FIG. 8.3 Dendrogram to show formation of phenons.

Discrimination

If taxonomic groups chosen for the study show overlapping of characters, discrimination should be used to select them. Various techniques, such as discriminant analysis, have been devised for such purposes. The best methods for delimiting taxa are based on the utilisation of maximum number of characters with similar weightage given to them.

Nomenclature and Numerical Taxonomy

Modern nomenclature does not concern itself with the problems of delimitation of taxa. It serves only as a reference point to the taxonomic names. The limits are debatable, subjective and forever changeable. Numerical taxonomy, on the other hand, is very useful in delimitation of taxa by exact estimation of affinities (although phenetic). Thus, there is no scope for "personal opinion" or "decision of taxonomists". The limits may be objective, utilitarian, permanent and fixed by common consent.

Applications of Numerical Taxonomy

The taxonomists who are interested in the study of similarities and differences are now using numerical methods on an increasing scale. There has been considerable work on bacteria, other micro-organisms and several animal groups, using numerical methods. However, its application in plant taxonomy has not been comparable to that in other groups. From angiosperms, genera such as *Oryza* (Morishima and Oka, 1960), *Solanum* (Soria and Heiser, 1961), *Sarcostemma* (Johnson and Holm, 1968) and other groups including Farinosae of Engler (Hamann, 1961) and a few others have been tried by numerical taxonomy for their delimitation. The results, in general, have been in confirmity with the earlier works based on classical methods. It is only in certain taxa (Farinosae-Hamann, 1961) that the earlier assemblages have been shown to be unnatural. Numerical taxonomic studies on the genus *Ononis* (Papilionaceae) by Cook (1969) are in confirmation with the system proposed earlier by Sirjaev (1932).

In general, the results achieved so far by numerical taxonomy, have not been appreciably different from those achieved by other methods. It is probably because the methods employed need much improvement. A colloquium held at Andrew's University, Scotland in 1968 brought out several modifications in methods, and since then many have attempted to reclassify a number of plant taxa but without any appreciable deviation from the formal taxonomic classification.

Merits and Demerits of Application of Numerical Methods

According to Davis and Heywood (1963), it would be better to welcome these procedures with caution, since these methods are only an extension of the orthodox procedures. They have raised some doubts. First, the methods will clearly be useful in phenetic classifications, not phylogenetic. Similarly, the proponents of "biological" species concept, may not accept the specific limits bound by these methods. Even the practicing taxonomist might use his brain more efficiently than the machine which is fed with non-relevant selection of characters. Character selection is the weak link in this approach. The statistical methods are likely to give less satisfactory solution if characters chosen for comparison are inadequate.

Stearn (1968) indicated that different taxonometric procedures may yield different results. A major difficulty for the beginner is to choose a procedure for his purpose. Another difficulty concerns the number of characters (from 40–100) needed in order to obtain satisfactory results by these mechanical aids. Taxonomists usually manage with far less characters. Further, so far it has not been seen that the results achieved by mechanical means are in any way more acceptable than those visualised by practicing taxonomists. It is desirable to ascertain whether a large number of characters would really give satisfactory results than those using a smaller number. Stearn (1964), after applying taxonometric procedures to the Jamaican species of *Columnea* and *Alloplectus* (Gesneriaceae), came to realise that it seemed a pity not to make further use of these. This survey, as Stearn (1968) has concluded, demonstrated the capacity of computer-aided taxonometric methods to build from an assemblage of characters a grouping of species comparable in validity to one made by conscious taxonomic effort. It also indicated that the number of characters used is less important than their range.

Johnson and Holm (1968), after analysing their data on the genus *Sarcostemma* (Asclepiadaceae) by various taxonometric methods, have concluded that the numerical classification based on correlation coefficients bears closer resemblance to the classical taxonomic classification. However, they expressed their view that thorough analysis of character sets will lead to a better understanding of the process of evolution and the role of environment in determining patterns of variation.

Dale (1968), while presenting the basic procedures which underlie numerical taxonomic methods, concluded that any taxonomist proposing to use such methods must be careful in his choice and be wary of what may seem to be unimportant details.

Cullen (1968), while reviewing the botanical problems of numerical taxonomy, extended his welcome to the advance of numerical techniques which, according to him, may well provide means of checking and improving classifications by orthodox taxonomists. He has also realised that the numerical classifications are not likely to supplant orthodox ones—they may either confirm them or, if very different, exist side by side with them.

Clifford (1970) seems to have used numerical methods for a better classification of the grasses and concluded that there is a greater probability of their evolution from the palms. This conclusion was also drawn by Meeuse (1966) on the basis of the ovarian structure and origin. In both palms and grasses, the ovary has an ecarpellate origin, with greater reduction in the grasses than the palms. Corner (1966) also has indicated that the embryos of *Archantophoenix* possesses a coleorrhiza as in grasses, a feature otherwise unknown in palms.

9
Plant Nomenclature

Any object that becomes known to human intelligence must possess a name since it may not always be possible or convenient to describe it in order to communicate ideas about it. The art of naming objects is, in fact, a science of application of names—*nomenclature.* Just as all known objects are given names or should be given names, plants also are given names for two main purposes: (i) as an aid to communication and (ii) to indicate relationship.

Names of human beings are different from those of other objects, living or non-living, in the fact that they are *individual* names while other objects are known by their *collective* names for individuals of any one kind.

Common Names

Many plants, because they are useful in some way or other, have common names or *vernacular* names or *local* names. Widely distributed plants have a large number of common names. Pansy (*Viola tricolor* L.) for example, is grown in most of the European and American gardens and has about 50 common English names. In a multilingual country like India, almost all useful plants have local names which differ from language to language and even from dialect to dialect. Not only this, but in *Ayurveda,* the ancient Indian literature on medicinal plants, the mango *(Mangifera indica* L.) is known by over 50 different names, all in the Sanskrit language.

The common names obviously have a limited usage and for wider use throughout the country or the whole world, these have proved to be unsatisfactory. Since they are neither universal nor methodical, they may be misleading and inadequate.

Scientific Names

To overcome the difficulties raised by common names, botanists have given scientific names to all the known plants. These are methodical and thus provide means for international communication. It was agreed by botanists of the world that scientific names should be in Latin. There are various reasons for this. The most important fact is that this language is not being used by any country or nation at present. Secondly, at one time it was a widely used language throughout the European countries and a lot of botanical literature has been written in Latin. It is from Latin that most of the European languages have evolved. Although it is now a "dead language". There was obviously no proposal for Sanskrit to be used for naming plants although much more botanical literature is written in this language. However, since Europe, and particularly Greece, has dominated the whole world in the field of science during 1600 to 1850 A.D. Latin is now a language of botany and other allied sciences. It has been found to be suitable for descriptive phases of natural science. The script, however, is Roman.

Early Attempts

Latin names were mostly taken from common names for the sake of precision but they had to be supplemented by adjectives. A single name thus used to be followed by one to many descriptive terms or adjectives. This gave rise to multiple terms. Thus the *polynomials* were evolved. They have been used by many taxonomists including Linnaeus (1753). In his *Species Plantarum,* Linnaeus intended to use polynomials and it was only for the sake of convenience that he used additional *trivial* names for these polynomials.

Binomial Nomenclature

Linnaeus thus adopted his system of trivial names unintentionally. However, he did it with consistency and it was found very convenient for the later workers to adopt a generic name followed by a trivial name. Thus the system of polynomials was replaced by binomials consisting of a generic name and a specific epithet (a trivial name). Although many of the Linnean names were from earlier authors, for practical purposes, botanists regarded the date of publication of *Species Plantarum* (1753) as the beginning of the present system of scientific nomenclature of most groups of plants—mainly Angiosperms, Gymnosperms and Pteridophytes. In the binomial, the first name or the generic name is a substantive (noun) while the second term or specific epithet is an adjective or noun. Thus a botanical name of a species is a combination of a generic name and a specific epithet.

How Names are Formed

Botanical names, as indicated earlier, are formed by Latinisation of *common plant names,* such as *Nelumbo* from Ceylonese, *Gantelbua* from South Indian, *Ravenala* from Madagascan, *Tsuga* from Japanese and many others or from many other sources. Many genera have been named in commemoration of some person, usually a botanist or a patron of botany. These include ***Bauhinia, Caesalpinia, Dodonaea, Edgeworthia, Fuchsia, Gerardinia, Hookerea, Jacobinia,*** etc. As stated by Core (1955), a whole history of botany could be written by reference to such names.

Some of the names are formed by combination of two or more Greek or Latin words, usually expressive of some feature of the plant. They are, for example, *Polygala,* "more milk", *Hygrophila,* "marsh loving", *Acanthospermum,* "spiny fruit", *Goniocaulon,* "angled stem", *Asteracantha,* "spreading spine", and so on.

Many specific epithets are coined after the habitat in which the plant grows, e.g. *arvensis* (of cultivated fields), *aquatilis* or *aquatica* (in water), *vulgaris* (of barren lands), etc. Others are named on the basis of their structure or other peculiarities, such as *squamosa* ("tubercled" fruit), *cordifolia* (cordate leaved), *grandiflora* (large flowered), *hirta* (hairy), *purpureus* ("purple" flowered), etc. Many specific epithets indicate names of the locality or country, e.g. *indica* (India), *americana, mexicana, mysorensis, zeylanica* (Ceylon), *chinensis* and many others. Specific epithets are also formed from a noun with a suffix indicating resemblance or relationship, as *boerhavifolia* (leaves like *Boerhavia), panduraeformis* (like violin), *portulacastrum* (like *Portulaca),* etc. A very common type of specific epithet is the commemorative name, in the honour of some person. These include *roxburghii, hookeriana, buchanani, griffithii, wallichii, linnaei,* etc.

Botanical names have to be written in a specific manner as prescribed by the rules. All generic names, irrespective of the source of derivation, *must* begin with a capital letter while the specific epithet should invariably begin with a small letter and it should agree with the gender of the generic name.

In Latin, three genders, masculine, feminine and neuter, are recognised. The generic names may have any gender. The rules governing the gender of Latin nouns are too complex to be explained here but in many cases the gender is recognisable by the ending. Masculine gender, for example, is indicated by *albus, japonicus, niger, viridis, repens, chinensis, pubescens, bromoides, vulgaris,* etc.; feminine by *alba, japonica, nigra, viridis, repens, chinense, pubescens, bromoides, vulgaris,* etc., while neuter gender is indicated by *album, japonicum nigrum, viride, repens, chinensis, pubescens, bromoides, vulgare* and so on. Generic names ending in *-a* are usually feminine, those ending in *-um* are neuter and those ending in *-us* are usually masculine, except for the names of many trees, which are feminine *(Quercus, Fagus, Populus, Pyrus).*

Organised Nomenclature

Publication of Linnaeus's *Species Plantarum* provided two very important tools to the enthusiastic students of botany. These were: (i) a definite system of naming the plants and (ii) a very convenient classification that was useful for identification of plants. In Chapter 2 it has been already pointed out as to how this publication initiated the extensive exploration of plants throughout the world. Within a period of about 60 years, huge collections were made and efforts were being made to name and classify them. Naming of the plant genera was felt difficult even by Linnaeus himself and in order to standardise generic names he had to struggle hard (c.f. *Critica Botanica,* 1737a translated by Sir A. Hort in 1938).

Some names were confusing and were repeatedly being used for different groups of plants prior to Linnaeus, but de Tournefort successfully compiled his *Elements de Botanique* (1694), later translated into Latin as *Institutiones Rei Herbariae* (1700) in three volumes containing descriptions of over 600 genera. Linnaeus largely drew upon Tournefort in his *Genera Plantarum* (1737d). He pronounced various laws or aphorisms for this nomenclature, which were later developed into *Laws of Botanical Nomenclature* by Augustine P. de Candolle in his *Theorie Elementaire de la Botanique* (1813). Many botanists adopted these suggestions. E.G. Steudel published his *Nomenclator Botanicus* (1821) containing a list of Latin names of all plants then known.

However, in different countries, nomenclature followed different patterns. National and personal jealousies further complicated the situation and the need for an international accord became increasingly apparent. At last, Alphonse de Candolle called for an assembly of botanists to outline a new system of rules. This first International Botanical Congress was held in London in 1866. But nothing could be settled. It was then that Alphonse de Candolle was entrusted with the task of the preparation of a draft of the Laws of Nomenclature, which was accepted in the Congress held in Paris in 1867 and published in 1868.

These laws consist of only three chapters with a total of 68 articles. The most important Article No. 15 states the *Principle of Priority*. But there was much confusion due to ambiguity of date, and following this policy of priority, O. Kuntze, in his *Revisio Generum Plantarum* (1891) changed 1000 generic names and more than 30,000 species names.

Subsequent Development of the Laws

The International Code of Botanical Nomenclature

The rules as adopted at Vienna in 1905 and Brussels in 1910 are substantially the same as those adopted in Paris in 1868 but with several clear improvements. The prescriptions were divided into *principles, rules* and *recommendations*. The principles are the foundation of the rules and recommendations. The rules govern the names or forms of nomenclature, and anything contrary to a rule cannot be maintained. Recommendations bear on secondary points for greater uniformity and clearness in nomenclature, and may or may not be accepted.

In the United States, a group of botanists met at Rochester in 1892 and formulated a set of rules based on the modifications of the Paris Code. These rules, referred to as the Rochester Code, first time recommended that each new species published was to be based upon a designated herbarium specimen, to be known as the *type specimen* for the new binomial. The advocates of the Rochester Code attempted to have their principles included in the proposed revision at Vienna but failed to do so. The dissatisfied American adherents of the Rochester Code, refused to accept the Vienna Code and published the new American Code in 1907. This created two opposing schools of thought.

At Cambridge, the fifth International Botanical Congress was held in 1930, where determined efforts were made to harmonise the differences between the Vienna Code and the American Code. Subsequent congresses held in Amsterdam (1935), Stokholm (1950), Paris (1954), Montreal (1959), Edinburgh (1964), Utrecht (1969) and Leningrad (1975) went on improving the Code and the recent International Code of Botanical Nomenclature appeared in 1978. This includes the type-specimen method or better known as *type method* as a principle. Articles 7 to 10 give detailed prescriptions concerning types.

Type Method

Since it is one of the important principles of the Code, it is desirable to know the type method in greater detail.

Article 7 of the Code states that the application of the names of taxa of the rank of family or below is determined by means of *nomenclatural types*. A nomenclatural type (typus) is that constituent element of a taxon to which the name of the taxon is permanently attached, whether as a correct name or as a synonym.

In note 1 of the article it is clearly stated that this nomenclatural type is not necessarily the most typical or representative element of a taxon; it is merely that element with which the name is permanently associated. Notes 2 and 3 indicate various kinds of types. Accordingly, *holotype* is the one specimen or other element used by the author or designated by him as the nomenclatural type.

In the earlier days when the rules of nomenclature were not standardised or when the type method was not followed, the authors of new taxa did not designate types. In such cases, or when the holotype has been lost or destroyed, a *lectotype* or *neotype* may be designated as a substitute for it.

An *isotype* is any duplicate of the holotype; it is always a specimen. Plant specimens are generally collected in sufficient numbers (minimum 4 specimens) out of which when one is selected as a holotype others are considered as isotypes. But if the author has not designated a single holotype and has used all or more than one specimen, then these are called as *syntypes*.

A *lectotype,* as stated above, is a specimen or other element selected from the original material to serve as nomenclatural type when no holotype was designated at the time of publication or as long as it is missing.

A *neotype* is a specimen or other element selected to serve as nomenclatural type as long as all of the material on which the name of the taxon was based is missing.

Obviously, a lectotype or a neotype is designated by others and not by the author himself. It is therefore necessary to select them carefully. The Code specifies in note 3, that lectotype must be selected either from isotypes or syntypes if such exist. If neither is available, a neotype may be selected from any other suitable source.

Further, it is strictly recommended by the Code that the original material, especially the holotype, of a taxon be deposited in a permanent responsible institution and that it is scrupulously conserved. When a living material is designated as a type (for Bacteria and Fungi only) appropriate parts of it should be immediately preserved.

Article 9 states that the nomenclatural type of a species or taxon below the rank of a species is a single specimen. Article 10 states that the nomenclatural type of any taxon between genus and species is a species, that of a family or of any taxon between family and genus is the genus.

The principle of typification does not apply to names of taxa above the rank of family. In the literature one finds occasionally mention of *cotypes* (the term identical with isotype) and *topotypes* (specimens collected subsequently from the same locality as that of the holotype). These, however, are not accepted by the present code. An additional type, a *paratype*, is sometimes used, which is a specimen other than an isotype or a syntype cited by the author while describing a taxon. In most cases, where no holotype was designated, there will also be no paratypes, since all the cited specimens will be syntypes. However, in cases where an author has cited two or more specimens as types, the remaining cited specimens are paratypes and not syntypes.

The Code has provided a guide to the determination or selection of the nomenclatural types of previously published taxa.

Other Important Aspects of the Code

The present Code consists of 6 principles, 75 rules set out in the Articles, 57 recommendations and a number of notes and examples. It also includes Appendices I, II and III and a guide for the determination of types and citation of botanical literature. Appendix I gives rules regarding names of hybrids and some special categories. Appendix II gives the list of conserved names of families and Appendix III gives the list of conserved and rejected generic names. Some of the more important rules are discussed in the following paragraphs.

Principle I of the Code states that botanical nomenclature is independent of zoological nomenclature. The necessity of this principle was felt since the *Species Plantarum* (1753) includes not only names of plants but also those of animals. There is a separate Code for zoological nomenclature. Further, certain organisms, originally assigned to the animal kingdom, have been transferred to the plant kingdom and vice versa. In such cases, the Code applies equally to the names of taxonomic groups treated as plants whether or not these groups were originally assigned to the plant kingdom. Articles 45 and 65 of the Code make special provisions for such taxa. Article 45 accepts the original dates of publication of taxa transferred from animals to plants. *Amphiprora,* for example, was published as the name of a genus of animals in 1843, but was transferred to the plant kingdom in 1844. It has priority in botanical nomenclature from 1843, not 1844.

On the other hand, Article 65 states that if a taxon is transferred from the plant kingdom to the animal kingdom, its name retains its status in botanical nomenclature for purpose of homonymy. This name is not used again for any other taxon. Similarly, the name of a plant must not be rejected merely because it is the name of an animal.

Principle II states that the names of taxonomic groups are determined by means of nomenclatured types. Various types have been already discussed.

Principle III states that the nomenclature of a taxonomic g oup is based on priority of publication. Thus, this is also known as the *Principle of Priority*—

the most important principle which has served to provide a stable method of naming taxonomic groups. Article 11 of the code states that each family or taxon of lower rank with a particular circumscription, position and rank can bear only one correct name (some exceptions are made under Articles 18 and 59).

It has already been pointed out that the huge collection of plant specimens from practically all over the world had to be identified and named. This was done by many botanists, but quite independently. As a result, the plant species occurring widely in various countries, received different names at the hands of these botanists. The same species was named differently in different parts of the world. Indian Coral tree (*Erythrina variegata* L.) for example, has as many as about 200 scientific names (Krukoff, 1972). Many economically important grasses, ornamental plants and plants of medicinal importance have numerous names—most of which are confusing.

This situation has been greatly rectified by this principle. The priority of names, whenever they are detected to be given to the same taxon, is based on the dates of their publication. The name *Cassia surattensis* was given to a taxon by Burmann *(Flora Indica)* in 1768. The same taxon was named by Lamark as *Cassia glauca* in 1785. When the Principle of Priority is applied to this situation, Burmann's name gets priority. Similarly, the name *Lawsonia inermis* L. (1753) has priority over *L. alba* Lamk (1789); *Mollugo pentaphylla* L. (1753) has priority over *M. stricta* L. (1762); *Foeniculum vulgarie* Gaertn. (1768) has priority over *F. capillaceum* Gillb. (1781), and so on.

It gave opportunity to many taxonomists to unearth earlier or earliest names and use them instead of current names. It often created much confusion instead of bringing the names into order. The rule ultimately had to be modified. Now there is a *limitation* of Principle of Priority, and for Spermatophyta and Pteridophyta 1st May, 1753 is taken to be the beginning. It means that one can unearth the earliest name only as far back as 1753 while the names used prior to this date have to be disregarded. For other groups of plants various other dates are prescribed, e.g. for mosses it is 1st January, 1801, for hepatics and lichens it is 1st May, 1753, and so on.

Similarly, by adhering strictly to the Principle of Priority, several changes were brought about in the current names of the plants. In order to avoid disadvantageous changes in the nomenclature of genera, families and intermediate taxa, the code provides lists of names that are conserved *(nomina conservanda,* Appendices II and III). One such example is *Desmodium* Desv., a leguminous genus. This was erected in 1813. But plants of this genus were included under two other genera, namely *Meibomia* Heist ex Fab. (1759) and *Pleurolobus* J.St.Hil. (1812). All these three genera have the same circumscription. According to the Principle of Priority. *Meibomia* should have been accepted as a correct name but since *Desmodium* is better known and widely used, it has been conserved.

Names of Families, Subfamilies, Tribes and Subtribes

Article 18 of the Code states that the name of a family is a plural adjective used as a substantive; it is formed by adding the suffix-*aceae* to the stem of a legitimate name of an included genus. Examples are, Malvaceae (from *Malva),* Rosaceae (from *Rosa),* Annonaceae (from *Annona),* etc. The following names sanctioned by long usage, are treated as exceptions to the rule. If, however, botanists intend to follow Article 18 rather strictly, they are authorised to use alternative names.

Conserved names	*Alternative names*
1. Cruciferae	Brassicaceae, type *Brassica* L.
2. Guttiferae	Clusiaceae, type *Clusia* L.
3. Leguminosae	Fabaceae, type *Faba* Mill.
4. Umbelliferae	Apiaceae, type *Apium* L.
5. Compositae	Asteraceae, type *Aster* L.
6. Labiatae	Lamiaceae, type *Lamium* L.
7. Palmae	Arecaceae, type *Areca* L.
8. Gramineae	Poaceae, type *Poa* L.

When Papilionaceae is regarded as a distinct family from the remainder of Leguminosae, that name is conserved and the alternative name is Fabaceae.

Article 19 states that the name of subfamily is a plural adjective used as a substantive. It is formed by adding the suffix *-oideae* to the stem of a legitimate name of an included genus, e.g. Rosoideae (from *Rosa),* Faboideae (from *Faba),* Pooideae (from *Poa),* Panicoideae (from *Panicum).*

A tribe is designated in a similar manner with the ending *-eae* and a subtribe with the ending *-inae.* Examples of tribe are, Paniceae (from *Panicum),* Phyllantheae (from *Phyllanthus),* Asphodeleae (from *Asphodelus),* etc. Subtribes are Malvinae (from *Malva),* Rutinae (from *Ruta),* Helianthinae (from *Helianthus),* etc.

Principle IV states that each taxonomic group with a particular circumscription, position and rank can bear only one correct name, the earliest in accordance with the rules.

Articles 29-45 include the conditions for effective and valid publication. Some of the important conditions are:

1. Publication is effected only by distribution of printed matter to the botanical institutions, libraries, etc. Thus, publication in a local newspaper, handwritten manuscripts, cyclostyled matter, etc. are not effective.
2. It must be accompanied by a description of the taxon or by a reference to previously and effectively published description.
3. A new name published after 1st January, 1953 must have clear indication of the rank of the taxon concerned.
4. The name of the taxon must be accompanied by a Latin diagnosis or reference to a previously and effectively published Latin diagnosis.
5. Publication on or after 1st January, 1958 of a name of a new taxon of the rank of a family or below must indicate nomenclatural type.

Principle V states that the scientific names of taxonomic groups are treated as Latin regardless of their derivation, and *principle VI* states that the Rules of nomenclature are retroactive unless expressly limited.

Citation of Author's Names

Article 46 states that for the indication of the name of a taxon to be accurate and complete, and in order that the date may be readily verified, it is necessary to cite the name of the author who first validly published the name concerned. It is recommended that if the author's name, is too long, it should be abbreviated.

Examples: *Hibiscus* L., *Hibiscus panuraeformis* Burm. f.,
Indigofera glandulosa var. *sykesii* Baker

Article 49 states that when a genus or a taxon of a lower rank is altered in rank but retains its name or epithet, the author who first published this as a legitimate name or epithet must be cited in parentheses, followed by the name of the author who effected the alteration.

Example: *Citrus aurantium* var. *grandis* L., when raised to the rank of a species becomes *C. grandis* (L.) Osbeck. Here L. is the first author while Osbeck effected the alteration.

Similar rule applies when a sub-division of a genus (Art. 54) or a species (Art. 55) is transferred to another genus or placed under another generic name.

Example: ***Saponaria* sect. *Vaccaria* DC. when transferred to *Gypsophila*.** becomes *Gypsophila* sect. *Vaccaria* (DC.) Godr. Similarly, *Oxalis sensitiva* L. when transferred to *Biophytum* becomes *Biophytum sensitivum* (L.) DC. and *Limonia aurantifolia* Christm. when transferred to *Citrus* becomes *Citrus aurantifolia* (Christm.) Swingle. *Hedysarum velutinum Willd.* When transferred to *Desmodium* becomes *Desmodium velutinum* (Willd.) DC.

Similar rules apply when infraspecific transfers or changes of ranks are effected.

Examples: *Sesbania aegyptiaca* var. *picta* Prain when transferred to *Sesbania sesban* becomes var. *picta (Prain) Santapau. Alysicarpus nummularifolius* DC. when reduced to variety it becomes *Alysicarpus vaginalis* var. *nummularifolius* (DC.) Baker.

Rejection of Names

Articles 62 to 72 indicate rules for rejection of names. Broadly, the conditions may be stated as follows:

1. A name must not be rejected merely because it is inappropriate or disagreeable.
2. A superfluous name must be rejected. A superfluous name is that which is given to a taxon when already some name is existing. *Chrysophyllum sericeum* Salisb. (1796), for example, is superfluous because this taxon already has a name *C. cainito* L.
3. A name must be rejected if it is a later *homonym.* Homonym is the same name given to another taxon. *Astragalus rhizanthus* Boiss (1843) is a later homonym of *Astragalus rhizanthus* Royle (1835) and must be rejected. If a name becomes a homonym after the transfer it also should be rejected.
4. A name must be rejected if it is not in accordance with the rules of

nomenclature, particularly not abiding by Articles 22, 45, 51, 54, 57, 60 or 64.

5. A name must be rejected if it is used in different senses and has become a persistent source of error.
6. A name must be rejected if it is a *tautonym,* i.e. if the specific epithet repeats exactly the generic name.
7. A name must be rejected if it is based on a type consisting of two or more discordant elements or based on monstrosity.

Names of Hybrids

Hybrids or putative hybrids between two species of the same genus are written by a formula consisting of a multiplication sign. For example, a hybrid between *Salix aurita* and *S. caprea* is named as *S. aurita* × *caprea.* Such hybrids may be given altogether a new name when parents are not definitely known. Thus, *Musa* × *paradisiaca* L. indicates that this species has a hybrid origin.

Bigeneric hybrids are designated by a formula such as × *Asplenophyllitis* (since it is a hybrid between species of two genera *Asplenium* and *Phyllitis).*

10
Plant Identification

It has already been brought out in the introductory chapter that identification of plants is one of the important functions of taxonomy. It has also been pointed out that in most cases this activity is done by comparison with the predetermined material. This determination is followed by naming of the plants correctly. There are various other methods employed for identification, and their choice largely depends on the nature of problem being handled. Since the activity of plant identification and nomenclature is carried out with the help of herbaria, botanic gardens and/or taxonomic literature, information in respect of these is essential.

Herbaria

An herbarium is a place where plant material is preserved using various techniques and arranged in the sequence of an accepted classification. Mostly this preservation includes drying and pressing of the plant material. Certain plants, which are either succulent or otherwise unsuitable for pressing and drying technique, may be fixed in suitable liquid preservations such as formaldehyde (2-5%), acetic alcohol or FAA (5 : 5 : 90).

Herbarium techniques involve: (i) collection, (ii) drying, (iii) poisoning, (iv) mounting, (v) stitching, (vi) labelling and (vii) deposition. These will be discussed briefly in the following paragraphs.

Collection

Collection of plant material for the herbarium should be done using aesthetic sense and scientific mind. One who collects must know what is to be collected. Indiscriminate collection may often prove to be worthless.

Angiospermic material must be so chosen that it is perfect and complete for determination, i.e. it must have fully grown leaves, complete inflorescence, flowers and fruits as far as possible. In forests with deciduous elements this may not be possible and satisfactory material may be obtained by repeated visits to the locality. Size of the material depends upon the requirement and availability. The woody elements can well be represented by flowering twigs 30-40 cm in length while herbaceous forms may be suitably collected along with the underground parts. There is no fixed rule for the number of specimens required but normally 4 to 6 twigs or complete plants may be enough for routine collections. Tiny herbaceous plants may be collected in large numbers since many can be made into a single herbarium sheet.

Diseased plants, depauperate specimens, infected twigs, etc. should be avoided as far as practicable. All such collections should be given field numbers, roughly one field number per species with about 4-6 duplicates. Relevant information in respect of all those aspects needed for determination must be noted in a field note-book. This should include notes on habit, habitat, flower colour, locality, altitude and other interesting features which cannot be preserved on herbarium sheets. Santapau (1955a, 1955b) has discussed this subject in greater details, bringing out a manual for botanical collectors and specific instructions to collectors of the Botanical Survey of India at the time of the reorganisation of that institute.

Drying and Poisoning

The numbered collections should then be pressed in ordinary newspaper folders, taking care that all the leaves are well spread and that there is no overlapping. The folders are then pressed in a field press. In the beginning the pressure has to be gentle. After return to the laboratory, the folders need a frequent change in order to avoid blackening and decay of plant material. The specimens need poisoning to keep away insects and fungal pests. This is normally done when specimens are partially dehydrated, using chemicals such as corrosive sublimate ($HgCl_2$) or any other suitable poisons. The specimens are again dried and kept ready for mounting. Details regarding preservation and drying techniques can be found in numerous articles published from time to time. Some of the more important references include publications by Adriano & Youzon (1933), Allard (1951), Altschul (1977), Anderson (1941), Andrews (1932), Archer (1950, 1952), Beard (1968), Blake (1935), Botha and Coetzee (1976), Camp (1946), Dewolf (1968), Fogg (1940), Franks (1965), Gates (1950), Gould (1968), Guillarmod (1976), Harrington (1957), Kanai (1964, 1974), Knudsen (1972), MacMillan (1968), Porter (1967), Radford *et al.* (1974), Scully (1937), Sheikh (1971), Smith (1971), Steenis (1950), and Williams (1970) in addition to several articles published in *Kew Bulletin, Rhodora, Taxon* and journals on museum techniques. Hicks & Hicks (1978) have provided a selective yet comprehensive bibliography of plant collecting techniques, preservation methods, herbarium procedures and practices, administrative problems and the role of herbarium as a repository of preserved specimens.

Mounting, Stitching and Labelling

Dried specimens are glued and stitched on herbarium sheets made up of thick card sheets cut to the required size (international size being 42 × 29 cm). The field data is then entered on the right hand side lower corner of the herbarium sheet. This sheet is now ready for further scrutiny. When identified satisfactorily, it is placed in thin paper folders—*species covers*—which are kept together in thicker paper folders—*genus covers*—and finally incorporated into the herbarium cupboard in their proper sequence.

Herbarium specimens preserved in this manner can normally remain in good condition for any length of time. But very often, poisoning during the process of drying is insufficient to keep off small insects such as book-worms, silver fish, etc. It is, therefore, necessary to spray the specimens with repellents or disinfectants such as DDT powder, dalf or copper sulphate solution at intervals of 4 to 6 months.

Details of various other techniques and preservation method have been described by many authors and the contributors's list is on the increase. Particular reference may be made to Core (1955), Davis & Heywood (1963), Jain & Rao (1977), Knudsen (1966), Lawrence (1951) and Porter (1959).

Important Herbaria

Plant specimens collected over the years have been preserved with great care in herbaria throughout the world and are available for reference and study. The herbaria were established as early as the eighteenth century but gradually there have been great many improvement and modern herbaria are very much different from those of say, Linnaeus in Sweden in the eighteenth century or Roxburgh's in India in the early nineteenth century.

Now there are many herbaria located throughout the world that are of great value to botanists and other workers who need information regarding plants. A detailed index of the world herbaria has been compiled by Lanjouw & Staffleu (1952, 1964) wherein about 850 institutions including 50 major herbaria have been reported. Most of these have long names and for the sake of brevity and convenience their names have been abbreviated. Some of the more important herbaria are listed here. Figures on the right-hand side indicate the approximate number of specimens and letters indicate their standard abbreviation.

Royal Botanic Gardens, Kew (K)	over 6,000,000
British Museum of Natural History (BM)	6,000,000
Museum of Natural History, Paris (P)	6,000,000
V.L. Komarov Botanical Institute of Azerbaijan Academy of Sciences of Baku, USSR (BAK)	4,000,000
Conservatoire at Jardin Botaniques de Geneve (G)	5,000,000
Royal Botanic Garden, Edinburgh (E)	1,500,000
National Herbarium of Victoria, Melbourne, Australia (MEL)	1,500,000
US National Herbarium, Washington D.C. (US)	3,860,000
New York Botanical Garden (NY)	4,000,000
Herbarium of Missouri Botanical Garden, St. Louis (MO)	2,357,000
Gray Herbarium of Harvard University, Cambridge, Mass. (GH)	1,694,206
Central National Herbarium, Calcutta (CAL)	2,000,000
Herbarium of the Forest Research Institute, Dehradun (DD)	300,000

Madras Herbarium, Coimbatore (MH)	150,000
Herbarium of the National Botanical Research Institute Lucknow (LWG)	80,000
Herbarium of the Botanical Survey of India, Central Circle, Allahabad (BSA)	26,440
Regional Herbarium of the Botanical Survey of India, Shillong (ASSAM)	86,400
Dehradun (BSD)	42,000
Pune (BSI)	120,000
Industrial Section Botanical Survey of India, Indian Museum, Calcutta (BSIS)	40,000

Functions of a Herbarium

There are two *primary* functions served by a herbarium, namely, accurate identification and alpha taxonomic research, both monographic and floristic. There are *secondary* functions which include a closer *interaction* between the student of general systematics and the herbarium.

Davis & Heywood (1963) distinguished between different kinds of herbaria according to the purposes which they serve. The *major* herbaria or *national* institutes with large herbaria adequately cover the flora of the world. They serve the dual purpose of research and identification. Cronquist (1968b) while writing about the functions of national herbaria of the United States, grouped them under four headings, viz., (i) their own research programmes; (ii) service as repositories of type and other historical plant materials; (iii) the loan of specimens for study at other institutions; and (iv) the training of graduate students. Brenan (1968) has brought out the purpose and functions of the three great national herbaria in Britain. He further has remarked that there is a close co-operation between them and thus overlapping of work has been greatly avoided. According to Brenan, the national herbaria were brought into existence primarily to fulfil public needs, since they are supported by public funds. This service must take a high place among other functions. The public interests embrace a wide range of people and bodies such as private ordinary members, amateurs of botany, research institutes and government departments.

Combining the above statements we can enumerate the functions of national herbaria as follows:

1. To fulfil public needs by way of supplying materials and scientific information in respect of plants, by arranging training courses, exhibitions, etc. on plant science and by providing research facilities and job opportunities to young workers.
2. To carry out their own research programmes of fundamental as well as applied value.
3. To preserve national plant wealth including type material and palaeobotanical collections.
4. To facilitate exchange and loan of preserved plant material for various purposes including research in botany and other branches, exhibitions, etc.

The relevance of national herbaria in carrying out modern taxonomic research has been adequately emphasised by Cronquist and Brenan and need not be repeated here.

Most of the developed and developing countries have smaller herbaria built up by private or government agencies. These can be classified into three main categories: (i) regional herbaria; (ii) local herbaria including personal collections; and (iii) herbaria of the educational institutions such as the universities, colleges and schools.

Regional herbaria mainly cover the above mentioned functions on the regional level and in most cases they are supported by government aid. In India, the Botanical Survey of India has established seven such regional herbaria in addition to the national herbarium. Local herbaria serve the purpose of a small area like that of a district and mainly represent the flora of that area. Thus, collectively, they serve to provide data for distributional studies. University or college herbaria are primarily used for teaching and post-graduate research in taxonomy. They also can help in the dissemination of scientific information to the needy public. In India, only a few universities have maintained herbaria with proper care. In some instances, herbaria maintained by colleges and schools are much more satisfactory than those maintained by the universities. A mention may be made of Bangalore, Baroda, Calicut, Delhi, Marathwada, Mysore, Trivandrum, Utkal and a few other universities where herbaria of some kind have been maintained.

Botanical Gardens

The relevance of botanical gardens to the development of taxonomy need to be overemphasised. As far as the available and authentic records go, it is from the time of Theophrastus (about 300 to 200 B.C.) that the gardens have contributed to this science of Botany. In the post-Linnean period, the botanical exploration of the world was accelarated because of interest in the development of private and public gardens.

Long before the dawn of history, man had begun to grow plants in gardens which were then known to him as useful raw material. In the ancient Indian culture, the cultivation of food and medicinal plants is known since 4000 to 2000 B.C. In the ancient Mediterranean civilisation, gardens were prominent features of the grounds of temples and palaces. The "Hanging gardens" of Babylon are counted among the wonders of the ancient world. The Romans gathered plants from the conquered lands and grew them chiefly in Italy. Similarly, the Chinese, Aztecs and Persians were also fond of gardening and grew plants for ornamental purposes as well as for perfumes.

During the Middle Ages, from about A.D. 600–1600, there was a general lapse in learning and little attention was paid to the introduction of plants. But it was during this rather peaceful period that the people grew various kinds of vegetables in their kitchen gardens. It was in the seventeenth century that there was a great awakening in respect of the science of healing. Garcia d'Orta's book on Indian medicinal plants appeared in 1565 and was translated into Latin. This attracted numerous visitors from Europe to India, and cultivation of medicinal plants was taken up in various countries. In the sixteenth century, herbalists acquainted the world with numerous plants, many of which were then grown in the gardens. The interest in learning lead to the establishment of the great universities and their botanical gardens. The number increased rapidly and by the eighteenth century most of the famous gardens known today had been established. Exhaustive accounts of botanical gardens of the world may be found in literature, e.g. Hyams & MacQuitty (1969), Holttum (1970). There are about 525 botanical gardens in various countries. Some of the more important ones have been listed in the following paragraphs.

Botanical Gardens of Europe

Padua Gardens, Italy

Orto Botanico of Padua is said to be the first of these gardens, started by the University of Padua. It was officially established as a botanical garden in 1545 primarily to meet needs of illustrative lectures in medicinal plants. Occupying an area of about 20,000 m², it is beautifully designed with squares, rectangulars and circles and is decorated with various grasses, alliums, irids, Paeonias, number of succulents, hydrophytes, etc. together with the busts of great botanists. This garden has played an important role in the introduction of large number of plants in Europe in the past.

Pisa, Italy

Almost as old (or probably older) as Padua is the botanical garden at Pisa, located on Via Luca Ghini. Luca Ghini (1543) was the first director and Andrea Caesalpino was the second (1554-1558). This garden was the first to introduce palaeontological practises for the study of plant fossils. Morison, John Ray, and Tournefort based their studies on the contributions of Andrea Caesalpino. Georgio Santi also published the flora of Tuscan for the first time (1782-1814).

The garden is known for various important trees such as *Magnolia grandiflora, Liriodendron tulipifera, Aesculus* sp., etc. which grow well here.

Palermo, Italy

Of the various Italian gardens which propagated the science of botany in the European countries, the Palermo Botanical Garden is probably the most famous. It is well known for specimens of *Dracaena draco,* xerophytic plants, fibre and fruit plants and medicinal plants.

Villa Taranto, Italy

This is the most beautiful garden of Italy having a large number of exotics and their display. It is of great importance from the horticultural point of view. The garden was a private property of Captain Neil McEacharn, who in 1910, gave it for a school of horticulture. It is now taken over by an institution and maintains a large collection of ornamental trees and shrubs.

Leiden, the Netherlands

The botanical garden of the University of Leiden, known as Hortus Botanicus Academicus Lugduno-Batavus, was established in 1587. Clusius is said to have been the first to do planting in this garden which by 1594 contained over 1000 species and varieties. The first greenhouse was probably established here in 1599 for the protection of some plants introduced from the Cape of Good Hope such as geraniums, mesembryanthemums, etc.

This important Dutch garden has offered scientific service for a long span of over four centuries. Many East Indian plants were introduced in this garden some time in the seventeenth century. Several famous botanists had an opportunity to work and enrich this garden, and today it enjoys the most important position among the gardens of the world.

Jardin de Jussieu, France

This is one of the earliest botanical gardens in France and was founded in 1593 under the University of Montpellier. It was then utilised for the study of medicinal plants. It was opened to the public in 1640 as the Jardin du Roy. Tournefort and Jussieu were connected with this garden.

Oxford University Botanic Garden, Great Britain

The first in Great Britain, this garden was established by the Earl of Dandy in 1621. Linnaeus demonstrated sexuality in plants for the first time in this garden. It has a rare collection of literature and monetory donations from all over the world.

Royal Botanical Garden, Edinburgh, Scotland

This garden was founded in 1670, the second oldest garden in Great Britain. James Sutherland was the first keeper. It is known for its beauty and is world famous for its rhododendrons and azaleas. Other interesting features include a demonstration garden, a glasshouse, an herbarium and a library. The rock garden is considered to be the finest in the world and is remarkable for its Himalayan alpine plants. In addition, it has a rich collection of interesting plants from all over the tropical countries.

The botanical garden at Cambridge University was established in 1762 and is also an important garden of Great Britain.

Several other great gardens were also founded in the seventeenth century. In Berlin, the Botanischer Garten, one of the world's greatest gardens was established in 1646. Among its famous directors have been J.G. Gleditsch, K.L. Willdenow, A.W. Eichler, Adolf Engler and L. Diels.

O.J. Rudbeck founded a botanical garden in Uppsala in 1655. Linnaeus was one of his earlier students and succeeded him as a director in 1742. C.P. Thunberg, a student of Linnaeus succeeded his teacher in 1784. The original garden is now maintained as a memorial of Linnaeus, with a principal university garden on a different site.

Early in the eighteenth century, two great gardens were founded in Russia, that of the University of Moscow in 1707 and the Druggist's Garden of Leningrad in 1713. Dr. Friedrich E.L. von Fischer was the first director of the latter. It is now known as the V.L. Komaróv Botanical Institute of the Academy of Sciences of the USSR. Its herbarium with over 4,000,000 specimens, is regarded as one of the largest in the world. This garden has contributed to the publication of the vast flora of the USSR.

Jardin Botanico de Madrid

This was founded in 1755. One of the famous directors was Antonio J. Cavanilles, noted for his "Icones" of American plants (1794). The *Hortus Botanicus* of the University of Budapest was founded in 1771.

Botanical Gardens of India

The Indian Botanical Garden, Calcutta, India

It is one of the greatest botanical gardens of the world and one of the first to be established in the tropics. It was founded at Calcutta in 1787 by Lt. Col. Robert Kyd not for the purpose of collecting rare plants but for establishing a stock for disseminating such articles as may prove beneficial to the inhabitants. The garden covers an area of about 273 acres of land and contains representative collections of the world's tropical plants.

William Roxburgh, who is considered as the "Father of Indian Botany" succeeded Robert Kyd in 1793 and held the post up to 1813. This garden was headed by many eminent botanists as directors including N. Wallich, W. Griffith, Voigt, T. Anderson, George King, David Prain, Gage, D. Chatterjee and others.

The garden, with its herbarium (the Central National Herbarium) is second to none in the East and has played a significant role in the floristics and botany of India since its inception. It continues to serve as a centre of intense taxonomic activity.

The garden and herbarium were handed over to the government of West Bengal after independence in 1947. Now it is under the control of the Botanical Survey of India. On account of the rich collection in the herbarium, including the type material of over 1000 Indian species of flowering plants, it forms the most valuable nucleus of specimens and deserves every attention from Indian botanists.

It has several interesting features including the great Banyan tree, *Ficus benghalensis,* about two centuries old and covering a large area with its pillar-like aerial roots. The palm houses, nurseries, various interesting shrubs and trees, the amazon lily *Victoria amazonica* (Nymphaeaceae) etc. add to the importance and beauty of the garden.

Other Botanical Gardens

During the nineteenth century many other great gardens were founded which continue to contribute to plant taxonomy. Some of the more famous gardens are: the Jardin Botanico do Rio de Janeiro, Brazil (1808), Universitets Botaniske Have at Oslo, Norway (1814), Conservatoire et Jardin Botaniques de Geneva (1817), Buitenzorg (Bogor) in Java (1817). The well known Royal Botanical Garden at Kew was officially opened in 1841. It is one of the chief attractions of the world. Originally, the Kew gardens belonged to Kew House, owned by Richard Bennett and was founded as early as 1759 when William Aiton took over as its Superintendent. It became the "botanical capital of the world" in the nineteenth century. Under the directorship of Sir William Jackson Hooker in 1841, there were many developments and the construction of a palm house, establishment of the herbarium which was greatly enriched by Sir J.D. Hooker with collections from India, cultivation of Rhododendrons which added excellence to the garden, publication of the *Flora of British India, Botanical Magazine, Icones Plantarum, Kew Bulletin* and the voluminous *Index Kewensis*. The famous Alpine house, rose garden, bamboo garden and a lily pond were also developed during this period. The succession of able directors including David Prain, Sir A.W. Hill, W.B. Turrill, M.W. Taylor, Heslop-Harisson, J.P.M. Brenan continued to maintain and enhance the importance of the garden. With the establishment of the Jodrell Laboratory a new era of experimental taxonomy was opened with special attention to anatomy, cytology and physiology sections. This laboratory has provided monumental publications in their fields of specialisation to the entire world.

The Cape Town Botanical Garden (1848), the Government Botanic Gardens, Jamaica (1857), the Singapore Botanic Garden (1859), the Missouri Botanical Garden, St. Louis (1859), the Universitets Botaniske, Copenhagen (1871), the Arnold Arboratum, Harvard University (1872), the New York Botanical Garden, one of the greatest in the United States (1891), etc. are some more important great gardens of the world.

Some of the later tropical gardens include the Sinhalese Botanical Garden, Peradeniya in Sri Lanka (1821), the Lloyd Botanical Garden, Darjeeling in the Himalayas; the National Botanical Garden, Lucknow; the Sahranpur Botanical Garden; the Tamil Nadu Government Botanical Garden, Ootacamand; Lalbag Gardens, Bangalore and many others.

Role of Botanical Gardens

Botanical gardens remain important for their records of local flora and as basis for continued monographic work. According to Holttum (1970), this work is far from complete in the equatorial tropics and it is an essential basis for all other studies of plants. The gardens also provide facilities for collection of living plant material for biosystematic studies.

Many of these gardens supply seeds and material for botanical investigation. Those supplying seeds have been listed by Heywood (1964), and many others have been added to the list since then. Most of the great botanical gardens are far more than merely gardens. They are usually botanical institutes in which, in addition to the outdoor garden, there are greenhouses, herbaria, library and research laboratory. The *International Association of Botanic Gardens* was established in 1962. Its members meet once a year in order to discuss various activities of the association. The 10th International Botanical Congress held in Edinburgh in 1964 recommended expansion of the activities such as supply of material and information for research in all botanical disciplines. It was also recommended to develop documented collections of authenticated taxa in botanic gardens throughout the world. At present there are over 125 botanic gardens with such documented collections. This association has published the *International Directory of Botanic Gardens* (1963).

Taxonomic Literature

There is a vast literature on this subject of botany and it would require several volumes to review the same. It is not the purpose of this chapter to enumerate all books, floras, magazines, etc. dealing with plant taxonomy but an attempt will be made to bring out some important aspects of taxonomic literature mainly being used for determination of various plant taxa and their natural classification.

It must be noted at this juncture that there have been sincere efforts in compiling information on plant wealth throughout the world including all the developing countries. But unfortunately, this country is lagging far behind. It is sad to note that even after 37 years of independence, the botanists have no other authentic literature on plants of India except the monumental work by Sir J.D. Hooker compiled during the last century. It is still more sad to know that the Indian taxonomists have to depend upon the opinion of the Westerners for confirmation of their plant identification. The picture, however, is gradually changing but at a very slow rate. It is for this reason that a greater cognizance has to be taken of the taxonomic literature compiled in Europe and North America. The following list includes a few important works under relevant headings. The literature already included in the earlier chapters is not repeated here.

General Indexes

These are the volumes compiled and continuously being compiled in respect of names of flowering plants published throughout the world.

Index Kewensis Plantarum Phanerogamarum 2 vols., 15 suppl., Oxford, 1893-1970. This is the most comprehensive index of the scientific names of seed plants and is essential to any study of the taxonomy of flowering plants. The original work, compiled under the direction of J.D. Hooker and B.D. Jackson in 1893-1895, consists of an alphabetical list of genera published from the time of Linnaeus down to 1885. Under each generic name is given, in alphabetic order, every specific epithet known to have been published, followed by the name of the publishing author, the place of publication and the native country of the plant. It includes over 375,000 entries. This work, thus, becomes an indispensable reference for all flowering plant taxonomists.

Gray Herbarium Card Index, Cambridge, Mass. This covers the flowering plants and ferns of the western hemisphere published since 1873 and numbering approximately 260,000 cards.

Genera Siphonogamarum, Berlin, 1907. A list of orders, families and genera of seed plants has been compiled by Dalla Torre and H. Harms and is arranged according to the Engler-Prantl system.

Index Londinensis to illustrations of flowering plants, ferns and fern allies, Oxford, 1920-1941. This is an alphabetical index to illustrations appearing from 1753 to 1935.

Floras, Manuals, etc.

A flora is a systematic enumeration of plant species occurring in a given region and ideally provides keys, descriptions and often illustrations. This helps in the determination of plant species described in the flora. A flora may cover any suitable area from a small patch of forest to a *Taluka,* city, district, state, country or even a continent.

Manuals differ from floras in certain minor aspects. They do not necessarily indicate place of deposition of plant specimens included. The main emphasis is placed on providing suitable keys and diagnostic descriptions.

In spite of the finer differences, the two words Flora and Manual, are used synonymously. Many a times, keys are provided either for the families or genera of plants occurring in a given area. These help only initial identification up to the level indicated therein and further confirmation has to be done by reference to other relevant literature. Some of the more important floras and manuals compiled for vast regions are listed here. A comprehensive account of them may be found in Blake (1961), Blake & Atwood (1942), Core (1955), Davis & Heywood (1963), Frodin (1964), Lawrence (1951), Reed (1969) and volumes of *Taxon.*

Africa

Various parts of Africa have been explored by the European botanists. Some of them have compiled floras, the more important of which include the following: D. Oliver *et al.* (1868-1937), ***Flora of Tropical Africa;*** Hutchinson & Dalziel (1927-1929), ***Flora of West Tropical Africa***; Adamson & Salter (1950), ***Flora of the Cape Peninsula;*** Humbert (1964), ***Flora of Madagascar;*** Milne-Redhead & Polhill (1966), ***Flora of Tropical East Africa;*** Merxmueller (1966-), ***Prodrumus einer Flora van Sudwestafrika,*** etc.

North America

Most of the United States have their regional floras or manuals. One of the earliest and most renowned manuals of American Botany was written by Asa Gray (1885) and it forms the basis of all the subsequent contributions. The first flora of North America appeared in 1905—Britton *et al.* (1905), *North American Flora*—but has remained incomplete up-to-date. Other floras include, Britton and Brown (1896-1898), *Illustrated Flora of North America;* Britton (1909), *Manual of the Flora of the Northern States and Canada;* J.K. Small (1933), *Manual of the Southeastern Flora;* Jepson (1909-1943), *A Flora of California,* etc. Some of the later floras include, Rydberg (1932), *Flora of Prairies and Plains* and (1922), *Flora of Rocky Mountains,* etc.

South America

There have been consistent efforts by taxonomists to bring out information on plant life of South American states, mainly because of its predominant tropical climate. Floristic studies on tropical America have particularly attracted attention of North American institutes. H. Ruiz and J. Pavon were probably the first taxonomists to publish *Florae Peruviana et Chilensis* (1798–1802). Subsequently, many other floras have appeared. Some of them include, Bonpland (1805-1818), *Plantae Aequinoctiales;* Martius (1829-1906), *Flora Brasiliensis*—one of the most sumptuous floras containing more than 20,000 pages, 3805 plates and account for 22,767 species. Other floras are, Alain (1946, 1951, 1953), *Flora de Cuba*' Conzattis (1939, 1943-1947), *Flora Taxonomica Mexicana*; Standley (1930), *Flora of Yuctan*; (1937-1938), *Flora of Costa Rica;* (1949), *Flora of Panama*; MacBride (1936-1949), *Flora of Peru*; Pulle (1932-1940), *Flora of Surinam*; Reiche (1896-1911), *Flora of Chile* and many others.

Asia

One of the largest continents and probably the richest in the world so far as plant wealth is concerned, unfortunately remained unexplored until about the seventeenth century. A few scattered publications, however, are on record from ancient Indian and Chinese literature. It would be proper to consider floristic work of this vast continent country-wise.

India: As early as 1565, Garcia d'Orta published the first account of Indian plants in the Portuguese language which was later translated in Latin by Clusius. The work entitled *Coloquios dos Simples e Drogas da India* became the basis of attraction of the European botanists to India. Subsequently, Hendrick von Rheede's (1670-1703), *Hortus Indicus Malabaricus;* Burmann's (1768), *Flora Indica*; Roxburgh's (1795, 1798, 1819), *The Plants of Coast of Coromandel* and (1820-1824), *Flora Indica* appeared. Several other explorers including Wallich (1830-1832), *Plantes Asiaticae Rariores*; Robert Wight (1838-1853), *Icones Plantarum Indiae Orientalis* and a few others also contributed to Indian botany. The most comprehensive flora ever written is that of Sir J.D. Hooker (1872-1897), *The Flora of British India* in seven volumes. Hooker's flora has provided the basis for the subsequent regional and district floras of this country. The Botanical Survey of India has recently taken up the publication of *Flora of India*.

Southeast Asia: G.E. Rumphius's (1741-1755), ***Herbarium Amboinense*** (published by Burmann much after the death of Rumphius in 1702) and Juan de Loureiro's (1790), *Flora Cochinchinensis* are probably the first comprehensive floras of Southeast Asia. K.L. Blume (1825-1826), ***Bijdragen tot de Flora van Nedelandsch Indiae*** appeared little later.

The Philippines: M. Blanco's (1837) *Flora de Filipinas,* was the first flora to appear from this country, and was subsequently revised. E.D. Merrill (1920-1925) published *Enumeration of Philippine Plants* and (1946) *Plant life of the Pacific World.*

All these contributions and intensive fresh collections are the basis of the recent voluminous work, *Flora Malesiana*. C.G.G.J. van Steenis is the general editor for flowering plants, i.e. Series I. The first volume of this flora appeared in 1948 and 8 volumes have been published up-to-date. Seven more volumes are scheduled to come. Backer and Bakhuizen's (1963-1967), *Flora of Java,* published in three volumes is another important flora of this region.

The floras of other parts of Asia are also written, e.g. Hara *et al.* (1966), *The Flora of Eastern Himalaya;* Guest (1966), *Flora of Iraq;* Zohari & Feinbrun-Dothan (1966-), *Flora Palestina;* Rechinger (1964-1970), *Flora Iranica* and others are either compiled or being compiled.

Australia

This continent together with New Zealand has been well studied botanically and has quite a few floras. Bentham's (1866), *Flora Australiensis* is one of the oldest flora. Subsequently, L.M. Bailey's (1899-1902), ***The Queensland Flora*** and Cheesman's (1906), ***Manual of the New Zealand Flora*** have appeared. More recent floras include, Black (1922-1929), ***Flora of South Australia***; Ewarl (1930), ***Flora of Victoria***; Moore (1961, 1970), ***Flora of New Zealand***; various authors (1966), ***Flora of New South Wales,*** etc.

Europe

This is probably the best known of all the continents botanically and has the largest number of floras. Some of the earlier floras are, Sibthorp & Smith (1801-1840), *Flora Graeca*; Willkomm & Lange (1861-1880), *Prodrumus Florae Hispanicae*; Halacsy (1901-1904), ***Conspectus Florae Graecae***; H. Coste (1900-1906), ***Flore descriptive et illustree de la France***; and Coutinho (1913), ***Flora de Portugal.*** More recent floras include, Clapham, Tutin & Warburg (1952, 1962), ***Flora of the British Isles;*** Komarov (1934-), ***Flora of the USSR;***

Tutin (1964-1976), *Flora Europea*; various authors (1965), *Flora of Leningrad Province*; Futak (1966-), *Flora Slovenska* and Soo & Karpati (1968), *Flora of Hungary*.

Monographs and Revisions

Monograph of a taxon such as a family or genus is a detailed treatment including all significant information of a morphologic or taxonomic nature concerning the taxon. Strictly speaking, it should cover the taxon as it exists throughout the world. However, the term is rather loosely used covering the treatments restricted to a continent or smaller area. Such treatments are better termed *revisions*. A revision may be based only on herbarium studies whereas a monograph should ideally cover the cytology, morphology, anatomy, genetics, chemistry, palaeobotany, geography and ecology of the group together with taxonomy. In other words, it should be based on biosystematic studies. Considering the vast disciplines that are to be undertaken, it can be realised that work of such a scope needs several years of patient study. This is the main reason why there are relatively few monographs on record up-to-date while revisions are numbered by thousands. Some of the well known monographs have been mentioned under 'Biosystematics' in Chapter 8.

Dictionaries, Pictorial Encyclopaedias, Cultivated Plant Manuals, Keys

Dictionaries and glossaries are invaluable in the subject matter. A glossary is an alphabetical list of difficult terms with their explanations. A botanical dictionary may include lists and descriptions of all known genera of certain plant groups. Some of the well-known glossaries and dictionaries are, Jackson's (1928), *A Glossary of Botanic Terms;* Kelsey & Dayton's (1942), *Standardized Plant Names*; Browns's (1954), *Composition of Scientific Words;* Schwarten & Rickett's (1958-1961), Abbreviation of Periodicals; Willis's (1966), *A Dictionary of Flowering Plants and Ferns;* Uphof's (1968), *Dictionary of Economic Plants;* Stearn's (1966), *Botanical Latin;* Watt's (1889-1896), *Dictionary of Economic Products of India,* etc.

Pictorial encyclopaedias and manuals provide all the available information on cultivated plants throughout the world. More famous among them are, Bailey's (1914-1917), *Standard Cyclopaedia of Horticulture*; Graf's (1961), *Exotica;* Bailey's (1949), *Manual of Cultivated Plants;* Bor's (1953), *Manual of Indian Forest Botany*; Brandis's (1906), *Indian Trees*; Britton's (1908), *North American Trees*; Coven's (1950), *Flowering Trees and Shrubs of India,* and various others.

Keys are provided in most of the manuals and floras in addition to the description but these are not being considered here. Keys prepared for the general purpose of identification of plant families are widely used, particularly in determining plants from rich botanical provinces. These include, J. Hutchinson's (1967), *Key to the Families of Flowering Plants of the World,* Davis & Cullen's (1965), *The Identification of Flowering Plant Families,* Hansen & Rahn's (1969),

Determination of Angiosperm Families by Means of a Punch-card System, Simpson & Janos's (1974), *A Punch-card Key to the Families of Dicotyledons*, etc., Saldanha & Rao's (1975), *Punched Card Key to the Dicot Families of South India*, Naik's (1977b), *Key to the Angiospermic Families and Certain Genera of Marathwada*, and Geesink *et al.* (1981), *Thonner's Analytical Key to the Families of Flowering Plants*.

Periodicals

Various herbaria and botanical societies throughout the world publish results of their taxonomic studies in periodicals. These being the authentic and learned treatises on concerned plant taxa, are greatly useful in taxonomic research. Some of the more important ones are:

Acta Phytotaxonomica et Geobotanica, USA
Adansonia, France
American Journal of Botany, USA
American Naturalist, USA
American Midland Naturalist, USA
Annals of the Missouri Botanical Garden, USA
Annals of Royal Botanical Gardens Calcutta, India
Australian Journal of Botany, Australia
Botanical Gazette, USA
Botanical Journal of the Linnean Society, England
Botanical Review, USA
Brittonia, USA
Blumea, the Netherlands
Bulletin of Botanical Survey of India
Bulletin of Torrey Botanical Club, USA
Botaniska Notiser, Sweden
Canadian Journal of Botany, Canada
Journal of Arnold Arboratum, USA
Journal of Indian Botanical Society, India
Journal of Japanese Botany, Japan
Journal of South African Botany, S. Africa
Kew Bulletin, England
Lloydia, USA
Notes from the Royal Botanic Garden Edinburgh, Scotland
Phytologia, USA
Reinwardtia, Indonesia
Sunyatsenia, China
Taxon, the Netherlands

Exhaustive lists of various periodicals have been provided by Lawrence (1951), Merrill & Walker (1938), Rehder (1911-1918), *Union List of Serials, A World List of Scientific Periodicals* and various issues of *Taxon*.

It has been rightly stated by Lawrence (1951) that the subject of taxonomy demands an almost encyclopaedic knowledge of the world's pertinent literature. Taxonomists must know the important sources of taxonomic literature. In India, all students of plant taxonomy must have a close co-operation of various botanical institutes including the Botanical Survey of India, Calcutta; the National Botanical Research Institute, Lucknow; the Forest Research Institute,

Dehradun; the Central Arid Zone Research Institute, Jodhpur and a few universities carrying out researches in plant taxonomy. They must also be in constant communication with famous herbaria and botanical institutes from all over the world.

Preparation and Use of Keys

A large collection meant for deposition in the herbarium needs indentification and proper labelling. Initial identification has to be at the family level and subsequently into genera, species, varieties and so on. As stated earlier, in most cases this is done by comparison with the predetermined material but specimens from newly explored areas need careful observation. Usually, identification of such material is done with the help of keys provided in the floras and manuals. There are a few keys prepared specially for this purpose (Hutchinson, 1967; Davis & Cullen, 1965; Saldanha & Rao, 1974; Naik 1977b, etc.) These are prepared in such a way that any one possessing working knowledge of morphological terms can be able to use them profitably.

According to Davis & Heywood (1963), the first aim of the key is to provide ease and certainty of identification. Obviously, it is often difficult to arrange taxa according to their natural relationship, and for the sake of convenience, it is many a times profitable to employ artificial separation of groups using one or two easily observable characters.

Keys are of two types: *punched cards* keys and *dichotomous* keys. The former can be tackled by school or college students who find it a most interesting exercise in taxonomic practice. The latter can be found in most of the floras and are of two types: *indented* and *bracketed.*

Punched cards keys consist of cards of suitable size with names of all the taxa (all families, genera or species for which the key is meant) printed on each one of them. Each card also has a number and any one character printed near one of the corners. All the taxa showing this character are indicated by a perforation in front of their names, while those lacking this character are without any perforation (see Fig. 10.1 for explanation). There are as many cards as there are characters chosen for the purpose. With a plant specimen to be identified in hand, only those cards showing characters possessed by the specimen, are selected. Character combination exhibited by the specimen will allow only one perforation through in the set of cards selected. The specimen is then referred to that family to which the card indicates this perforation.

Dichotomous keys consist of pairs of contrasting characters (couplets) each statement of which is a lead. The leads are numbered and both begin with the same word as far as possible. The characters to be used for this purpose should be easily observable, constant and thus dependable. Quantitative characters should usually be preferred to qualitative ones. In closely related taxa with overlapping characters, it is profitable to employ more than one contrasting character so that the combination of characters is taken to decide the similarity or difference between the taxa. The following examples are adopted from the author's publications (Naik, 1977b, 1979) to exemplify bracketed and indented key respectively.

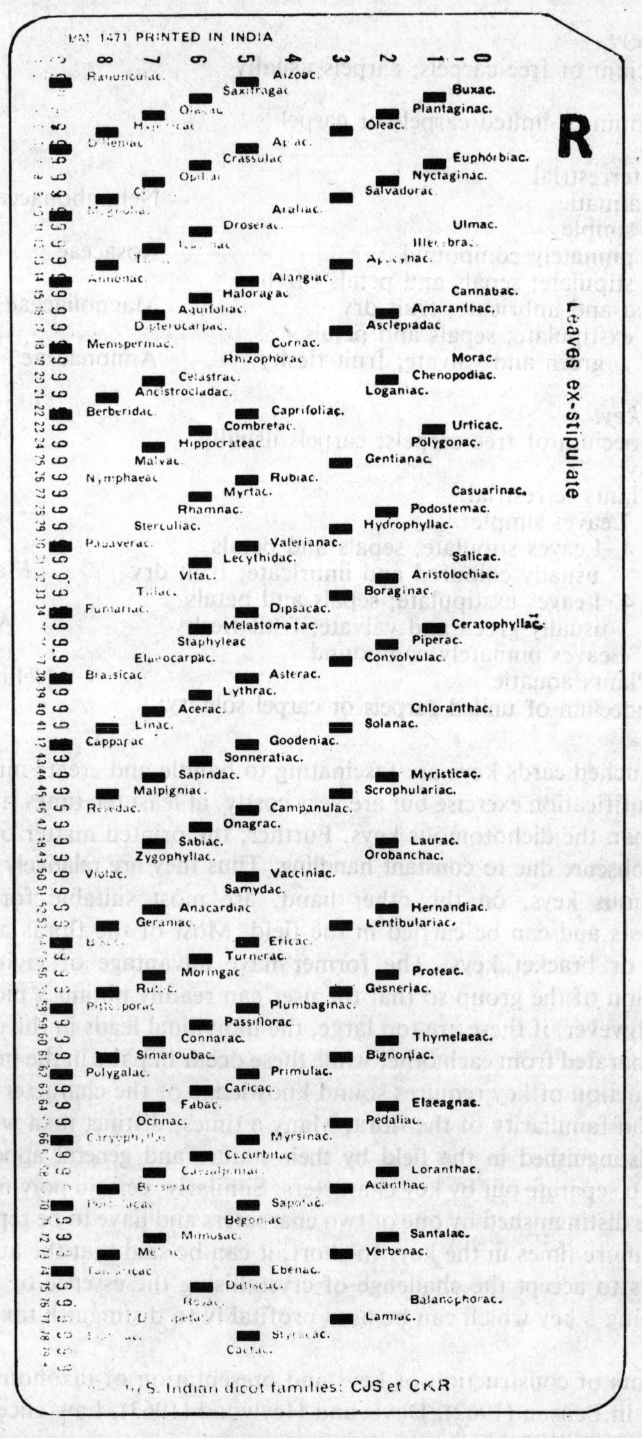

FIG. 10.1 A specimen card of punched cards key. All the available families in the area are listed. The letter 'R' on the right-hand side indicates the number of character state of exstipulate leaves. Perforations before certain families indicate presence of this character.

Bracket key:

<table>
<tr><td>1. Gynoecium of free carpels; carpels usually many</td><td></td><td>2</td></tr>
<tr><td>Gynoecium of united carpels or carpel solitary</td><td></td><td>5</td></tr>
<tr><td>2. Plants terrestrial</td><td></td><td>3</td></tr>
<tr><td>Plants aquatic</td><td>Nelumbonaceae</td><td></td></tr>
<tr><td>3. Leaves simple</td><td></td><td>4</td></tr>
<tr><td>Leaves pinnately compound</td><td>Rosaceae</td><td></td></tr>
<tr><td>4. Leaves stipulate; sepals and petals often coloured and imbricate; fruit dry</td><td>Magnoliaceae</td><td></td></tr>
<tr><td>Leaves exstipulate; sepals and petals usually green and valvate; fruit fleshy</td><td>Annonaceae</td><td></td></tr>
</table>

Indented key:

1. Gynoecium of free carpels; carpels usually many:
    2. Plants terrestrial:
        3. Leaves simple:
            4. Leaves stipulate; sepals and petals usually coloured and imbricate; fruit dry — Magnoliaceae
            4. Leaves exstipulate; sepals and petals usually green and valvate; fruit fleshy — Annonaceae
        3. Leaves pinnately compound — Rosaceae
    2. Plants aquatic — Nelumbonaceae
1. Gynoecium of united carpels or carpel solitary:

The punched cards keys are fascinating to handle and create much interest in the identification exercise but are very costly, at least ten times (if not more) costlier than the dichotomous keys. Further, the printed matter on the cards becomes obscure due to constant handling. Thus they are relatively short-lived. Dichotomous keys, on the other hand, are most suitable for practicing taxonomists and can be carried in the field. Most of the floras adopt either indented or bracket keys. The former have advantage of giving a visual presentation of the group so that the user can readily obtain a picture of the taxon. However, if these are too large, the individual leads in the couplets get widely separated from each other while these occur in pairs in the bracket keys.

Construction of key requires sound knowledge of the character differences and a good familiarity of the flora. Many a times, distinct taxa which can be readily distinguished in the field by their stature and general appearance, are difficult to separate out by key characters. Similarly, certain polymorphic taxa cannot be distinguished by one or two characters and have to be repeated twice or many more times in the key. In short, it can be said that the author of the group has to accept the challenge of crystallising the essence of his work in constructing a key which can be used profitably to distinguish taxa in a given area.

Accounts of construction of keys and presentation of taxonomic data will be found in Benson (1962), Davis and Heywood (1963), Lawrence (1951) and Radford *et al.* (1974).

Diagnosis, Descriptions and Illustrations

Diagnosis may be defined as a brief listing of the most important characters which can be used to distinguish a given group from other related taxa. The International Code of Botanical Nomenclature insists on Latin diagnosis for a new taxon being described. This is generally accompanied by a detailed description. On closer examination of a larger number of individuals with the help of a detailed description, it becomes easier to detect minor or major variations. Accumulation of such variations over a period allows recognition of a new taxon.

Descriptions of plants may be ***original, redescriptions*** or ***short*** ones depending upon the purpose of the same. Original descriptions should be fairly complete avoiding repetition, suitable for identification of a taxon and should include exact measurements to be precise. Redescriptions are recommended in cases where the original description is inadequate, incomplete or faulty. Short descriptions should include all essential and diagnostic features while at the same time they should not be lengthy. Any character which has not been included in the key may be of great help when inserted in short descriptions, thus supplementing the information for identification.

Very often a single accurate illustration serves the purpose of keys, diagnosis as well as description. It is therefore, recommended by the Code that in the absence of any authentic specimen (Holotype or Lectotype), an illustration can serve as a Neotype to represent a taxon. Many such illustrations from Wight's *Icones* (1838-1853), Hooker's *Icones* (1836), and Royle's *Illustrations* (1833-1840) can serve as neotypes.

Photographs of type specimens or close-ups of floral parts serve the same purpose and are more impressive. Many cultivated plants, which are generally difficult to identify due to enormous variations, can be satisfactorily determined with the help of pictorial manuals such as Graf's *Exotica* (1961).

Need for Accurate Identification

Researchers in the specialised fields of botany other than taxonomy, often do not care much for the accurate determination of a taxon with which they work. This obviously leads to misinterpretation of the data and misuse in disciplines like pharmacognosy, biochemistry and such others. The success of Ayurvedic medicine entirely depends upon the accurate determination of natural plant wealth. In these and many other instances, the role of the experienced taxonomist need not be overemphasised. He has to rely on various resources for accurate identification as described above in addition to his own judgement acquired through long experience and critical observation.

11 Phytogeography

Taxonomy is a science of classification, and the classification, in turn, should largely be based on natural affinities between the taxa. In order to construct a more acceptable and natural classification, it should be based on much evidence as is available for construction of groups. The full significance of the interrelationships of plant taxa can be appreciated only after it is understood that the related plants have or have had through common ancestors, common or interrelated geographic distributions. Plant geography is such a branch of botany that deals with the distribution of plants in present and the past (Good, 1974). It is, therefore, necessary for a student of plant taxonomy to be familiar with the spatial relationships of the groups concerned and the floras affecting distributional patterns. He cannot remain satisfied by studying only the present day distribution of plants but also has to know their distribution in time. The various textbooks on plant geography have discussed some of the great changes in the distribution of plants that have taken place in the course of geological time. It will appear that the primary cause of these changes can be attributed to physiological reaction of plants to ecological factors and consequently, to a considerable extent on climate. Climate is the most far reaching of the natural elements controlling plant life. The second, and probably equally important factor that has influenced plant distribution, is animal life on this globe. Man, in particular, is apt to have the greatest influence of all. These factors will be considered here in a broad way. Detailed account of these can be found in exhaustive treatments on the subjects by renowned phytogeographers such as Daubney (1855), Pickering (1876), Schimper (1903), Warming (1909), Campbell (1926), Wulff (1943), Cain (1944), Croizat (1952), Good (1953, 1964, 1974), Turrill (1953) and Polunin (1960).

Climatic Groupings

Climatic factors that affect plant life include chiefly, light, temperature, precipitation, evaporation and wind. Other factors such as radiation, cloudiness, storms, etc. are also considered under special circumstances. These components are often interdependent and their various combinations form the characteristic climates of different parts of the world. The three main climatic zones, namely, the *polar, temperate* and *tropical* regions, are primarily temperature zones.

The climates of polar regions and high altitudes are mostly rigorous with the mean annual temperature much below 10°C. Precipitation is mostly in the form of snow and is often less than 25 cm per annum. Relative humidity is fairly high due to low temperature and low evaporating power. There are wide seasonal and diurnal fluctuations. In the extreme polar regions there is continuous light in summer and continuous darkness in winter.

The climates of temperate and adjacent lands are mostly fairly warm and moist, at least in the favourable periods. Seasonal and diurnal fluctuations are well marked and vary from place to place. The mean annual temperature is a little above 10°C and rainfall more than 76 cm.

In the tropical and subtropical regions, the climate is warm and humid. The mean annual temperature is usually above 15°C and rainfall ranges between 200 and 400 cm. Frost and snow are usually unknown, the conditions being torrid and equable with often little or no seasonal and diurnal variation.

Other climatic regions include, "oceanic" with even climate and "continental" with uneven climate. These regions, however, are irrespective of latitudinal temperature zones and are found in all the primary climatic zones. In general the oceanic extreme occurs along coastal regions while continental extreme is found far inland from the ocean.

Physical Geographic Regions

There are four subjects of physical geography of the world that must be taken into consideration in plant geography. These are the continents and oceans, the islands, the mountains and the deserts.

There are six main land masses known as continents, namely, Eurasia, Africa, Australia, North America, South America and Antarctica. The last named is completely devoid of plant life at present and covered with ice and snow although in former ages it possessed considerable vegetation.

Most of these land masses are chiefly distributed in the northern hemisphere of the globe and are exactly opposite those of the southern hemisphere. In other words, where there is land in the north, there is sea in the south and vice versa. The absolute level of edges of continents varies considerably. In most places they stand clear of the water to their very boundaries but in others they pass gently below the sea level before their actual abrupt edges are reached.

It is for this reason that the seas or oceans of the world are classified as deep seas or oceans proper bound by the true edges of the continents and shallow or marginal seas which are really shallow flooding of the peripheral parts of the continents. These latter are appropriately called epicontinental seas.

In addition to these continents, there is a very large number of lesser island land masses. The distribution and size of these islands are significant to phytogeographic problems. Such islands include, Greenland, Ireland, the British Isles, the Canaries, the West Indies, Madagascar, the Seychelles, the Aleutians, Japan, Formosa, the Philippines, Malaya, New Caledonia, New Guinea, New Zealand, Tasmania and the Hawaiian Islands.

The relative positions of continents and islands are of particular importance to students of plant taxonomy. The land masses below the equator of South America, Africa and intermediate islands, for example, are far more remote from one another than are similar masses at an equivalent northern latitude. Many islands are an integral part of an adjoining continental platform and thus are termed continental islands. Others are surrounded by deep seas and are called oceanic islands. The latter are more common in the Pacific than in the Atlantic and include the Bonnins, the Mariannas, the Galapagos and the Hawaiian Islands. Oceanic islands are generally regarded as older in age and more permanent than the young and more fluctuating continental ones.

Most of the land masses are quite uneven rising at certain places into great heights thus giving rise to mountains. These are important to a phytogeographer since the climate of mountains changes appreciably with altitude. Thus many mountain ranges situated in the tropical or subtropical latitudes have arctic climates on high altitudes.

The great mountain systems of the world are only three, namely, the western American system comprising the rocky mountains in the north and the Andes in the south, the Eurasian-Australian system comprising the Pyrenees, Alps, Caucasus, the plateaux of Central Asia, the Sino-Himalayan mountains, the mountains of Malaya and those of New Zealand, and the African system.

On the leeward side of mountain ranges, because of great heights, the rain-bearing clouds from the sea discharge before they pass further inland thus creating rain-shadow areas or deserts. Deserts have been defined as areas where, because of the climatic conditions, there is no continuous covering of vegetation. When such a climate persists in the northern latitudes or at great elevations in the tropics, they are known as *cold deserts* in contrast to *warm* or *hot deserts* formed in the tropics or at low elevations. Hot deserts of the world include the Great Basin in North America, the North Mexican desert, western Argentina, Peru and Chile in South America and the greatest deserts of Africa and Asia. The latter include the Sahara, Arabian and Persian deserts. The deserts of Turkestan, Tibet and Mongolia (Gobi) are cold deserts.

The Sahara is one of the most typical and absolute of all deserts, and over much of its surface there is sand bearing no plant life. Other deserts include the warm deserts of West Pakistan and Kutch, southern Africa, and Australia, and the cold deserts of Arctic and Antarctic.

There is a considerable difference of opinion as to the age of the present deserts. According to one view, at least some of the deserts have been a feature of the world throughout the geological time and have been here longer than the history of angiosperms. Another opinion is that the desert conditions may have occurred at intervals throughout the geological time but that all the present deserts are modern. Some hold that desert conditions were unknown anywhere until the late geological time. Good (1974) considers all the present deserts to be of different ages.

Phytogeographic Regions

Three latitudinal zones mentioned earlier are very broadly defined and are symmetrical about the equator. However, for, most practical botanical purposes a fourth zone, namely, subtropical zone, is added. Hansen (1920) subdivided the earth's surface into 7 zones on either side of the equator. These zones with corresponding latitudes are as follows:

1. Equatorial zone	0° to 15° on either side
2. Tropical zones	15° to 23.5° on either side
3. Subtropical zones	23.5° to 34° on either side
4. Warm temperate zones	34° to 45° on either side
5. Cold temperate zones	45° to 58° on either side
6. Sub-Arctic zones	58° to 66.5° on either side
7. Arctic zones	66.5° to 72° on either side
8. Polar zones	72° to 90° on either side

These zones would indicate the major distribution of plants, were it not that it ignores one factor, namely, the influence of elevation of land. The climate of various latitudinal zones can be experienced in the altitudinal zones of mountain ranges. The vegetational zonation of mountains has been much studied. These zones in the tropical mountains are summarised as follows:

0-600 metres above mean sea level	Zone of palms and bananas
600-1200 metres above mean sea level	Zone of tree ferns and figs
1200-1900 metres above mean sea level	Zone of myrtles and laurels
1900-2600 metres above mean sea level	Zone of evergreen trees
2600-3200 metres above mean sea level	Zone of deciduous trees
3200-3800 metres above mean sea level	Zone of coniferous trees
3800-4450 metres above mean sea level	Zone of alpine shrubs
4450-5050 metres above mean sea level	Zone of alpine herbs
5050 metres and above	Zone of permanent ice and snow

Altitudinal and latitudinal zonation combined together may be represented as shown in Fig. 11.1

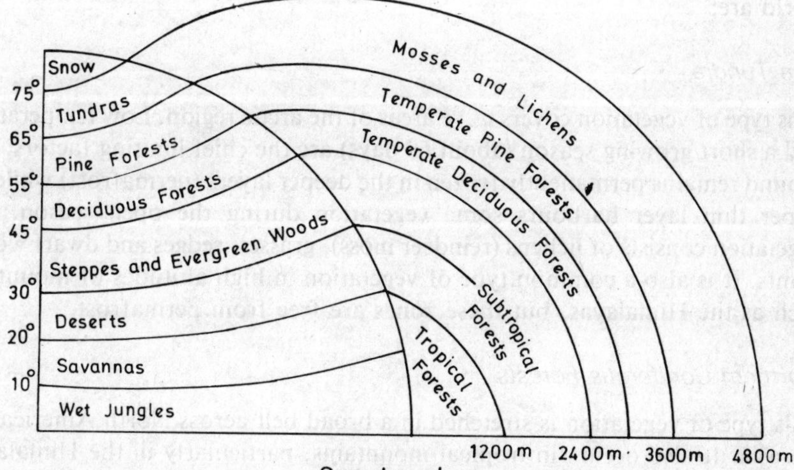

FIG. 11.1 Diagrammatic representation of the vegetation zones of latitude and altitude. (Redrawn from *Outlines of Phytography* by Herbertson 1913, by permission of Edward Arnold, London.)

Even these altitudinal or latitudinal zonations do not harbour similar or same kinds of plants or plant species in different parts of the world. This is because the average range of species is comparatively small and further, factors such as local soil conditions, day length, slopes of mountains, etc. play a significant role in determination of the types of species that can grow in a particular area. It is for this reason that a phytogeographer must classify plant life of the world from vegetational as well as floristic points of view. Vegetational classification of plant life includes aspects of quantitative structural characters. These structural characters are closely related to climatic conditions and hence the same kind of vegetation—or dominant growth form such as trees, shrubs or herbs etc.—tends to recur in many parts of the world. Evergreen forests, for example, are found in Peninsular India, Eastern Himalaya, Southeast Asia, Africa, South America and other parts of the world. In all these forests, the dominant components are evergreen trees.

Floristic classification, on the other hand, is based on the kinds of plant species occurring in the area. Thus evergreen forests in different parts of the world mentioned above, are dominated by different tree species. The guttifers dominate the peninsular Indian forests, while the Eastern Himalayan forests have the dipterocarps as their dominants and so on. Thus the distribution of floras is quite different from that of the vegetation. Flora is chiefly a matter of quality while vegetation is a matter of quantity.

Types of World Vegetation

Regional climates interact with the regional plants and substrate to produce large communities. In a given unit of community, the life-form of the climatic climax vegetation is uniform. Thus the climax vegetation of evergreen forest is evergreen trees and that of a grassland is grass although the species of dominant components may vary in different parts. The major plant formations of the world are:

The Tundra

This type of vegetation covers large areas of the arctic region. Low temperatures and a short growing season (about 60 days) are the chief limiting factors. The ground remains permanently frozen in the deeper layers (permafrost) while the upper thin layer harbours some vegetation during the open season. The vegetation consists of lichens (reindeer moss), grasses, sedges and dwarf woody plants. It is also a common type of vegetation in high altitudes of mountains such as the Himalayas, but these zones are free from permafrost.

Northern Coniferous Forests

This type of vegetation is stretched in a broad belt across North America and Eurasia. It also occurs in tropical mountains, particularly in the Himalayas. The dominant components are needle-leaved conifers such as the species of *Pinus, Picea, Abies* and others. There is a poor development of shrubs and herbs.

Moist Temperate Coniferous Forests

Along the west coast of North America and in the Eastern Himalaya, the fairly high temperatures and humidity support a distinctive type of coniferous forest. These forests are dominated by conifers but are floristically and ecologically very different from northern coniferous forests. ***Tsuga, Pseudotsuga, Abies, Thuja, Cryptomeria,*** etc. are some of the dominant components. The world's tallest and giant redwoods ***(Sequoiadendron gigantea*** and species of ***Sequoia)*** occur in such forests of California. Shrubs and mosses are abundant, most of the latter being epiphytic.

Temperate Deciduous Forests

Deciduous forest communities develop in the areas where there is evenly distributed moderate rainfall (about 75-150 cm per annum) and moderate temperatures with distinct seasonal pattern. They are found chiefly in eastern North America, all of Europe, parts of Japan, Western Himalaya, Australia and the tip of South America. In these parts, the seasonal variation in temperature is extreme, causing the trees and shrubs to shed leaves during winter. Shrubs, herbs and ground vegetation is well developed. Since the deciduous forests of temperate region are scattered, they exhibit a variety of species composition.

The regions represent one of the most important biotic regions of the world since "white man's civilisation" has achieved its greatest development in these areas. These forests are, therefore, greatly modified by man and many of them are replaced by cultivation and forest edge communities (Odum, 1971; Collinson, 1977).

Subtropical Evergreen Forests

These forests develop where there is relatively high humidity and less pronounced seasonal fluctuations in temperature. They are mainly found in central and southern Japan, parts of Florida along the Gulf and South Atlantic coasts, and at moderate altitudes in eastern India. Various species of ***Quercus, Magnolia, Ficus,*** certain palms dominate these forests.

Temperate Grasslands

Vast tracts of the temperate latitudes are covered by grasslands and have been extremely important from the agricultural point of view. They occur in the areas with lesser rainfall (between 25 and 75 cm) and generally in the interior of continents. In North America, grasslands are chiefly dominated by tall grasses and therefore are called *prairies*. The European grasslands have mid or short grasses. Dominant species vary from place to place depending upon edaphic factors and moisture.

Tropical Savannas

They are grasslands occurring widely throughout the tropics with scattered trees or clumps of trees. In warm regions of the tropics with about 100-150 cm rainfall but having a long dry season, the savannas are best developed. The largest area of this type is in Africa but sizable tropical savannas occur in South America, South India and Australia. ***Panicum, Pennisetum, Andropogon*** and ***Imperata*** are some of the dominant genera of grasses while trees are chiefly fire-resistant and mostly legumes, euphorbias and palms.

Tropical Rain Forests

The low altitude zones near the equator experience well spread heavy rainfall (between 200 and 250 cm) and equable humid climate. This supports the development of tall, broad-leaved evergreen forest communities. Such forests occur chiefly in the Amazon and Orinoco basins of South America and the central American isthmus, the Congo, Nigeria and Zambezi basins of central and western Africa and Madagascar and the Indo-Malay-Borneo-New Guinea regions. These differ from each other in species composition but all are extremely rich in variety of plant and animal lives. Rain forests are highly stratified. Trees generally form three layers, then are shrubs and tall herbs and the rich ground vegetation develops in the clearings and margins of the forests.

There are some variants of rain forests, for example, ***montane rain forests*** develop in mountainous areas and are dominated by relatively dwarf tree species; ***cloud forests*** develop in still higher altitudes and with a very high number of epiphytic species; ***gallary forests*** are seen along banks of rivers (these are also termed as ***riverine forests***) etc. Exhaustive accounts of rain forests may be found in Richards (1952, 1973), Janzen (1975), Walter (1971), Whitmore (1975), etc.

Tropical Scrub and Deciduous Forests

In the areas where the moisture conditions are intermediate between desert and savanna on the one hand and rain forests on the other, tropical scrub or thorn forests and tropical deciduous forests may occur. They are scattered in many parts of the tropics including South America, India (Deccan) and Australia.

Phytogeographic (Floristic) Regions of the World

Although vegetation types are common in many parts of the world, each continental area tends to have its own special flora. Islands often differ greatly from mainlands. Wallace and Darwin were the first to recognise systems of phytogeographical regions and many others have contributed to the subject since then. Presently, it is considered that the earth flora can be broadly classified into six main kingdoms, namely:

1. Boreal—stretching from North America to Eurasia;
2. Paleotropical—with three subdivisions, (i) African, (ii) Indo-Malayan and (iii) Polynesian;

3. South American or neotropical;
4. South African;
5. Australian; and
6. Antarctic.

Good (1974) has classified these further into about 37 floristic regions and a number of provinces. The Indian region, for instance, falls under the Indo-Malayan subkingdom of the Palaeotropical kingdom and was divided into nine provinces by Hooker (1907). Hooker's provinces in the present limits of political boundaries of India are:

1. the Eastern Himalayas extending from Sikkim to the Mishmi mountains in Upper Assam;
2. the Western Himalayas extending from Kumaon to Chitral;
3. the Indus Plain including the Punjab, Rajasthan, west of Aravali range, Kutch and Gujarat;
4. the Gangetic Plain from the Aravali range to Bengal, plains of Assam and low country of Orissa;
5. the Malabar including the humid belt of hilly or mountainous country along the western side with the Konkan, Kanara, Malabar, Cochin, Travancore and the Laccadive Islands;
6. the Deccan which is the dry elevated table land of India east of Malabar and south of the Satpuda range; and
7. eastern Assam and the hilly ranges of Khasi, Naga and Mizo hills, and the Andaman-Nicobar Islands.

Two more provinces include Sri Lanka and Baluchistan which are no more in the Indian boundary.

General Characters of the Flora of India

According to Hooker (1907), who thoroughly worked out the flora of British India (1872-1897) and recorded his findings in a 7-volume work, the flora of this country is "more varied than that of any other country of equal area in the Eastern hemisphere, if not in the globe." This is due to its geographical expanse and varied physical features. But at the same time he has doubted as to whether the flora is richer in the number of genera and species than any other area of equal dimensions on the globe; it is certainly far poorer in endemic genera and species than many others, especially, China, Australia and South Africa. This, however, has not been accepted by subsequent workers like Chatterjee (1940) who holds that the percentage of endemic genera is sufficiently high (about 49%) and endemic species are abundant in the Eastern Himalayan region (about 28%).

In any case, in spite of huge barriers such as the lofty Himalayas on the north and the sea on the other three sides, the flora of India is dominated by migratory elements, particularly from the Malaya and SE Asia. Similarly, out of about 2300 total genera, well over 500 are European and quite a few are from Africa, Arabia, Tibet, Burma, China and Japan. It is also evident that the flora presents few anomalies from the phytogeographic point of view.

Lakhanpal (1970) reconstructed the palaeogeography of India during the early Eocene and Miocene epochs. According to him, geologically, India is divisible into three units, (i) peninsular, (ii) extrapeninsular and (iii) Indo-Gangetic plain. He has divided Tertiary floras of India into Palaeogene and Neogene; the former is found only in the Peninsular India while the latter occurs in both Peninsular and extra-Peninsular regions. They are predominantly tropical floras made up of genera now largely confined to the Old World.

Some of the peculiar features of the living Indian flora are: (i) the *Rhododendron* belt in the high Eastern Himalaya; (ii) gregarious trees of Sal *(Shorea robusta),* Eng *(Dipterocarpus turbinatus),* Sissoo *(Dalbergia sissoo),* Khair *(Acacia catechu)* and Babhul (Acacia nilotica); (iii) indigenous palms such as *Corypha* spp., *Phoenix sylvestris, Borassus flabellifer* and *Cocus nucifera. Calamus* is another interesting genus of climbing palms found throughout the tropical forests; (iv) about 20 species of tree ferns; (v) thickets of *Strobilanthes (sensu lato)* in the western ghats; (vi) certain aquatic plants such as *Nymphaea* spp., *Nelumbo nucifera* and *Euryale ferox*; (vii) certain peculiar sand hill plants such as *Phoenix farinifera, Ipomoea pes-caprae* and *Spinifex littoralis.*

The total number of species listed in Hooker's flora is about 15,900 under 176 families of flowering plants. The largest family in India is Orchidaceae of which more than 1600 species are recorded. This family with majority of epiphytic species is largely distributed in the Eastern Himalaya, Khasi hills and the western ghats. In other parts of the country, Leguminosae, Gramineae and Euphorbiaceae are the dominant families. Ten dominant families in their numerical sequence are:
1. Orchidaceae, 2. Leguminosae, 3. Gramineae, 4. Rubiaceae, 5. Euphorbiaceae, 6. Acanthaceae, 7. Compositae, 8. Cyperaceae, 9. Labiatae, 10. Urticaceae (including Moraceae, Ulmaceae and Cannabaceae).

The proportion of monocotyledons to dicotyledons is approximately 1 : 2.3; of genera to species is about 1 : 7. About 220 species of palms, 120 bamboos, 22 conifers and 5 Cycadaceae members are also recorded. The genera with 100 or more species include *Dendrobium, Impatiens, Syzygium, Pedicularis, Strobilanthes, Ficus, Bulbophyllum, Eria, Habenaria* and *Carex.*

Of the botanical provinces mentioned above, the provinces of the Eastern Himalayas and Assam are the richest of all in number of species. The former contains about 4000 species while the latter (including Burma) contains 6000 species. The poorest region is the dry province of the Indus plain with about 1500 species. The characteristic vegetation of these provinces is summarised below.

Eastern Himalayas

This is the most humid tract of the Himalayan ranges and includes Sikkim, Bhutan and the whole of Arunachal Pradesh. The flora is disposed in three altitudinal zones: tropical, temperate and alpine. The tropical zone is dominated by trees of which there are about 250 species belonging to Magnoliaceae, Annonaceae, Guttiferae, Sterculiaceae, Tiliaceae, etc. The temperate zone is dominated by lower non-coniferous belt, upper coniferous belt and the highest *Rhododendron* belt. Numerous shrubs are also common in this zone. The alpine zone is predominantly a zone of herbaceous species.

Western Himalayas

These ranges are much greater in length and breadth than the eastern ranges but the climate is cooler and drier. This results in the non-representation of about 12 Eastern Himalayan families in this province. The ranges include Kashmir, the Punjab and the northern parts of Haryana, Himachal Pradesh and Uttar Pradesh. The chief dominant families are mostly herbaceous and many genera and species are common to European flora.

The Indus Plain

A vast portion of this phytogeographical area is now occupied by Pakistan and only a portion of the southeastern side may be considered here. This part includes the Punjab, Rajasthan, Gujarat and other regions west of Aravali range. The climate in general is dry and the vegetation is dominated by desert shrubs and herbs. Most of the shrubs and small trees are totally leafless in hot season and herbaceous flora is witnessed during the short growing season. The total species estimated are about 1500 belonging to 112 families. Grasses and legumes are the most dominant components.

The Gangetic Plain

The entire plain stretching towards the eastern side from River Yamuna forms an alluvium of the Ganga. This is roughly divisible into (i) most dry western portion, (ii) Bengal proper, which is relatively more humid, and (iii) the Sunderbans, now a part of Bangla Desh. The total number of species may be same as that for the Indus plain but the eastern part covered by Bengal being relatively humid is dominated by some evergreen tree species such as ***Polyalthia longifolia* Benth & Hook f.**, ***Pterospermum acerifolium* Willd**, ***Artocarpus heterophyllus* Lam** and species of ***Terminalia.***

Malabar

A narrow strip of land west of the Sahyadris extending from Bombay southwards being relatively more humid owing to heavy precipitation, harbours one of the most luxuriant vegetation of the country. The evergreen as well as the semi-evergreen forests on the western slopes of Sahyadris and the coastal vegetation together have about 4000 species of flowering plants belonging to 150 families. The most distinctive characters of the Malabar flora are (i) the presence of Guttiferae, Dipterocarpaceae, Myristicaceae, many palms and bamboos, (ii) the great excess of species of Malayan type, (iii) the highest representation of Podostemaceae and (iv) a close similarity of vegetation of some of the high hills like Nilgiri, Pulney, etc. with that of the northern hills, particularly the Khasi hills and Naga hills.

The Deccan

The vast table land extending from the Satpura ranges in the north to the Nilgiri and Pulney hills in the south and eastwards of Malabar is made up of basaltic rock. It is in the rain shadow of the Sahyadris and is characterised by the tropical deciduous forest type of vegetation. This main type of vegetation is dominated, in certain hilly pockets, by *Shorea robusta, Tectona grandis,* etc., while in most of the exposed situations they are replaced by other drought resistant species and thorny shrubs. The vegetation has, in general, a close resemblance with that of the western Gangetic plain.

The eastern-most coastal region of the Deccan plateau is slightly different from the main land and is designated as the Coromandel coast.

Assam and Andaman-Nicobar Islands

This eastern land of the country has the richest vegetation dominated by evergreen tree species and a large number of epiphytes. The variety of plant life reaches its highest limit in these forests. The number of species, which is only roughly estimated, amounts to 6000 under 161 families. These forests have been considered by some (Takhtajan, 1969) to be the *cradle of angiosperms* chiefly because of the rich representation of primitive taxa such as the members of Magnoliaceae, Winteraceae, Annonaceae and many vesselless genera. One of the world's highest concentration of orchids and bamboos is found in these forests. The area is also characterised by a large percentage of endemic genera. The vegetation in general bears a close similarity with that of Burma and Malaya.

Evolutionary Background

It has been repeatedly brought out that the present day plants have not arisen all of a sudden. So also they have not occupied the present areas in all the geological ages. The pattern presented by the living plants and their distribution is a result of a slow process beginning in the remote past and governed by various factors. Here the evolutionary background of the vegetation that covers the globe has to be considered.

The phytogeographers and geologists recognise four major areas in the geological time sequence. It is believed that the earth had its beginning about 4,500,000,000 years ago and the oldest known rocks were formed about 3,300,000,000 years ago. The first geological era extends from the rock age to about 550,000,000 years ago and is termed the Pre-Cambrian. This era has been divided into the older Archaeozoic and the younger Proterozoic. It was probably in this latter time that relatively simpler forms of algae, sponges, some fungi and bacteria were widespread. The pre-Cambrian was followed by the Palaeozoic era of the large pteridophytes. It extended from the Cambrian some

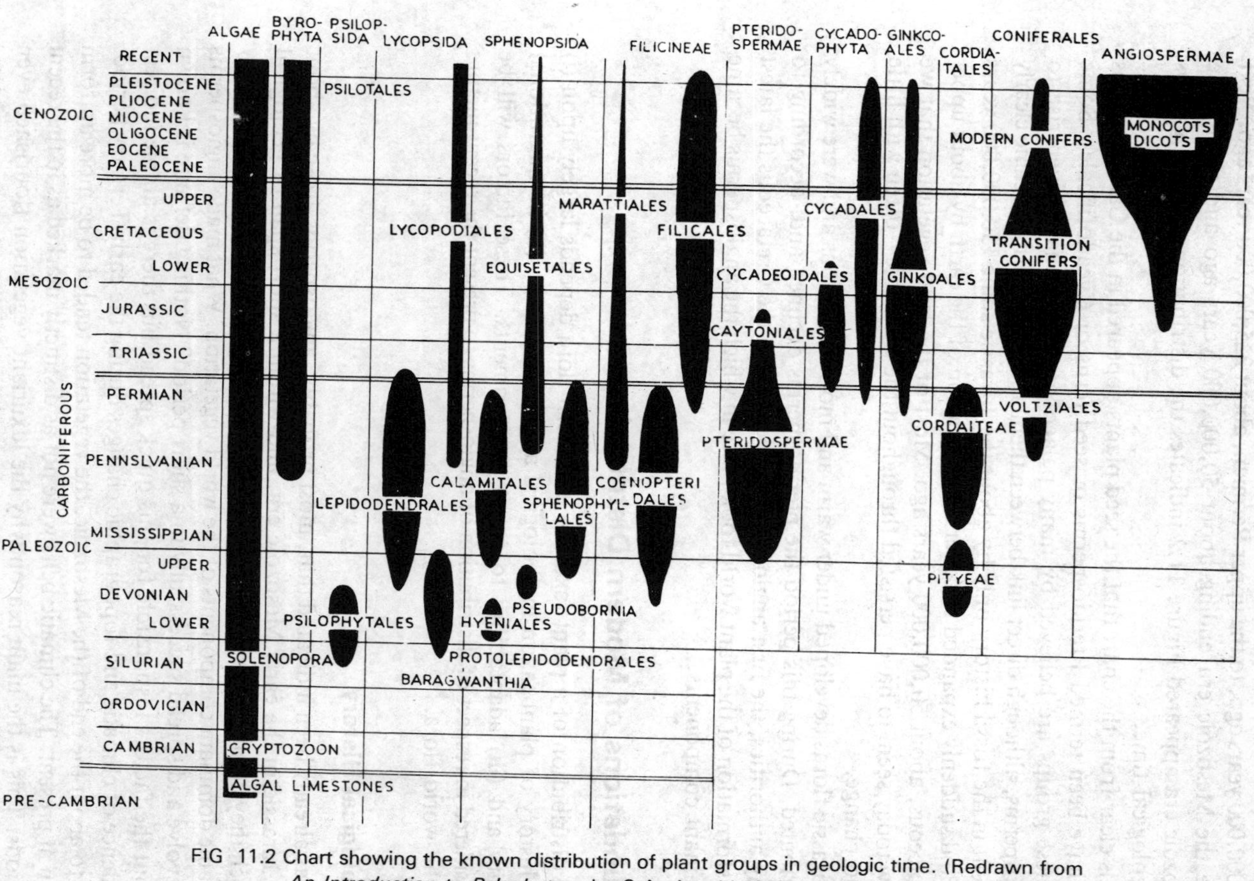

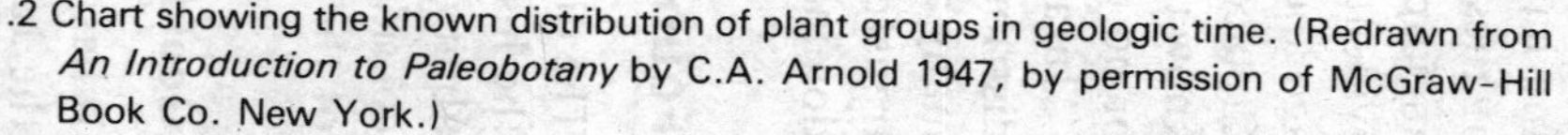

FIG 11.2 Chart showing the known distribution of plant groups in geologic time. (Redrawn from *An Introduction to Paleobotany* by C.A. Arnold 1947, by permission of McGraw-Hill Book Co. New York.)

550,000,000 years ago, to the upper Permian, about 225,000,000 years ago. Next came the Mesozoic era ending about 50,000,000 years ago and finally the Cenozoic era appeared. Figure 11.2 indicates the distribution of plant groups in geological time.

It is clear from the chart that the seed plants appeared in the Carboniferous and have been termed Pteridosperms or seed ferns or Cycadofilicales. Some of these groups are believed by many palaeobotanists to have given rise to angiosperms, although direct link between them and angiosperms became clearly evident in the fossil history only by about the Jurassic some 150,000,000 years ago and suddenly expanded to cover major portion of the earth by about upper Cretaceous, about 50,000,000 years ago. Most of the land vegetation that we know today seem to have persisted throughout the Cenozoic—often with little or no change.

Jurassic floras developed under warm and moist conditions and were widely distributed. During this period the pteridosperms declined and, according to many authorities, the first angiosperms appeared. In the Cretaceous the latest transformation of the plant world took place in which the angiosperms became dominant components.

Foundations of Modern Distribution

The distribution of a plant taxon of a modern flora depends largely upon (i) the history of plant taxon in geological and recent times, (ii) its migrational ability and (iii) adaptability to newer environments. These factors will be considered in respect of distribution of angiosperms to present the recent picture of the world flora.

Geological History

It has already been indicated that, most probably, angiosperms arose by about the Jurassic in the early Mesozoic era, and within a short span of geological epoch they became distributed all over the globe. By the upper Cretaceous, they became dominant components of the world vegetation. What made angiosperms to evolve and spread successfully in a short period? Nothing definite is known about the factors responsible for this quick spread but there is ample indirect evidence of climatic and topographic changes during the early Tertiary period. Up to about the end of the Mesozoic, the vegetation tended to be more uniform than at present. The climatic belts were not as distinctly marked as in the recent periods. This is the main reason why the luxuriant vegetation flourished even in the polar regions. However, from the Miocene onwards there were marked local changes in conditions. At the close of the Tertiary or beginning of the Quaternary, although the vegetation of the tropical and adjacent zones continued in considerable luxuriance, there was a marked lowering down of temperature in most other regions that led to the covering of some by the glaciers and to complete change in the floras of others.

Although evolution in general is a gradual process, it seems to have accelerated by sudden changes in the habitat conditions. Thus the violent upheavals of the earth's crust or direct changes of climate appear to have induced sudden inherent and hereditary changes involving the abrupt creation of new races and in time, of new species. It is due to these reasons that the floras might have migrated from more severe climates to equable conditions.

Besides direct climatic changes and geological revolutions, there have been changes in the confirmation of land and sea. Following are some of the leading theories that have been advanced to explain the current distribution of particular plants.

Continental Drift

The theory of continental movement was first proposed by Dr. Alfred Wegener in his *Die Entstehung der Kontinente und Oceane* published in 1915 and subsequently translated into English in 1924. The theory runs as follows: During the early part of the Palaeozoic era, the continents of the world as we know them today, were all joined together in one huge land mass or *Pangaea,* but subsequently separated and drifted apart until they have come to reach the positions they now occupy. This movement centred on Africa, which, with the main land of continental Asia, has retained its original position, more or less unchanged. The theory also postulates a movement or wandering of the poles, in order to account for the considerable alterations in the distribution of climatic zones. After the publication of Wagener's book, the theory of Continental drift received a great deal of attention (Campbell, 1942; DuToit, 1937, 1944; Holland, 1942-43; Longwell and Bailey, 1944; Sahni 1936; Adams & Ager, 1967; Dietz & Sproll, 1966; Hsu, 1971; Tarling, 1971, 1972; Schopf, 1970). DuToit (1937), in particular, brought together in one volume much of the relevant matter relating to these theories. According to this latter author, there are seven criteria of drift. These are discussed here.

1. *Physiographic:* The general similarity in shape of many opposed coastlines such, for instance, as those of eastern South America and western Africa. The correspondence of physiographical features in lands now widely separated. The occurrence of various submarine features producible by drifting blocks.
2. *Stratigraphical:* The occurrence of similar geological formations on opposite coasts. Other geological resemblances on separate masses.
3. *Tectonic:* The occurrence of comparable geosynclines, fold systems, fault systems and rift valleys on different continental masses.
4. *Volcanic:* Similarity between the volcanic geology of separated masses.
5. *Palaeoclimatic:* The peculiar distribution of glacial deposits and of other extreme climatic types of deposits over the different continents.
6. *Palaeontological:* The floral relation between America and Africa, present distribution of organisms, etc.
7. *Geodetic:* Evidence afforded by the actual measurements of longitudinal and latitudinal values.

There are, however, differences of opinion about the course of continental drift and also about the condition of the world at the time it began. So far as the distribution of angiosperms is concerned, one difference between the views of Wegener and DuToit is of considerable theoretical importance. Wegner postulated that in the late Palaeozoic, all the continents were joined together into a single mass—Pangaea. DuToit, on the other hand, believed that the original distribution of continents was into two masses, viz. Laurasia or the present north and Gondwanaland or the south and that these two were separated by an ocean called the Tethys Sea, the residue of which is said to be represented today by the Mediterranean Sea. If this latter view is correct then the history of angiosperms will have been largely conditioned by how long this separation of the world's land surface into two lasted. If wide separation persisted until after the evolution of the angiosperms as a group then obviously there are three possibilities. They may have originated in the northern Laurasia or in the southern Gondwanaland or independently in each of these.

According to some advocates of the theory, the drifting of the continents is still proceeding and actually demonstrable in the case of Greenland. To many of the botanists who support this theory, it seems to constitute the most plausible working hypothesis upon which they can base their suppositions as to the history of plant ranges.

Geologists and geophysicists, however, believe that the major displacement of continents has occurred much before the beginning of the Mesozoic when angiosperms were yet to originate. Obviously, in such a situation it would be of little help in explaining the striking similarities of flora in certain areas that are now widely separated by the oceans. Even in such a situation, certain phytogeographers (Du Rietz, 1929) believe that the same taxonomic entity may have arisen independently in more than one area. The flora of New Zealand, for instance, is contrary to the hypothesis of continental drift, as it bears similar relationships to both its east and west.

Land-Bridges

If the hypothesis of two land masses put forward by DuToit and supported by others is accepted, it becomes necessary to imagine that these masses might also have come together at the time of angiosperm evolution. There are obviously two methods by which these units may be joined. Either one has moved towards the other or both towards one another. In still another way they can be joined, i.e. by a bridge across them (Schuchert, 1932). In the first case, it is the displacement theory while in the second case it is the theory of land-bridges which supposes that there has existed in the past great additional land surfaces which served to unite the now severed continents in various ways.

The occurrence of marine deposits on what is now land and the occurrence of land or fresh-water deposits where there is now sea, might be taken at first sight to afford evidence of the former existence of bridges or at least of the sort of geographical changes which might produce them. This is certainly the simplest way of explaining similarities of plant and animal life between such areas as Europe and eastern North America, or Australia and South America. It seems that the theory of land bridges is justified to the extent that such phenomena come and go nowadays on a small scale. Also, there can be little doubt that such bridges created by relative change of level of water have existed on a bigger scale in the past. According to Darlington (1957), Central America, is in fact, a land bridge which has existed only since the Pliocene. Recently, van Steenis (1962) has given an elaborate presentation of many of the facts and arguments in support of the theory of land bridges.

Although comparatively small elevations would serve to link what are now widely separated areas, the land bridges proper, to explain many of the phytogeographic facts, are land areas crossing the main oceans. There is no adequate evidence for such cases. According to Good (1974), the theory of continental drift explains the peculiarities and leading features of angiosperm distribution more simply than any other hypothesis. Further, angiosperms have spread all over the world with a degree of completeness and constancy, which is inconceivable if the continents had never been more closely adjacent than they are at present. Taking the several facts put forward by Good (1951), into consideration, it seems almost an inescapable conclusion that angiosperms must have achieved a great part of their distribution during a period prior to the sundering of a super continent into its constituent parts. Recently, Lakhanpal (1970) has envisaged that there were large-scale migrations and intermingling of floras over Malaysia, India, Arabia and East Africa during the Neogene time.

Shifting of Poles

The theory of polar oscillations or shifting of poles, sometimes called the ***pendulum theory*** also explains the basis of incidental earlier climatic changes and some phenomena of plant distribution. It is presumed that changes in climatic zones were caused by changed location of continents in relation to the sun's orientation. Periodic changes have occurred owing to the position of the geographical poles oscillating back and forth like a *pendulum* or at least "wandering" quite widely.

Increasing support for the view that there may have been a real or apparent shift in the positions of poles in the past, is now available. It is this shift that has caused infinite variety of climatic changes.

Theories of Differentiation and Natural Selection

In terms of natural selection, there is a slow divergence of forms, resulting from gradual accumulation of variations leading to successive appearance of species, genera and higher categories. In such cases evolution proceeds upwards from smaller units to the higher ones. In terms of large mutations, there is sudden, abrupt and discontinuous divergence without intermediate links producing new forms which become at once foundation members of larger groups and subsequently resolve into their constituent genera and species. Here the evolution proceeds downwards from higher to lower units. The former process may be thought of as one of accumulation, the latter as one of differentiation.

The theory of differentiation was first proposed by Guppy (1903, 1906, 1912, 1917, 1919a and 1919b), later by Willis (1922, 1925, 1931, 1940 and 1949) and still later by Croizat (1947, 1952, 1958). Guppy was of the opinion that there are two natural groups of families of flowering plants, some wide-ranging primitive families and the others restricted derived families. This, according to him, is in response to the more or less constant climate of the historical times and diversified climate of later history. He postulated (1919b) for terrestrial plants a slow diversification in all directions during the early history, with equable climates. Willis, after increasing familiarity with tropical plant life, proposed (1922) a *theory of age and area,* which states that the area, in individual cases, may be closely related, it would not apply in all the cases. The hypothesis would serve as a general application only when it is considered that circumstances in which evolution has proceeded have been uniform for all the time, which is not the case.

Croizat (1958), in his voluminous work, *Pangeography,* described differentiation as "form-making in an orderly process through time and over space. It takes place by the breaking down of the ancestral group around essentially local centres of progressive differentiation."

The Cycle of Distribution

When a new species is formed, it consists of a few individuals having no distribution in space. Gradually, through successive generations, the number of individuals increases and it occupies more and more area. If a new species is biologically sound it will compete with the pre-existing species and will tend to increase its range roughly in accordance with the number of individuals. At some point or other, various external factors may tend to restrict its spread. If this checking point is encountered soon after the origin, the new species will never be wide spread. On the other hand, if the check is long delayed, the species will gradually attain a considerable range. In the course of time this process of formation of new species may continue until at last the original genetic stock is exhausted and no new forms can be produced. When the power of producing new forms will decrease or cease altogether, the taxon will face great difficulties in maintaining itself against the competition of younger and more virile strains. The range of a species may eventually contract; ultimately it may die out altogether.

Thus, the history of a species or a genus, expressed in its geography, will normally consist of four successive stages. This view has been called "the theory of generic cycles" (Cain, 1944). The first stage is a juvenile stage in which the species establishes itself and gradually extends its range to the maximum. In the second stage, the species matures and gives rise to new forms. In the third stage, the species enters into obscurity, no longer producing new forms and gradually contracting in its distribution, ultimately attaining the last stage of complete disappearance.

All species need not follow this cycle in its exactness, and the actual details will depend on many other considerations. One or the other stage may be unduly prolonged or shortened, depending upon extraneous circumstances. Some species may never attain an appreciable range while others may be widely distributed. The evolutionary vitality to produce more and more newer forms varies from species to species, in different circumstances and in different places (Sinnott, 1916). It is also true that certain parts of the world have favoured rapid evolution while certain others have retained status quo.

Types and Areas of Natural Distribution

Every plant species has its own particular distribution or range which is dependent on its history, migrational ability and adaptability. Generally, no two species have the same range or distribution and the distributions continue to change all the time.

The term *area* or *range* in plant geography is applied to the entire region of occurrence of a particular taxon or vegetational unit. Within this range, the local distribution is termed *topography*. Although climate is mainly responsible for the limitation of distribution of a taxon, other considerations such as topography and edaphic and biotic factors also have their effect and often delimit the ranges drastically.

Endemism and Endemic Areas

A taxon which has very restricted distribution or is confined to one particular country or region, is termed as *endemic*. The range of a taxon varies according to its size and obviously, higher taxa such as families, normally occupy very large areas and are widely distributed. If, however, a particular family has a distribution restricted to a relatively smaller area such as a single continent, it may be said to be endemic to that continent. Genera may show smaller areas of their distribution and species still smaller. Certain species may be endemic to a very small area such as the peak of a mountain. Evidently, smaller areas normally will have fewer endemic species while large ones will tend to have relatively more endemics.

An *endemic area* is the area of a taxon, in its distribution, limited to some single natural region or habitat.

There are two main types of endemics. The old ones whose range was once far more extensive than it is today, and which being remnants or survivors of former floras may be called *relic endemics* or *epibiotics*. These are particularly abundant on ancient islands and mountain massifs. New Zealand flora, for example, has as many as about 72% of its species endemic to that region. Similarly, St. Helena has the percentage of endemic species as high as 85. *Sequoia* (red wood), *Metasequoia* of N. America, *Ginkgo* of China, *Manglietia*. *Talauma* of SE Asia, *Degeneria* of Fiji islands are some of the examples of this type.

The other type of endemic is relatively young, usually below the rank of a species and in the newer situations such as forest clearings, etc. When ecological conditions change within the limits of some natural region, there is a tendency of new forms to evolve. The new forms naturally will show a small distributional range since they are physically unable to spread beyond their confines. Such plants may be termed *neo-endemics*.

The determination of proportion of these main types of endemism in a particular flora is an important factor in its analysis, capable of expressing its age and history. The relic endemics are particularly useful in indicating antiquity, isolation and diversification of habitats. All these factors tend to produce additional endemics and aid their survival. Such endemics are deficient in biotypes and have smaller amplitude of variation, which leads to their restriction to narrow ecological conditions. They have relatively small chromosome number and show a retrogressive nature. Neo-endemics, on the other hand, being secondarily derived types, commonly have larger chromosome numbers and are relatively aggressive.

Other minor types of endemics are classified as *micro-endemics*—endemics at infraspecific level; *pseudoendemics*—apparently mutants encountered in certain areas; *ecological endemics* which have arisen in relation to particular habitat conditions; *local endemics* that are confined to very limited areas such as small island or a mountain peak and so on.

Endemism may be qualitative as well as quantitative. Two floras, for instance, may well have the same percentage of endemic taxa but in one of these the endemics may be closely related to each other and differ little from the non-endemics, while in the other they may be very different from other taxa in the flora. The endemism in the latter flora clearly expresses a higher degree of distinctiveness and better quality of endemism.

The type of distribution exhibited by certain families and genera, in terms of endemism, may be illustrated here. Of the 544 families (Willis, 1966) of angiosperms distributed in the whole world, about 72 are endemic to America (both N and S), 48 to Africa including Madagascar, 52 to Asia and 20 to Australia. Similarly, out of 475 well-known genera of angiosperms, only 50 are distributed throughout the world while 305 are endemic to tropical countries, 90 to the temperate region and 30 are confined to the southern hemisphere (Good, 1974). Appreciably high incidence of endemism is encountered in the oceanic islands such as the Hawaii, Kerguelen, Tahiti, Samoa, Fiji, St. Helena, New Caledonia, the Galapagos, etc.

Continuous Intercontinental Ranges

The area of a taxon or of a vegetational feature is never really continuous. But the distribution which involves spreading over a whole territory, may be termed as continuous. The interruption in the continuity may occur due to lack of suitable intermediate habitats. Four main types of continuous ranges are recognised, namely (i) cosmopolitan, (ii) circumpolar, (iii) circumboreal, and (iv) pantropical. Cosmopolitan means distributed all over the globe where growth conditions are suitable. Such plant taxa are wide ranging and rather indifferent to environmental conditions and are termed as *cosmopolites* or *panendemics*. Obviously, such taxa at and below the rank of a genus are rare. The taxa distributed around the north and south poles are circumpolar in distribution while those distributed around the boreal zone are termed circumboreal in distribution. There are quite a few taxa which have distribution practically throughout the tropics and subtropics and indicate pantropic distribution.

Discontinuous Ranges

In discontinuous or disjunct ranges the plants are separated by wider gaps than the dispersal capacity of their propagules would normally bridge. The causes of discontinuity may be environmental or biotic. About five such types are described, viz. (i) *diffuse,* when the distribution range is broken into small and numerous equal parts, (ii) *bipartite,* when it is composed of only two separate parts in the same hemisphere, (iii) *bipolar,* when it is composed of two parts widely separated into northern and southern hemispheres, (iv) *altitudinal*, and (v) either *homogeneous* with identical populations or *heterogeneous* having related or unrelated forms. The most familiar discontinuous ranges are the (i) Arctic-Alpine, (ii) North Atlantic, (iii) North Pacific, (iv) North-south American, (v) Europe-Asian, (vi) Mediterranean, (vii) Tropical, (viii) South Pacific, (ix) South Atlantic, and (x) Antarctic.

Vicarious Areas

These are areas belonging to closely related taxa (vicariads) derived from the same common ancestor and tending to be mutually exclusive of one another in naturally occupying separate areas. From their very nature, ecotypes, for example, often tend to be vicarious. This means that the process of formation of geographical races is the main basis of formation of vicarious areas. In general, it is the marginal or peripheral segregation of a parent population which readily adapts to the newer environment.

Most of the well known subspecies described in the modern taxonomic monographs are good examples of vicariads. Several species with wide distribution are represented either by a large number of ecotypes which in turn tend to form subspecies and species or several varieties. These can be considered as vicariads and the areas occupied by them as vicarious areas.

It is often difficult to distinguish between true and false vicariads since many morphologically similar species evolve in response to environmental conditions quite independently through convergent evolution. All succulents, for example, occupying arid and semi-arid situations, are not necessarily interrelated. Experimental studies based on genetic characters are obviously needed for confirmation of the vicarious nature of apparently similar species or other taxa. True vicariads, depending upon the manner of their separation, may be classified as (i) horizontal or geographical, (ii) altitudinal or physiographic, (iii) habital or ecological, and (iv) seasonal.

Most systematic vicariads consisting of pairs or sets of higher taxa which are vicarious belong to the first or geographical category, a good example being the various races of *Pteridium aquilinum* (Pteridaceae), *Solanum nigrum* (Solanaceae), species of the genera *Podophyllum* (Ranunculaceae *sensu lato*),

Platanus (Platanaceae), *Senecio* (Compositae) and various others (c.f. Fernald, 1931; Cain, 1944; Camp, 1947 and Stebbins, 1950).

Examples of physiological vicariads inhabiting lower and higher altitudes respectively are *Myosotis sylvatica* and *M. alpestris, Phleum pratens* and *P. alpinum,* etc. Ecological vicariads grow in different habitats, some of them are *Scirpus lacustris* and *S. tabernaemontanii, Geum rivale* and *G. urbanum* and others.

The origin of vicarious populations is explained by a few hypotheses. One is that they have always been separated and migration took place by long-distance dispersal of seeds. The second is that the present disjunct areas are relicts of a former continuous distribution of a group. Stebbins (1950) has suggested five different methods of origin of vicarious areas, (i) long distance dispersal, (ii) past greater proximity, (iii) past continuity, (iv) stepping stones, and (v) divergent migration from a third area. Combinations of these methods may also be possible.

Each of these explanations is true for different ones of the modern vicarious areas. Long distance dispersal has most probably been the method of colonisation of remote oceanic islands, like Juan Fernandez, St. Helena and the Canary Islands. A continuous distribution over past land bridges to explain the origin of the flora of all the Pacific Islands has been proposed by Skottsberg (1925, 1938-1939). Cain (1944) has suggested the "stepping stone" method of long distance dispersal as the most likely one to explain the Antarctic migration and radiation of plants. Vicarious areas in the North and South America of the genera *Chorizanthe, Acaena, Godetia, Phacelia, Mimulus, Madia* and *Agoseris* can be explained more satisfactorily by this method. All the members of these genera have very different methods of seed-dispersal.

The explanation of divergent migration is the most likely one for the disjunct distribution of many Arctic and boreal species (Hulten, 1937). Similarly, complete and partial continuity of distribution in the past has also been strongly supported by the evidence from fossils in the case of certain modern disjunctions. Fossils of woody genera such as *Carpinus, Castanea, Fagus, Juglans, Quercus* and *Ulmus,* for example, are known from a great number of localities in both the Old and New World (Chaney, 1940, 1947).

Polytopy

It is the occurrence of a species or any other taxon in two or more separate areas. Such taxa are called *polytopic* or *polyendemic*. Several taxa which are distributed over vast but discontinuous ranges involving disjunct areas are examples of polytopy.

It is believed by some that approximately polytopic forms may have had an independent origin in their existing plurality of areas whose populations are similar because of parallel descent from a common ancestor. This would explain discontinuity on the basis of the species concerned having evolved independently in two or more separate areas. Although this seems possible where a common near-ancestry and minor taxa are concerned, it scarcely seems conceivable for members of major species whose common ancestry was remote and whose distinctive characters are numerous. Some hold that polytopic taxa in different areas have had an independent origin from taxonomically different ancestors and have arrived at their present similarity through convergent evolution.

The more widely accepted is the hypothesis that polytopic forms are immediately related, the intervening tracts having been bridged in the past either by a continuous series of populations or by long distance dispersal. If the theories of continental drift, land bridges and climatic changes are accepted, the explanation of discontinuous ranges and polytopy can be satisfactorily explained.

Centre of Origin

The area of a taxon normally above the level of a species in which the largest number of the constituent taxa of subordinate rank are concentrated, is termed as the centre of origin. But it is often not so easy, particularly in the absence of extensive palaeobotanical evidence. One of the ways in which areas are indicated is by *isoflors.* These are lines delimiting regions supporting equal number of species, for example, belonging to a single genus. The number of species may be expected to decrease regularly, from the generic centre outward, and to assume a pattern which suggests the tracts of past migration. Even here, palaeobotanical confirmation is essential. Groups also have their single or multiple *centres of variation,* where the greatest diversity and wealth of forms are concentrated (also called as the *mass centre*), and their *centres of frequency,* where the greatest numbers of individuals are accumulated.

In case of a single species with infraspecific taxa, there is a tendency to decrease the number of individuals towards the periphery of its area. But this is closely connected with adaptability to definite habitat conditions. The area is generally indicated by the shape enclosed by connecting all the peripheral points of its distribution on the map. The *potential area* of a species may be demonstrated by artificial introduction of its individuals. Each species has, besides its own natural area of distribution, a wider potential area, where it can be grown in cultivation or otherwise in the virtual absence of competition.

Intraneous, Extraneous and Other Elements

Certain plant species, occurring in a given floristic region or area, may be classified as *intraneous* when it is occurring within the area of its distribution and *extraneous,* if it is near its periphery. The components of such grouping form *special elements* in the flora. They are termed as *floral elements* which are closely related to their migration. In addition to these main general elements, a flora generally includes the *aliens* and *wides* (migrated from other floristic areas having extensive range). The detailed analysis of all these elements together with the endemics helps in establishing the genesis of the flora.

The Theory of Tolerance

Ronald Good (1931) proposed a theory to express the range of tolerance in plants and their distribution. This is known as the Theory of Tolerance, which states as follows:

Each and every plant species is able to exist and reproduce successfully only within a definite range of climatic and edaphic conditions. This range represents the tolerance of a species to external conditions.

The tolerance of a species is a specific character subject to the laws and processes of organic evolution in the same way as its morphological characters, but the two are not necessarily linked.

Change in the tolerance may or may not be accompanied by morphological change and morphological change may or may not be accompanied by change in tolerance.

Morphologically similar species may show wide differences in tolerance, and species with similar tolerance may show very little morphological similarity.

The relative distribution of species with similar ranges of tolerance is finally determined by the result of the competetion between them.

The tolerance of any larger taxonomic unit is the sum of the tolerances of its constituent species.

The author of this theory had discussed various points in details and summarised that:(i) any species shows a definite range of tolerance to external conditions at any given time—the whole picture of plant distribution, according to him, is very intimately related to the distribution of external factors so that no other view can be maintained; (ii) the supporting evidences are furnished by the behaviour of plants in cultivation, by the non-occurrence of acclimatisation, by the concept of adaptation to environment and by such matters as phasic development and vernalisation; and (iii) certain more details of the application of the theory are debatable since the environmental changes have been more rapid in the recent past than changes in the tolerance or morphology.

Some Relevant Information about Angiosperms

The Number and Size of Families

Various systems of classification brought out in Chapter 5 indicate to some extent their basis and total number of families of angiosperms. Here is the synopsis of these systems in tabular form, given for ready reference.

System/author	*Total no. of families*
Bentham & Hooker (1862-1883)	202 (including 3 families of gymnosperms)
Engler & Prantl (1887-1915)	285
Engler & Diels (1936)	303
Bessey (1915)	300
Lemee (1929, 1943)	300

Hutchinson (1926, 1934)	342
Hutchinson (1959, 1969, 1973)	368, 411, 418
Cronquist (1968)	354
Dahlgren (1975, 1980)	440, 438
Thorne 1976	321-450 (approx.)
Willis' Dictionary (1966)	500
Good (1974)	544

Twenty large families in the order of sequence

Family	*Genera*	*Species*
Compositae	1000	20,000
Orchidaceae	750	20,000
Papilionaceae	440	10,750
Gramineae	620	10,000
Rubiaceae	500	9,000
Euphorbiaceae	300	5,750
Labiatae	185	4,550
Scrophulariaceae	235	4,150
Cyperaceae	90	4,100
Melastomataceae	240	3,700
Myrtaceae	95	3,600
Asclepiadaceae	255	3,300
Cruciferae	375	3,200
Acanthaceae	250	3,100
Verbenaceae	75	3,000
Umbelliferae	320	2,850
Palmae	250	2,500
Lauraceae	32	2,500
Solanaceae	88	2,300

Geographical Classification of Families

Cosmopolitan

Gramineae, Compositae, Cyperaceae, Caryophyllaceae, Orchidaceae, Papilionaceae, Labiatae, Scrophulariaceae, Liliaceae, Boraginaceae and Gentianaceae

Subcosmopolitan

Cruciferae, Umbelliferae, Ranunculaceae, Rosaceae, Campanulaceae, Juncaceae, Onagraceae, Polygonaceae, Primulaceae, Convolvulaceae, Malvaceae, Solanaceae, Urticaceae, Rubiaceae, Euphorbiaceae, Lythraceae, Alismataceae, Elatinaceae, Hydrocharitaceae, Lemnaceae, Najadaceae, Nymphaeaceae, Potamogetonaceae.

Tropical

Amaryllidaceae, Aquifoliaceae, Araceae, Aristolochiaceae, Asclepiadaceae, Cucurbitaceae, Dioscoreaceae, Loranthaceae, Tiliaceae, and Ulmaceae. These families, however, have some members distributed in temperate countries. Certain other families with predominant tropical distribution are, Acanthaceae, Apocynaceae, Araliaceae, Gesneriaceae, Menispermaceae, Moraceae, Sapotaceae, Smilacaceae and Vitaceae. Less strikingly tropical families include Amaranthaceae, Anacardiaceae, Buddlejaceae, Caesalpiniaceae, Capparidaceae. Commelinaceae, Mimosaceae, Nyctaginaceae and Strychnaceae.

Temperate

Adoxaceae, Aceraceae, Betulaceae, Cannabaceae, Caprifoliaceae, Carpinaceae, Corylaceae, Diapensiaceae, Elaeagnaceae, Fumariaceae, Grossulariaceae, Juglandaceae, Monotropaceae, Podophyllaceae, Polemoniaceae, Salicaceae, Sambucaceae, Saxifragaceae, Scheuchzeriaceae, Trilliaceae and Vacciniaceae.

Endemic

These are indicated by numbers against respective continents, countries etc. America—2, N. America—9, Tropical America—47, S. America—10, Tropical Africa and Madagascar—36, S. Africa—11, Asia and Malaysia—15, Continental Asia, Japan and Formosa—22, Australia—19, New Caledonia—5, Malaysia—5, India—none.

Some Arborescent Compositae

Giant species of *Senecio* from tropical Africa, *Vernonia abrorea* in some forests of tropical Asia and Malaysia, species of *Olearia* from Australia and New Zealand, species of *Commidendron, Melanodendron* and *Petrobium* endemic to St. Helena, *Wilkesia, Argyroxiphium* and *Hesperomannia* endemic to Hawaiian Islands, *Robinsonia, Rhetinodendron* and *Dendroseris* endemic to Juan Fernandez Islands, *Brachyglottis* from New Zealand, *Dendrocacalia* from Bonin Islands, *Fitchia* on Islands of the Pacific, *Scalesia* endemic to Galapagos Islands.

Number and Size of Genera

Taxonomically the size of the genus is estimated by the number of species it contains. A great many are monotypic, i.e. they consist of only one species, while several others contain more than 1,000 species.

Total number of genera of flowering plants	approx. 12,500
Average number of species per genus	18
Genera with more than 1,000 species	14

These are: *Senecio* 2,500, *Astragalus, Euphorbia, Piper* and *Carex* each containing 2,000, others with about 1,000 to 2,000 species are *Bulbophyllum, Dendrobium, Epidendrum, Eugenia, Eupatorium, Peperomia, Psychotria, Solanum* and *Vernonia* and probably also *Begonia, Ficus* and *Pleurothallis*.

Genera containing more than 100 species	500

These are distributed as follows:

More or less cosmopolitan	50
Tropical	305
Temperate	90
Southern	30

Endemic genera:

Arctic flora	3 to 4
Euro-Siberian region	about 70
Sino-Japanese region	over 300
Western and Central Asiatic region	200
Mediterranean region	250
Macaronesia	30
Atlantic North America	100
Pacific North America	300
North Africa-Indian Desert	50
Tropical Africa	300
Sudan and West Africa	250
Madagascar	350
St. Helena	5
South Africa	500
India	120
Southeast Asia	300
Malaysia	400
Polynesian subkingdom	250
Hawaii	40
New Caledonia	130
Tropical America	3,000
Australia	500

Distribution of Species

Total number of species approx. 2,25,000

Cosmopolitan and Very Wide Species

Really speaking no species can be said to be cosmopolitan in the true sense of the word but there are quite a few which have very wide ranges, e.g. *Phragmites communis* is the most widely distributed of all angiosperms. Many other fresh-water aquatics are also relatively widely distributed. They include species of *Lemna, Potamogeton pectinatus, Typha latifolia, Ceratophyllum demersum, Cladium mariscus, Cyperus flavescens, Glyceria fluitans, Myriophyllum spicatum, Najas marina, Phalaris arundinacea, Scirpus* spp. and *Zannichellia palustris*. The most common temperate weeds naturalised in the tropics are *Capsella bursa-pastoris, Chenopodium album, Erigeron canadensis, Euphorbia helioscopa, Plantago major, Poa annua, Polygonum aviculare, Solanum nigrum, Sonchus oleraceus, Stellaria media, Taraxacum officinale* and *Urtica dioica*. The tropical extending into temperate zones are *Amaranthus angustifolius, Asclepias curassavica, Cynodon dactylon, Echinochloa crusgalli, Gnaphalium luteo-album, Paspalum distichum, Portulaca oleracea* and *Setaria verticillata*.

Pan-Tropical Species

About 115 species, most of them belonging to Malvaceae, Amaranthaceae, Compositae, Gramineae and Leguminosae are widely spread throughout the tropics. Many of them are temperate in origin and have escaped from cultivation.

Endemic Species

Of the total species of flowering plants, nearly 90% have a very restricted distribution and can be considered as endemic. Endemism in different parts of the world is as follows:

Arctic and Subarctic region	Low percentage
Arctic-Alpine	Low percentage
Euro-Siberian region	Low percentage
Sino-Japanese region	High endemism
Western and central Asiatic region	High endemism
Mediterranean	High endemism
Macronesian	High endemism
Atlantic North America	High endemism
Pacific North America	30-50%
North American-Indian desert	Poor endemism
Sudanese Park Steppe	Average
NE Africa	Average
W. Africa	Considerable
E. Africa	Average
Tropical Africa	Considerable
Madagascar	85% species
St. Helena	Only 3% species
S. Africa	High percentage
India	About 33%
SE Asia	40% species
Malaya	High percentage
Hawaiian region	Over 90% species
New Caledonia	Over 80% species
Melanesia, Micronesia and Polynesia	High percentage
Caribbean region	High percentage
Venezuela and Guiana	Probably high
Amazon Basin	Considerably high
South Brazil	Very high
Andes	42% species
Pampas	Small percentage
Juan Fernandez	70% species
N & E Australia	20% species
SW Australia	Over 75% species
Central Australia	Probably 100%
New Zealand	Over 75% species
Patagonian region	10% species
South temperate oceanic islands	About 50%

Glossary

Abaxial Away from the axis
Accessory Extra or additional
Actinomorphic Symmetrical in all planes
Actinomorphy Symmetry in all planes
Adaptability Ability to adapt
Adaptation Changed or modified form of growth in response to environmental conditions
Adaxial Towards the axis
Aestivation Arrangement in bud condition, e.g., arrangement of floral parts
Adnate Grown together or attached
Affinity Closeness due to relationship
Agamospermy Formation of seed without meiosis and fertilisation, i.e. without formation of gametes
Albian Stratigraphic period of the Cretaceous
Alete Without furrow (pollen)
Aliens Elements migrated from other floristic regions
Ament Dense, bracteate spike of unisexual and naked flowers; a catkin
Amentiferae A group of plants having ament inflorescence
Amentifers Catkin-bearers
Amphimixis Fusion of male and female gametes, fertilisation
Amphitropous ovule Half inverted or horizontal ovule having funiculus and micropyle at right angles to each other
Anatropous ovule Fully inverted ovule having funiculus and micropyle close together
Androecium Third whorl of a typical flower consisting of stamens
Anemogamous Wind-pollinated (and subsequently fertilised)
Anemogamy Fertilisation due to wind pollination
Anemophilous Pollinated by wind
Anemophily Pollination by wind
Aneuploidy A series of chromosome numbers without simple numerical relationship
Angiosperms A group of plants characterised by having the ovules enclosed in an ovary
Anisocytic (Stoma) with unequal subsidiary cells
Anomalous Abnormal
Anomocytic (Stoma) without distinct subsidiary cells
Antarctic South polar region
Anthesis The period during which a flower is fully expanded and functional
Anthocyanin A chemical class of flavonoid pigments, ranging in colour from blue to violet or purple or red; often found in petals
Anthostrobilus A flower-like cone (imaginary)
Anthoxanthin A group of flavonoid pigments, ranging in colour from yellow to orange to red, found in petals

Antibodies Bodies developing in the blood serum in reaction to foreign material and causing clumping of the blood.
Antigens Bodies occurring in red blood cells. They cause clumping of blood
Antisera Serum from immunised blood
Antipetalous In front of petals
Antisepalous In front of sepals
Aperturate Having aperture or opening
Apetalous Without petals
Apetaly A condition of petallessness
Aphanisis Reduction of perianth
Apocarpous With the carpels free from each other
Apomixis Failure of fertilisation or development of fruit without fertilisation
Apotracheal (Parenchyma) away from the vessels
Apotropous ovule An ovule, when erect, has a ventral raphe or when pendulous, has a dorsal raphe; a sapindaceous ovule
Aptian Stratigraphic period of the Cretaceous
Archegonium A specialised multi-cellular structure enclosing an egg
Archetype Structure with a common ground plan; presumably a primitive taxon
Arctic North polar region
Aril A specialised outgrowth from the funiculus which covers or is attached to the mature seed
Arillate (Adj.) with aril
Autogamy Self-fertilisation
Barremian Stratigraphic period of the Cretaceous
Bennettitales A group of the Mesozoic, cycad-like fossil pteridosperms
Betacyanin A chemical class of nitrogenous, water-soluble pigments, ranging in colour from blue to violet or purple or red; often found in petals of some kind of plants
Betalain A chemical class of pigments consisting of betacyanins and betaxanthins
Betaxanthin A chemical class of pigments, ranging in colour from yellow to orange to red; found in petals of some kind of plants
Binomial Consisting of two names
Biosystematics Taxonomy of living populations
Biotype A member of the individuals having the same or similar genotype
Binucleate With two nuclei
Bisporangiate strobilus A strobilus with both, micro- and megasporangia
Bisporic embryo-sac An embryo sac derived from two megaspores
Bitegmic ovule An ovule with two integuments
Calyx Outermost whorl of a typical flower, made up of sepals.
Campylotropous ovule An ovule with curved embryo and micropyle lying close to chalaza and funiculus
Cantharophilous Pollinated by beetles
Cantharophily Beetle-pollination
Capsule A dry, dehisent fruit composed of more than one carpel
Carboniferous A period in the Palaeozoic era
Carpel The fertile leaf (megasporophyll) of an angiosperm, which bears the ovules
Category A level or a rank of taxonomic group
Cauliflorous Plants bearing flowers on old stem
Caytoniales A group of the Mesozoic pteridosperms
Cenospecies A biosystematic category roughly corresponding to a section or a subgenus

Centrifugal From the centre to periphery (applied to the maturation sequence of flowers in the inflorescence or stamens in the flower)

Centripetal From the periphery to the centre (applied to the maturation sequence of flowers in the inflorescence or stamens in the flower)

Chalaza The part of the ovule or seed lying at the opposite end from the micropyle of the embryo sac

Chemotaxonomy Chemical based taxonomy

Chromosomes Thread-like bodies carrying hereditary material, enclosed in the nucleus

Classification Formation and arrangement of groups in a sequential manner

Collateral Side by side

Colpate pollen grain A pollen grain with slit-like aperture

Colporate pollen grain A pollen grain with both slit-like and pore-like apertures superposed on each other

Comparium A biosystematic category corresponding to a genus

Concrescence Fusion and growth together

Coniferales A group of conifers

Connate Grown together or attached; applied only to similar organs

Connective The tissue which connects the pollen sacs of an anther

Consolidation Putting together, applied to data collected by different persons

Constitutive Constant and not variable within smaller groups

Convergence Coming together although arising from widely separated positions

Convergent One that comes together in spite of widely separated origin; applied to evolution of groups of organisms

Contorted (aestivation) Arranged so that each member (either sepal or petal) has one edge exposed and the other edge covered

Corolla Second whorl of a typical flower consisting of petals

Corona Appendages between corolla and androecium

Corticatae A group name for the monocotyledons

Cotyledon Embryonal leaf in the seed

Cotypes The term identical with isotype

Crassinucellate ovule An ovule with massive nucellar tissue, at least at the micropylar end

Cretaceous A major period of the Mesozoic era

Cryptogams Non-flowering plants

Cupule a cup-like envelope enclosing the seed

Cyanogenetic Producing cyanide

Cycadales A group of living gymnosperms

Cycadofilicales A group of the Mesozoic seed ferns

Cymose (Applied to inflorescence) having determinate growth of the main axis due to development of terminal flower and giving lateral branches from below the flower

Cytotaxonomy Cytology based taxonomy

Deciduous Falling off; applied to leaves of certain plants, or floral parts such as sepals, petals, etc.

Dermogram Diagramatic representation of epidermal peculiarities

Dermotype Representation of cell types in the epidermis

Dibasic With two different basic numbers; applied to chromosome numbers or ploidy level

Dicotyledons Plants with two cotyledons in their seeds

Dioecious Bearing male and female flowers on separate individuals

Diplostemonous With two whorls of stamens

Distichous Arranged in two vertical longitudinal rows

Ecospecies A biosystematic category roughly corresponding to a species

Ecotype/s	A population adapted to a particular ecological habitat
Embryo sac	The female gametophyte of an angiosperm
Encyclopaedic	Considering all known information
Endemic/s	With a restricted distribution; applied to plant or animal groups occurring in a narrow range of distribution
Endemism	Restricted distribution of a taxon
Endogamy	Self-breeding behaviour
Endomorphic	Pertaining to internal structure
Endosperm	Food storage tissue of a seed that is derived from triple fusion nucleus of the embryo sac
Entomogamy	Fertilisation due to insect pollination
Entomophily	Insect-pollination
Entomophilous	Insect-pollinated flowers
Epibiotic/s	Endemics of relict nature
Epigyny	The inferior ovary
Epipetalous	Attached to the petals
Epiphyte	A plant growing attached to another plant but not deriving its food or water from it
Euploidy	True multiples; applied to chrmosome numbers when they exhibit multiple relationship within a group
Eurypalynous	Taxa with different pollen morphology
Exine	The outer wall layer of a pollen grain or spore
Exogamy	Out-breeding or cross-breeding
Exomorphic	Pertaining to external form
Extant	Living presently
Extinct	Not living presently
Extinction	Total disappearance from the site
Extraneous	From outer regions; applied to organisms migrating from outside the boundary under consideration
Follicle	A fruit derived from a single carpel, which dehisces along one suture at maturity
Foraminae	More or less circular openings scattered over the entire surface of pollen exine
Forate	(A pollen grain) with foraminae
Fortuitous	Characters showing no functional relationships
Fossilization	A process by which plants and/or animals are preserved in the form of half-burned specimens
Free-central placenta	A placenta consisting of free-standing column from the base of the compound unilocular ovary
Funiculus	A stalk of an ovule
Gametophyte	A generation that produces gametes or reproductive cells
Gamopetalous	With petals connate
Gamosepalous	With sepals connate
Genecology	A combined discipline consisting of genetics and ecology
Genetics	A study of genes and their behaviour; often deals with the study of heredity or hereditary mechanism
Genonomy	A discipline dealing with the study of genes and their behaviour; generally considered to be synonymous with genetics
Genotype	A member of the genetically identical population or simply genetic constitution
Geophilous	Marsh loving
Geophytes	Marsh plants
Glossopteridale:	A group of fossil pteridosperms of the Gondwanaland
Glumaceous	Glume-bearing or glume-like

Glume/s	A dry bract subtending a flower; applied to bracts of grasses, sedges and allied groups of plants
Gnetales	A group of living gymnosperms having many similarities with dicotyledons
Gymnosperms	A group of plants characterised by naked ovules
Gynobasic style	A style which is attached directly to the receptacle as well as to the base of the carpel/s
Gynoecium	The innermost whorl of a typical flower consisting of carpels
Gynandrophore	A common stalk of the gynoecium and androecium
Gynophore	A stalk of the gynoecium
Gynostemium	A composite structure formed from the fusion of gynoecium and androecium
Habitat	A precise locality; a natural home
Haemolyse	To destroy
Haemolysis	The destruction
Haplocheilic	With a single lip; applied to stoma derived from a single guard-cell-mother cell along with its subsidiaries
Haplostemonous	With a single whorl of stamens
Helobial endosperm	Endosperm in which the first division of the primary endosperm nucleus is followed by cell-plate formation, after which successive divisions follow nuclear or cellular pattern
Herbal/s	A book/s with descriptions and illustrations of medicinal plants
Herbalist/s	Author/s of herbal/s
Herbarium	A place where dried plant specimens are preserved
Herbarium sheet	A hard paper on which dried plant specimen is mounted
Herbarium specimen	A dried plant specimen mounted on a hard paper
Heterobathmy	Different evolutionary grades
Heterogamy	Fusion of unlike gametes
Heterogeneous	Dissimilar groups derived from different ancestral stocks
Heterotrophic	Dependent for nutrition; parasitic or saprophytic
Heterotypic	Applied to different types (taxa); used in connection with names of taxa
Heteroxyly	Presence of two types of elements in the wood or xylem, e.g. vessels as well as tracheids. In short, presence of vessels in the xylem as in majority of angiosperms
Hilate	(Applied to spore) with hilum, i.e. more or less circular pore at the proximal end
Holarctic	Entire region near the north pole
Holophytic	Self-sufficient (with regard to nutrition) plants, i.e. green plants
Holotype	The specimen used by the author for naming the taxon
Homogeneous	Similar individuals/groups related to each other through common ancestry
Homologous	Similar (organs) with common ancestry
Homology	Similarity due to common ancestry
Homonym	Same name given to two or more different taxa
Homotypic	Applied to same taxon; used with regard to names of taxa
Homoxyly	Xylem or wood with similar tracheal elements, i.e. wood without vessels as in majority of pteridophytes and gymnosperms
Hydrophilous	Pollinated through the agency of water
Hydrophily	Pollination through the agency of water
Hypanthium	A cup-like structure developed from the adnation of sepals, petals and stamens
Hypogynous	With perianth and stamens arising from beneath the gynoecium
Hypothesis	A thesis without evidence
Hypothetical	Consideration without evidence, imaginary

Hysterophytic Dependent (for nutrition) plants, i.e. non-green plants
Identification Recognition of identity
Imbricate Arranged in a tight spiral so that the outermost member has both edges exposed, the innermost member has both edges covered and the rest with one edge covered and the other exposed
Immutable Incapable of sudden inheritable change or mutation
Imperfectae A group name given to non-flowering plants such as algae, fungi, mosses, etc.
Indicator The character or a feature showing the highest average correlation with similar other characters
Inferior ovary An ovary with calyx, corolla and androecium attached to its summit
Inflorescence Arrangement of flowers often on a leafless branch
Integument One of the one or two layers of nucellar envelop; the fore-runner of the seed coat
Intercalary meristem A meristem detached from the apical meristem, which produces primary tissues
Intervascular Between the conducting elements or tissues
Intraneous Occurring within the limits; applied to floristic elements, i.e. indigenous
Inventory One which is useful for invention. In case of plant identification it is a flora or a manual
Involucre Any structure which surrounds another structure; in angiosperms usually applied to a whorl of bracts beneath the inflorescence
Isoetales A group of living, aquatic, heterosporous, pteridophytes
Isoflor/s The lines delimiting regions supporting equal number of species
Isolation Separation into distinct units; applied to plant groups which are separated from the rest by certain characteristics such as genetic, geographic etc.
Isomerous With same number, e.g., stamens isomerous with the petals
Isotype One or few specimens that are duplicates of, holotype
Karyotype Morphology of chromosomes at somatic metaphase
Laesura A longitudinal furrow at the proximal end of a spore
Laminar Thin and flat
Laminar placentation An arrangement of ovules on the entire surface of the carpel
Laticifer A cell or a tube containing latex
Lectotype/s A specimen or any other element designated to serve as a nomenclatural type in the absence of holotype
Leucoanthocyanins Colourless anthocyanins
Loculicidal Dehiscing along the median line of each locule
Megasporangium A sporangium which produces megaspores
Megaspore A spore which may develop into a female gametophyte
Megasporophyll A sporophyll which bears one or more megasporangia
Mesogeneous A stoma in which subsidiary cells as well as guard cells originate from the single common mother cell
Mesophytes Plants adopted to ordinary amount of water stress
Mesozoic The middle era approximately 250-100 million years ago, of the geological history
Micropyle An opening formed by integuments of an ovule to the nucellus
Microsporangium A sporangium which produces microspores
Microspore A spore which may develop into a male gametophyte
Microsporophyll A sporophyll which bears one or more microsporangia
Monocarpic Blooming only once and then dying; applied to certain perennials such as century plant
Monoecious With unisexual flowers, both types borne on the same individual

Monograph	A treatment dealing with all the available data
Monographic	Considering all the available data
Monolete	A spore with a single longitudinal furrow at the proximal end
Monophyletic	Evolved from a single common ancestry
Monophylesis	Evolution from a single common ancestry
Monosomic	An individual with one chromosome less than the normal i.e. $2n-1$
Monosporic	Derived from a single spore
Morphology	Study of form and structure
Multilacunar node	A node with many leaf-gaps
Multipalynous	With varied pollen morphology
Neoteny	A synchronic disharmony in which a plant attains sexual maturity while remaining permanently juvenile in some vegetative features
Neotype	A specimen or any other element chosen to serve as nomenclatural type in the absence of a holotype or syntypes
Node	A place of attachment of the leaf on a stem
Nomenclature	Application of a name
Nomina conservanda	A name or names conserved to avoid confusion, although they may not be according to the rules of nomenclature
Nucellus	A tissue of the ovule lying inside the integuments and which encloses the female gametophyte
Nullisomic	An individual having one pair of chromosomes less than the normal, i.e. $2n-2$
Oligocarpy	A condition with one carpel
Ontogeny	The developmental history of an individual
Orthotropous ovule	A straight ovule with the micropyle at the opposite end of the stalk
Palaeobotany	Botany of fossils
Palaeontological	Based on developmental studies of historical (fossil) plants
Palaeozoic	A great era, approximately 450-250 million years ago, of the geological history
Pangaea	A hypothetical single land mass from which the present continents are believed to have separated
Parallelism	Similar development of features in the related groups of plants
Paratracheal	Applied to the parenchyma, lying in close association with the vessels
Paratype	A specimen or any other element other than the isotype or syntype cited by the author while describing the taxon
Parietal placenta	A placenta along the walls or on the intruded partial partitions of a compound unilocular ovary
Pentoxylales	A group of fossil pteridosperms, similar to the living order Pandanales
Perfectae	A group name given to flowering plants
Perforation	An opening in the end wall of the vessel element
Perianth	All the sepals and petals of a flower collectively
Perigenous	Applied to stoma in which subsidiary cells and guard cells originate from different cells
Perigynous	Having perianth and stamens united into a cup-like structure distinct from the ovary, generally around the base of the gynoecium
Perigyny	A perigynous condition
Phenetic	Pertaining to the expressed characteristics of an individual, without regard to its genetic nature
Phenon/s	Groups of similar organisms recognised by numerical methods

Phenotype Pertaining to the external similarity without regard to the genetic nature

Phyllospermae With the ovules borne on specialised or modified leaves

Phyllotaxy Arrangement of leaves

Phylogenetic Based on evolutionary history of a group

Phylogeny Evolutionary history of a group

Phytochemistry Plant chemistry

Phytogeography Plant geography

Placenta Tissue of the ovary to which ovules are attached

Placentation Disposition of placenta in the ovary

Plasticity Capacity to modify

Pleiomerous Pertaining to the effects of genes when a single gene is responsible for many effects. When applied to flowers, it means flowers with many parts

Pleiotropy Multiple effect of a single gene

Pollen A mass of young male gametophytes

Pollination Transfer of pollen from anthers to the stigma of the same or other flower

Pollinium A coherent cluster of pollen grains, transported as a unit during pollination

Polycarpy A condition of many carpels

Polynomial A name consisting of many, often more than two, terms

Polyphyletic Of more than one evolutionary origin

Polyploid With more than two sets of chromosomes

Polyploidy Doubling of chromosomes

Polysomaty Duplication or multiplication of any one pair of chromosomes

Polysomic Individual with duplication or multiplication of any one pair of chromosomes

Polythetic Groups derived by using multiple attributes

Polytopic A taxon occurring in two or more separate areas

Polytopy Occurrence of a taxon in two or more separate areas

Population A group of individuals of the same species

Poricidal Opening by pores

Posteriori With previous experience or valid reasons

Precipitin Pertaining to the reaction in which the two types of proteins or a protein and a serum form precipitate

Primitive Similar to the ancestral condition

Priori Without past experience or a valid reason, i.e. intuitive

Pro-angiosperms A hypothetical group of plants which is believed to have given rise to angiosperms

Proteophylls Probable ancestors of the subclass Rosidae

Pseudanthium A cluster of small or reduced flowers, collectively appearing like a single flower

Psilate Pertaining to a pollen grain having more or less circular distal aperture with smooth margin

Pteridophytes Ferns or vascular cryptogams

Pteridosperms Seed ferns

Raceme An inflorescence having pedicillate flowers arising in acropetal sequence from an unbranched central axis

Racemose Pertaining to a broad class of inflorescences characterised by flowering in acropetal sequence

Raphe The part of the funiculus which is permanently attached to the integument of the ovule, commonly visible as a line or ridge on the mature seed coat

Raphide	A needle-shaped crystal of calcium oxalate occurring in special sac-like cells in certain plants
Recapitulation	Duplication of events or repetition of events
Revision	In taxonomic studies it means re-investigation of a particular group with additional data, e.g. revision of a family, genus, etc. occurring in a particular geographical region
Rugae	Slit-like apertures of pollen grains occurring all over the surface
Rugate	Pollen grains with global distribution of elongate apertures
Samara	An indehiscent winged fruit
Sarcotesta	An outgrowth from an integument
Satellite	A terminal globular portion of the chromosome cut off by the secondary constriction
Scalariform	Ladder-like, with cross-bars connecting vertical members
Scales	Dry, leaf-like outgrowths
Sclerophyllous	With hard reduced leaves
Semantides	Molecules of DNA, RNA, and various amino-acids in the form of proteins
Senomanian	A stratigraphic period of the Cretaceous
Septicidal	Opening along the septa
Septum	A partition
Serology	Study of antigen-antibody reaction by employing known serum
Sero-taxonomy	Serology based taxonomy
Speciation	Formation or evolution of new species
Sporangia	Chambers which produce spores
Sporangium	Singular of sporangia
Sporophyll	A special leaf which bears sporangia
Stachyosporous	With the ovules borne terminally on telomes
Stele	The primary vascular structure of the stem or root, together with any other tissue which may be enclosed
Stenopalynous	With uniform pollen morphology
Stratigraphic	Belonging to various strata
Strobilus	A cluster of sporophylls on an axis; a cone
Subsidiary cells	The modified epidermal cells immediately adjacent to the guard cells
Sulcus	A longitudinal furrow at the distal end of the pollen grain
Superior ovary	An ovary situated at a higher level on the receptacle than the attachment of other flower parts
Supernumerary	More than the normal number; pertaining to the chromosomes
Sympetalous	With united petals
Symphysis	Connation or lateral fusion of floral parts
Synangium	A cluster of sporangia
Syncarpous	With the carpels united to form a compound ovary
Syncotyly	Fusion of cotyledons
Syndetocheilic	Pertaining to stoma in which subsidiary cells and the guard cells arise from different cells
Syndrome	A group of characters
Syntype	Specimens or any other elements used by the author for naming a taxon without indication of a holotype or isotypes
Tautonym	A binomial in which the generic name and the specific epithet are exactly the same
Taxogram	A diagram showing relationship of taxonomy with other disciplines
Taxon	Any taxonomic group of whatever rank
Taxonomy	A synthetic discipline in which organisms are identified, named and classified according to their natural affinities

Telome	An ultimate branch of a dichotomously branching stem
Tenuinucellate ovule	An ovule with the nucellus consisting of a single layer of cells
Terrestrial	Of the land
Tetrad	A group of four
Tetrapetalae	A group name for the crucifer-like plants
Tetrasomic	With four sets of an individual chromosome when others are in two sets, i.e. $2n + 2$
Tetrasporic embryo sac	An embryo sac derived from four megaspores
Topotype/s	Specimens collected at various times from the same locality
Triaperturate	With three apertures
Trilete	A spore with three longitudinal furrows at its proximal end and radiating from a point
Trimerous	With parts in sets of threes
Trisomic	With one extra chromosome similar to any one pair, i.e. $2n + 1$
Tunicatae	A group name given to the dicotyledons
Ulcus	A more or less circular distal aperture of the pollen grain
Uniaperturate	With one aperture
Unipalynous	With similar or uniform pollen morphology
Unitegmic ovule	An ovule with a single integument
Valvate aestivation	Arranged with the margins of the petals or sepals adjacent throughout their lengths, without overlapping
Venation	Arrangement of veins
Vessels	The xylem tubes formed from several vessel elements joined end to end
Vicariad/s	Closely related taxa
Vicarious areas	Areas belonging to closely related taxa
Wides	Taxa having extensive range
Wood	Secondary xylem
Xeric	Dry, deficient in water
Zygomorphic	Symmetrical in one plane only; applied to floral parts

Bibliography

Abbott, H.C. des (1886), Certain chemical constituents of plants considered in relation to their morphology and evolution, *Bot. Gaz.*, **11**: 270-272.

Adams, C.G. and D.V. Ag(Ed.) (1967), *Aspects of Tethyan Biogeography,* Systematists Assocn., London.

Adanson, M. (1763), *Familes des Plantes,* Vols. I & II, Vincent, Paris.

Adriano, F.T. and E. Youzon (1933), Natural colour preservation of Philippine plant materials for museum and exhibition purposes, *Nat. Appl. Sci. Bull.*, **3**: 121-125.

Afzelius, B.M. (1954), La Structure du sporoderme vue au microscope electronique, *Int. Bot. Congr. Paris, Rapp. Comm. Sect.*, **6**: 241.

_______ (1956), Electron microscopic investigations into exine stratification, *Grana Palynologica,* **12**: 22-37.

Airy Shaw, H.K. (1952), Note on taxonomic position of Nyctanthes L. and Dimetra Kerr., *Kew* Bull., **1952**: 271-272.

Allard, H.A. (1951), Drying herbarium specimens slowly or rapidly, *Castanea,* **16**: 129-134.

Altschul, Siri von Reis (1977), Exploring the herbarium, *Sci. Amer.*, **236**: 96-134.

Amelunxen, F., K. Morganorth and T. Picksak (1967), Untersuchungen au der epidermis mit den stereoscan Elektronen mikroskop, *Z. Pflanzen Physiol.*, **57**: 79-95.

Anderson, E. (1941), Mass collections—the technique and use of mass collections in plant taxonomy, *Ann. Missouri Bot. Gard.*, **28**: 287-292.

_______ (1949), *Introgressive hybridization,* John Wiley & Sons, New York.

_______ (1953), Introgressive hybridization, *Biol. Rev.*, **28**: 280-307.

Anderson, E. and G.L. Stebbins (1954), Hybridization as an evolutionary stimulus, *Evolution,* **8**: 378-388.

Andrews, F.M. (1932), Preservation of dry plant material, *Ind. Acad. Sci. Proc.*, **41**: 80-81.

Arber, A. (1925), *Monocotyledons, A Morphological Study,* Cambridge Univ. Press, Cambridge.

Archer, W.A. (1952), Aerosol for controlling herbarium pests, *Science,* **116**: 233-234.

Arber, E.A.N. and J. Parkin (1907), On the origin of angiosperms, *J. Linn. Soc. Bot.*, **38**: 29-80.

Arekal, G.D. (1963), Embryological studies in Canadian representatives of the tribe Rhinantheae, Scrophulariaceae, *Canad. J. Bot.*, **41**: 267-302.

Arnold, C.A. (1947), *An Introduction to Paleobotany,* McGraw-Hill, New York.

Avdulov, N.P. (1931), Karyo-systematische untersuchungen der Familie Gramineen, *Trudy Prikl. Bot. Genet. Selek.* (Suppl.) **43**: 1-428.

Axelrod, D.I. (1952), A theory of angiosperm evolution, *Evolution,* **6**: 29-59.

_______ (1959), Poleward migration of early angiosperm flora, *Science,* **130**(3369): 203-207.

_______ (1960), The evolution of flowering plants, *in:* S. Tax (Ed.), *The Evolution of Life,* Univ. Chicago Press, Chicago, pp. 227-305.

_______ (1970), Mesozoic palaeogeography and early angiosperm history, *Bot. Rev.*, **36**: 277-319.

Ayensu, E.S. (1970), *Anatomy of Monocotyledons—VI. Dioscoreales,* Clarendon Press, Oxford.

_______ (1970a), Comparative anatomy of *Dioscorea rotundata and Dioscorea cayenensis, in:* N.B.K. Robson, D.F. Cutter and M. Gregory (Ed.), *New Research in Plant Anatomy,* Academic Press, London. pp. 127-136.

Babcock. E.B. (1942), Systematics, cytogenetics and evolution in *Crepis, Bot. Rev.*, **8**: 139-190.

_______ (1947), *The Genus Crepis,* Parts I & II, Univ. California Publ. Bot., **21**: 1-198; **22**: 199-1030.

Babcock, E.B. and D.R. Cameroon (1934), Chromosomes and phylogeny in *Crepis*-II. The relationships of 108 species, *Univ. California Publ. Agr. Sci.*, **6**: 287-324.

Babcock, E.B., G.L. Stebbins and J.A. Jenkins (1937), Chromosome and phylogeny in some genera of the Crepidinae, *Cytologia Fuji Jub. Vol.*, pp. 188-210.

Bailey, I.W. (1944), The development of vessels in angiosperms and its significance in morphological research, *Amer. J. Bot.*, **31**: 421-428.

_______ (1949), Origin of Angiosperms: need for a broadened outlook, *J. Arnold Arbor.*, **30**: 64-70.

_______ (1951), The use and abuse of anatomical data in the study of phylogeny and classification, *Phytomorphology*, **1**: 67-69.

_______ (1956), Nodal anatomy in retrospect, *J. Arnold Arbor.*, **37**: 269-287.

Bailey, I.W. and B.G.L. Swamy (1949), The morphology and relationships of *Austrobaileya*, *J. Arnold Arbor.*, **30**: 211-226.

_______ (1951), The conduplicate carpel and its inital trends of specialization, *Amer. J. Bot.*, **38**: 373-379.

Baker, H.G. (1959), Reproductive methods as factors in speciation of flowering plants, *Cold. Spring Harb. Symp. Quant. Biol.*, **24**: 177-191.

_______ (1961), Rapid speciation in relation to changes in the breeding systems of plants, *in:* D.L. Bailey (Ed.), *Recent Advances in Botany*, Toronto Univ. Press, Toronto, pp. 881-885.

Bakker, E.M.V.Z. (1953), *South African Pollen Grains and Spores*, Balkema, Amsterdam.

Banks, H.P. (1968), The early history of land plants, *in:* E.T. Drake (Ed.), *Evolution and Environment*, Yale Univ. Press, New Heaven.

Barber, H.N. (1955), Adaptive gene substitutions in Tasmania Eucalypts. I Genes controlling the development of glaucousness, *Evolution*, **9**: 1-14.

_______ (1956), The natural history of natural selection, *Austr. J. Sci.*, **1956**: 148-159.

Barber, H.N. and W.D. Jackson (1957), Natural selection in action in *Eucalyptus*, *Nature*, **179**: 1267-1269.

Barua, P.K. and A.C. Dutta (1959), Leaf sclereids in the taxonomy of *Thea* camellias-II, *Camellia sinensis* L., *Phytomorphology*, **9**: 372-382.

Bate-Smith, E.C. (1948), Paper chromatography of anthocyanins and related substances in petal extracts, *Nature*, **161**: 835-838.

_______ (1958), Plant phenolics as taxonomic guides, *Proc. Linn. Soc.*, **169**: 198-211.

_______ (1962), Phenolic constituents of plants and their taxonomic significance, *J. Linn. Soc.* (Bot.), **58**: 95-173.

Bate-Smith, E.C. and T. Swain (1966), The asperuloides and the aucubins, *in:* T. Swain (Ed.), *Comparative Phytochemistry*, Academic Press, London, pp. 159-174.

Bauhin, G. (1623), *Pinax Theatri Botanici*, L. Regis, Paris.

Beard, J.S. (1968), Drying specimens in humid weather, *Taxon*, **17**: 744.

Beck, E.B. (1976), *Origin and Early Evolution of Angiosperms*, Columbia Univ. Press, New York.

Behnke, H.D. (1965), Uber das phloem der Dioscoreacean unter besonderer Beeucksichtingung ihrer phloem becken II. Mittellung: Electronenoptische untersuchungen zur Feinstruktur des phloem-beckens, *Z. Pflanzen.*, **53**: 214-244.

_______ (1967), Uber den Aufbau der Siebelement Plastiden einiger Dioscoreacean, *Z. Pflanzen.* **57**: 243-254.

_______ (1969a), Die siebrohen-plastiden der monocotyledonen. Vergleichende undersuchungen uber Feinbau und Verbreitung eine characteristichen plastiden-types, *Planta*, **84**: 174-184.

_______ (1969b), Ultrastructure of angiosperm sieve-tube plastids in relation to systematics. Abstr. XI, *Intern. Bot. Congr.* (Seattle), p. 12.

_______ (1972), Sieve-element, plastids in relation to angiosperm systematics. An attempt towards a classification by ultrastructural analysis, *Bot. Rev.*, **38**: 155-197.

_______ (1975a), P-type sieve-element plastids: A correlative ultrastructural and ultra-histochemical study on the diversity and uniformity of a new reliable character in seed plant systematics, *Protoplasma*, **83**: 91-101.

_______ (1975b), The basis of angiosperm phylogeny: Ultrastructure, *Ann. Missouri Bot. Gard.*, **62**: 647-663.

Behnke, H.D. (1977), Transmission electron microscopy and systematics of flowering plants, *in:* K. Kubitzki (Ed.), *Plant Systematics and Evolution,* Suppl. 1 Springer Verlag, New York, pp. 155-178.

Bell, W.A. (1956), Lower cretaceous floras of western Canada, *Geol. Surv. Canada Mem.,* **285**: 1-331.

_______ (1957), Flora of the upper cretaceous Nanaimo group of Vancouver Island, British Columbia, *Geol. Surv. Canada Mem.,* **293**: 1-84.

Benson, L. (1957), *Plant Classification,* D.C. Heath & Co., Boston.

_______ (1962), *Plant Taxonomy,* Ronald Press, New York.

Benson, M. (1904), *Telangium scottii,* a new species of *Telangium* showing structure, *Ann. Bot.,* **18**: 161-177.

Bentham, G. & J.D. Hooker (1862-1883), *Genera Plantarum* Vols. I–III, Reeve & Co., Williams & Norgate, London.

Benzig, D. (1967), Development patterns in stem primary xylem of woody Ranales, I & II, *Amer. J. Bot.,* **54**: 805-823.

Berry, E.W. (1934), Former land connection between Asia and North America as indicated by the distribution of fossil trees, *Proc. Fifth Pacif. Sci. Congr.,* 3093-3106.

Bertarelli, E. (1902), il metodo biologico ele sue applicazione all diagnoi differenziable delle farine delle leguminose, *G. Acad. Med. Torino,* **8**: 489-492.

Bessey, C.E. (1883), Evolution and classification, *Bot. Gaz.,* **18**: 329-332.

_______ (1897), Phylogeny and taxonomy of angiosperms, *Bot. Gaz.,* **24**: 145-178.

_______ (1915), The phylogenetic taxonomy of flowering plants, *Ann. Missouri Bot. Gard.,* **2**: 109-164.

Bhandari, N.N. (1971), Embryology of the Magnoliales and comments on their relationships, *J. Arnold Arbor.,* **52**: 1-39, 285-304.

Bhoj Raj (1961), Pollen morphological studies in the Acanthaceae, *Grana Palynologica,* **3**(1): 3-108.

Bierhorst, D.W. (1971), *Morphology of Vascular Plants,* Macmillan & Co., New York.

Bjorkman, S.O. (1960), Studies in *Agrostis* and related genera, *Symb. Bot. Upsal.,* **17**: 1-112.

Bjorkman, O.S. and P. Molmgren (1963), Adaptability of the photosynthetic apparatus to light intensity in ecotypes from exposed and shaded habitats, *Physiologia Pl.,* **16**: 889-914.

Blackwelder, R.E. (1962), Animal taxonomy and the new systematics, *in:* B. Glass (Ed.), *Survey of Biological Progress,* **4**: 1-57.

Blair, W.F. and B.L. Turner (1972), The integrative approach to biological classification, *in:* J.A. Behnke (Ed.), *Challenging Biological Problems,* Oxford Univ. Press, New York, pp. 193-217.

Blake, S.F. (1935), Better herbarium specimens, *Rhodora,* **37**: 19.

_______ (1961), *Geographic Guide to Floras of the World,* Part II, U.S. Dept. Agr. Misc. Publ., 797.

Blake, S.F. and A.C. Atwood (1942), *Geographic Guide to Floras of the World,* Part I, U.S. Dept. Agr. Misc. Publ., 401.

Blakeslee, A.F. and J. Belling (1924), Chromosomal mutations in the Jimson weed *Datura stramonium, J. Heredity,* **15**: 195-206.

Bloch, R. (1946), Differentiation and pattern in *Monstera deliciosa,* The idioblastic development of the trichosclereids in the air-roots, *Amer. J. Bot.,* **33**: 544-551.

Bocher, T.W. (1943), Studies on variation and biology in *Plantago lanceolata* L., *Dansk, Bot. Arkiv.,* **11**(3): 1-18.

_______ (1970), The present status of biosystematics, *Taxon,* **19**: 3-5.

_______ (1972), Comparative anatomy of three species of the apophyllous genus *Gymnophyton, Amer. J. Bot.,* **59**: 494-503.

Bondeson, W. (1952), Entwicklungsgeschichte und Bau der Spaltoffnungen ble den Gatungen *Trochodendron* Sieb. et Zucc., *Tetracentron* Oliv. und *Drymis* J.R. et G. Frost, *Acta Hort. Berg.,* **16**: 169-218.

Bonner, R.E. (1964), On some clustering techniques, *IBM Res. Dev.,* **8**: 22.

Bonnett, H.T. and E.H. Newcomb (1965), Polyribosomes and cisternal accumulations in root cells of radish, *J. Cell. Biol.,* **27**: 423-432.

Borrill, M. (1961), The pattern of morphological variation in diploid and tetraploid *Dactylis, J. Linn. Soc. Bot.,* **56**: 441-452.

Botha, D.J. and J. Coetzee (1976), A portable dryer for herbarium specimens, *J. African Bot.,* **42**: 42-44.

Boyden, A. (1942), Systematic serology: A critical appreciation, *Physiol. Zool.,* **15**: 109-145.
_______ (1964), Perspectives in systematic serology, *in:* C.A. Leone (Ed.), *Taxonomic Biochemistry and Serology,* Ronald Press, New York, pp. 75-99.
Boyle, J. (1945), Development lines in pollination mechanism in the Coniferales, *Sci. Proc. R. Dublin Soc.,* **24**: 43-62.
Bradshaw, A.D. (1957), Population differentiation in *Agrostis tenuis.* I. Morphological differentiation, *New Phytol.,* **58**: 208-227.
_______ (1965), Evolutionary significance of phenotypic plasticity in plants, *Adv. Gen.,* **13**: 115-155.
Braun, A. (1859), *Flora der Provinz Bradenburg,* W. Englemann, Leipzig.
Bremekamp, C.E.B. (1939), Phylogenetic interpretations and genetic concepts in taxonomy, *Chron. Bot.,* **5**: 390.
_______ (1944), Materials for a monograph of Strobilanthinae (Acanthaceae), *Verb. Nederl. Acad Wet. II,* **40**(1): 1-306.
Brenan, J.P.M. (1968), The relevance of national herbaria to modern taxonomic research, *in:* V.H. Heywood (Ed.), *Modern Methods in Plant Taxonomy,* Academic Press, London. pp. 23-32.
Brewbaker, J.L. (1967), The distribution and phylogenetic significance of binucleate and trinucleate pollen-grains in the angiosperms, *Amer. J. Bot.,* **54**: 1069-1083.
Brown, R.W. (1954), *Composition of Scientific Words,* Smithsonian Institution Press, Baltimore.
Brown, W.V. (1958), Leaf anatomy in grass systematics, *Bot. Gaz.,* **119**: 170-178.
Brunswick, H. (1920), Uber das Vorkommen von Gripskristallen bei der Tamaricaceae, *Sber Acad. Wiss. Wien (Math. Naturw. Kl.,* Abst. I, **129**: 115-136.
Buchholz, J.T. (1939), The embryogeny of *Sequoia sempervirens,* with a comparison of the sequoias, *Amer. J. Bot.,* **26**: 248-257.
Burger, W.C. (1977), The piperales and the monocots. Alternative hypothesis for the origin of monocotyledons flower, *Bot. Rev.,* **43**(3): 345-393.
Burkill, I.H. and D. Prain (1936), An account of the genus *Dioscorea, Ann. Roy. Bot. Gard. Calcutta,* **14**: 1-528.
Butterfield, B.G. and B.A. Maylan (1972), Scalariform perforation plate development in *Laurelia novae—Zeylandiae* A. Cunn. A scanning electron microscope study, *Austr. J. Bot.,* **20**: 253-259.
Buxbaum, F. (1925), Vergleichend Anatomichen der *Melanthioideae, Repert. nov. spec.,* Regn. Beihefte **29**: 1-80.
_______ (1927), Nachtrag dazu, *Bot. Zbl. Beihefte I, Abst.* **44**: 255.
_______ (1936), Die Entwicklungslinien der Lilioideae, *Bot. Arch.,* **38**: 242-293.
Cain, A.J. (1958), Logic and memory in Linnaeus' system of taxonomy, *Proc. Linn. Soc. London,* **169**: 144-163.
_______ (1959a), The post-Linnaean development of taxonomy, *Proc. Linn. Soc. London,* **170**: 233-244.
_______ (1959b), Function and taxonomic importance, *Systematics Asson. Publ. No.* **3**: 5-19, London.
Cain, S.A. (1944), *Foundations of Plant Geography,* Harper & Row, New York.
Camerarius, R.J. (1694), *De Sexu Plantarum Epistola,* Tubingen. Quoted from Maheshwari (1950).
Camp, E.H. (1946), On the use of artificial heat in the preparation of herbarium specimens, *Bull. Torrey Bot. Club,* **73**: 235-243.
Camp, W.H. (1947), Distribution patterns in modern plants and the problems of ancient dispersals, *Ecol. Mono.,* **17**: 159-183.
Camp, W.H. and C.L. Gilly (1943), The structure and origin of species, *Brittonia,* **4**: 323-385.
Campbell, D.H. (1926), *An Outline of Plant Geography,* Harper & Row, New York.
_______ (1928), The phylogeny of angiosperms, *Bull. Torrey Bot. Club,* **55**: 479-496.
_______ (1930), The phylogeny of angiosperms, *Ann. Bot.,* **44**: 311-331.
_______ (1942), Continental drift and plant distribution, *Science,* **95**: 69-70.
Candolle, A.P. de (1804), *Essai Sur les Propeietes medicales des plantes compares avec leur formes exterieures et leur Classification Naturelle,* Edin. I., Mequignon, Paris.
_______ (1813), *Theorie Elementaire de la Botanique,* Deterville, Paris.
Candolle, A.P. de *et al.* (1824-1873), *Prodrumus Systematis naturalis regni Vegetabilis,* Vols. I-XVII, Trenttel & Wintz, Paris.

Canright, J.E. (1955), The comparative morphology and relationships of the Magnoliaceae. IV. Wood and nodal anatomy, *J. Arnold Arbor,* **36**: 119-140.

Cave, M.S. (1953), Cytology and embryology in the delimitation of genera—A symposium on plant genera, their nature and definition, *Chron. Bot.,* **14**: 140-153.

_______ (1959), Embryological characters of taxonomic value, *Proc. 9th Int. Bot. Congr. Montreal,* **2**: 62.

_______ (1962), Embryological characters of taxonomic significance, *Lillea,* **31**: 171-182.

Celakovsky, L.F. (1892), Gedanken uber eine Zeitgemasse Reform der Theorie der Blutenstande, *Bot. Jahrb. Engler,* **16**: 33-51.

Chandler, M.E.J. (1958), Angiosperms fruits from the lower cretaceous of France and the lower Eocene (London clay) of Germany, *Ann. Mag. Nat. Hist.,* Ser. 13, **1**: 354-358.

Chandler, M.E.J. and D.E. Axelrod (1961), An early cretaceous (Hauterivian) fruit from California, *Amer, J. Sci.,* **259**: 441-446.

Chaney, R.W. (1940), Tertiary floras and continental history, *Bull. Goel. Soc. Amer.,* **51**: 469-488.

_______ (1947), Tertiary centres and migration routes, *Ecol. Mono.,* **17**: 139-148, 159-183.

Chatterjee, D. (1940), Studies on the endemic flora of India and Burma, *J. Asiat. Soc. Bengal,* **5**(1): 19-67.

Cheadle, V.I. (1953), Independent origin of vessels in the monocotyledons and dicotyledons, *Phytomorphology,* **3**: 23-44.

Chouard, P. (1931), Types de development de l'appareil vegetatif chez les Scillees, *Ann. Sci. Nat.,* Ser. 10, **13**: 131-132.

Chung, T.I. and L.R. Heckard (1972), Seed coat morphology in *Cordylanthus* (Scrophulariaceae) and its taxonomic significance, *Amer. J. Bot.,* **59**: 258-265.

Clausen, J. (1951), *Stages in the evolution of Plant Species,* Cornell Univ. Press, Ithaca.

_______ (1960), A simple method for sampling of natural populations, *Report, Scottish Pl. Br. Stn.,* **1960**: 69-75.

Clausen, J. and W.M. Hiesey (1958), *Experimental Studies on the Nature of Species-IV. Genetic Structure of Ecological Races,* Carnegie Inst. Washington Publ., **615.**

Clausen, J., D.D. Keck and W.M. Hiesey (1939), The concept of species based on experiment, *Am. J. Bot.,* **26**: 103-106.

_______ (1945), *Experimental Studies on the Nature of Species*-II. *Plant Evolution through Amphiploidy and Autoploidy, with Examples from Madiinae,* Carnegie Inst. Washington Publ., **564**: VI + 174 pp.

_______ (1948), *Experimenal Studies on the Nature of Species*-III. *Environmental Responses of Climatic Races of Achillea,* Carnegie Inst. Washington Publ., **581**: III + 129 pp.

Clifford, H.T. (1970), Monocotyledon classification with special reference to the origin of the grasses (Poaceae), *in:* H.B.K. Robson, D.F. Cutter and M. Gregory (Ed.), *New Research in Plant Anatomy,* Academic Press, London, pp. 25-34.

Cole, G.T. and H.D. Behnke (1975), Electron microscopy and plant systematics, *Taxon,* **24**: 3-16.

Collinson, A.S. (1977), *Introduction to World Vegetation,* London: George Allen & Unwin.

Cook, C.D.K. (1968), Phenotypic plasticity with particular reference to three amphibious plant species, *in:* V.H. Heywood (Ed.), *Modern Methods in Plant Taxonomy,* Academic Press, London, pp. 97-111.

Cook, M.T. (1906), The embryology of some Cuban Nymphaeaceae, *Bot. Gaz.,* **42**: 376-392.

Cook, R.B. Ivimey (1969), The phenetic relationship between species of *Ononis, in:* A.J. Cole (Ed.), *Numerical Taxonomy,* Academic Press, London and New York, pp. 68-85.

Coonen, L.P. (1939), The chromosomes of *Ranunculus, Amer. J. Bot.,* **26**: 49-58.

Core, E.L. (1955), *Plant Taxonomy,* Prentice-Hall, Englewood Cliff, N.J.

Corner, E.J.H. (1946), Centrifugal stamens, *J. Arnold Arbor.,* **27**: 432-437.

_______ (1949), The durian theory or the origin of the modern tree, *Ann. Bot.,* **52**: 367-414.

_______ (1951), Review of P. Maheshwari, *An Introduction to Embryology of Angiosperms, Phytomorphology,* **1**: 243.

_______ (1954a), The durian theory extended-II. The arillate fruit and the compound leaf, *Phytomorphology,* **4**: 152-165.

_______ (1954b), Thd durian theory extended-III. Pachycauly and megasperm, conclusion, *Phytomorphology,* **4**: 263-274.

Corner, E.J.H. (1964), *The Life of Plants,* Oxford Univ. Press, London.

_______ (1966), *The Natural History of Palms,* Weldenfield & Nicholson, London.

_______ (1981), *Angiosperm classification and phylogeny—A criticism, Bot. J. Linn. Soc.,* **82**: 81-87.

Cowan J.M. (1950), *The Rhododendron Leaf: A Study of the Epidermal Appendages,* Oliver & Boyd, London.

Crawford, R.M.M. and D. Wishart (1967), A rapid multivariate method for the detection and classification of groups, *J. Ecol.,* **55**: 505-524.

Crawshay-Williams, R. (1961), In report on: the mathematical assessment of taxonomic similarity including the use of computors, *Taxon,* **10**: 97-101.

Croizat, L. (1947), *Trochodendron, Tetracentron* and their meaning in phylogeny, *Bull. Torrey Bot. Club,* **74**: 60-76.

_______ (1952), *Manual of Phytogeography,* Junk, The Hague.

_______ (1958), *Panbiogeography,* Vols. I-III, Caracus (Venezuella, S.A.): Published by the author

Cronquist, A. (1957), Outline of a new system of families and orders of dicotyledons, *Bull. Jard Bot. Brux.,* **27**: 13-40.

_______ (1968a), *Evolution and Classification of Flowering Plants,* Nelson,New York.

_______ (1968b), Relevance of national herbaria to modern taxonomic research in the United States of America, *in*: V.H. Heywood (Ed.), *Modern Methods in Plant Taxonomy,* Academic Press, London, pp. 15-22.

Cronquist, A. (1977), On the taxonomic significance of secondary metabolites in angiosperms, *in*: K. Kubitzki (Ed.), *Plant Systematics and Evolution,* (Suppl. 1) Springer-Verlag, New York, pp. 179-189.

Cronquist, A., A. Takhtajan and W. Zimmermann (1966), On the higher taxa of Embryobionta, *Taxon,* **15**: 129-134.

Cullen, J. (1968), Botanical problems of numerical taxonomy, *in:* V.H. Heywood (Ed.), *Modern Methods in Plant Taxonomy,* Academic Press, London, pp. 175-184.

Dahlgren, R.M.T., B. Hansen, K. Jakibson and K. Larsen (1974), *Angiospermenes Taxonomi* (In Danish), Akademisk Forlag, Kobenhavn.

Dahlgren, R.M.T. (1975), A system of classification of the angiosperms to be used to demonstrate the distribution of characters, *Bot. Notiser* (Lund.), **128**: 119-147.

_______ (1977), A commentary on a diagrammatic presentation of the angiosperms in relation to the distribution of character states, *in:* K. Kubitzki (Ed.), *Plant Systematics & Evolution* (Suppl. 1), Springer-Verlag, New York, pp. 253-283.

_______ (1980), A revised system of classification of the angiosperms, *Bot. J. Linn. Soc.,* **80:** 91-124.

_______ (1981), Angiosperm classification and phylogeny—A rectifying comment, *Bot. J. Linn. Soc.,* **82**: 89-92.

Dale, M.B. (1968), On property structure, numerical taxonomy and data handling, *in*: V.H. Heywood (Ed.), *Modern Methods in Plant Taxonomy,* Academic Press, London. pp. 185-198.

Darlington, C.D. (1936), The external mechanics of the chromosomes. I-V, *Proc. Roy. Soc. Britain* **121**: 264-319.

_______ (1937), *Recent Advances in Cytology,* 2nd edn., Blakiston, Philadelphia.

Darlington, P.J. (1957), *Zoogeography,* John Wiley & Sons, New York.

Darwin, C. (1859), *On the Origin of Species by means of Natural Selection or the Preservation of Favoured Races in the Struggle for Life,* J. Murray, London.

Daubeny, C. (Ed.) (1855), *Popular Geography of Plants: Or A Botanical Excursion Around the World,* L. Reeve, London.

Davey, V. McM. and J.M.S. Lang (1939), Experimental taxonomy III. Correlation of characters within a population, *New Phytol.,* **38**: 32-61.

Davis, G.L. (1966), *Systematic Embryology of the Angiosperms,,* John Wiley & Sons, New York.

Davis, P.H. and V.M. Heywood (1963), *Principles of Angiosperm, Taxonomy,* Oliver & Boyd, Edinburgh.

_______ and J. Cullen (1965), *The Identification of Flowering Plant Families,* Oliver & Boyd, Edinburgh & London.

DeBary, A. (1884), *Comparative Anatomy of Vegetative Organs of the Phanerogams and Ferns,* Clarendon Press, Oxford.

De Beer, G.R. (1954), Archaeopteryx Lithographica, A study based upon the British Museum *Specimen,* Brit. Mus. Nat. Hist. London.

Desborough, S. and S.T. Peloquin (1969), Acid disc gel electrophoresis of tuber proteins from *Solanum* species, *Phytochemistry,* **8**: 425-429.

Dewolf, G.P.J. (1968), Notes on making an herbarium, *Arnoldia,* **28**: 69-111.

Dietz, R.S. and W.P. Sproll (1966), Equal areas of Gondwana land and Laurasia, *Nature,* **212**: 1196-1198.

Dobzhansky, T. (1935), A critique of the species concept in biology, *Philos. Sci.,* **2**: 344-355.

_______ (1950), Mendelian populations and their evolution, *Amer. Nat.,* **84**: 401-418.

_______ (1970), *Genetics of Evolutionary Process,* Columbia Univ. Press, New York.

Don, D. (1827), On the affinities of Empetraceae, a natural group of plants, *Edinburgh New Phil. J.,* **2**: 59-63.

Dorf, E. (1936), A late tertiary flora from South Western Idaho, *Carnegie Inst. Washington Pub.,* **476**: 75-124.

_______ (1938 & 1942), Upper cretaceous floras of the rocky mountain region I & II, *Carnegie Inst. Washington Pub.,* **508**: 1-78 and 79-159.

Doyle, J. (1945), Development lines in pollination mecahnism in Coniferales, *Sci. Proc. R. Dublin Soc.,* **24**: 43-62.

Duke, J.A. (1961), Preliminary revision of the genus *Drymaria, Ann. Missouri Bot. Gard.,* **48**: 173-268.

Du Rietz, G.E. (1929), Factors controlling the distribution of species in vegetation, *Proc. Int. Congr. Pl. Sci. Ithaca.*

Du Toit, A.L. (1937), *Our Wandering Continents,* Oliver & Boyd, Edinburgh.

_______ (1944), Tertiary mammals and continental drift, *Amer. J. Soc.,* **242**: 145-163.

Eames, A.J. (1936), *Morphology of Vascular Plants, Lower Groups,* McGraw-Hill, New York.

_______ (1953), Floral anatomy as an aid in generic limitation, *Chron. Bot.,* **14**: 126-132.

Eames, A.J. (1961), *Morphology of the Angiosperms,* McGraw-Hill, New York.

Echlin, P. (1968), Pollen, *Sci. Amer.,* **218**(4): 80-90.

Eglington, G. and R.J. Hamilton (1967), Leaf epicuticular waxes, *Science,* **156**: 1322-1335.

Ehlrich, P. (1891), Experimentalle Untersuchung uber Immunitat I. Uber Ricin. II. Uber Abin, *Dt. Med. Wachr.,* **17**: 976-1218.

Ehlrich, P.R. and P.N. Raven (1964), Butterflies and plants: A study of co-evolution, *Evolution,* **18**: 586-608.

_______ (1969), Differentiation of populations, *Science,* **165**: 1228-1232.

Ehrendorfer, F. (1964), Cytologie, taxonomie und evolution bei same pflanzen, *Vistas in Botany,* **4**: 99-186.

_______ (1968), Geographical and ecological aspects of interspecific differentiation, *in*: V.H. Heywood (Ed.), *Modern Methods in Plants Taxonomy,* Academic Press, London, pp. 261-296.

Eichler, A.B. (1876), *Syllabus der Vorlesungen uber Phanerogamen Kunde,* 2nd edn. (1880); 3rd edn. (1883), Gebruder Borntraeger, Berlin.

_______ (1875-1878), *Bluthendiagramme,* Vols. 1 and 2, W. Engelmann, Leipzig.

Engler, A.H.G. (1879, 1882), *Versuch einer Entwicklungageschichte der Pflanzenwilt insbesondre der Florengbiete, seit der Tertiarperiode,* Vols. I and II, W. Engelmann, Leipzig.

_______ (1892a) *Syllabus der Vorlesungen,* W. Engelmann, Leipzig.

_______ (1892b) *Syllabus der Pflanzenfamilien* Gebruder Borntraeger, Berlin; 2nd edn. (1898); 3rd edn. (1903); 4th edn. (1904); 5th edn. (1907); 6th edn. (1909); 7th edn. (1912); 8th edn. (1919).

Engler, A.H.G. and E. Gilg (1924), *Syllabus der Pflanzenfamilien,* 9th and 10th edn., Gebruder Borntraeger, Berlin.

Engler, A.H.G. and Diel (1936), *Syllabus der Pflanzenfamilien,* 11th edn., Gebruder Borntraeger, Berlin.

Engler, A.H.G. and K. Prantl (1887-1915), *Die Naturlichen Pflanzenfamilien,* Vols. 1-23, 2nd edn. (1924-) (Incomplete), W. Engelmann, Leipzig.

Erdtman, G. (1943), *An Introduction to Pollen Analysis,* Ronald Press, New York, 2nd edn. (1954).
________ (1952), *Pollen Morphology and Plant Taxonomy Angiosperms,* Almquist & Wicksell, Stockholm.
________ (1954), Pollen morphology and plant taxonomy, *Bot. Not.,* **1954**: 65-81.
________ (1956), Current trends in palynological research work, *Grana Palynologica,* **1**: 127-139.
________ (1959), UV micrographs and photomicrographs from the palynological laboratory, Stockholm, Solna, *Grana Palynologica,* **21**: 36-39.
Erdtman, G., J. Praglovski and S. Nilsson (1963), *An Introduction to a Scandinavian Pollen Flora* II, Almquist & Wicksell, Uppsala.
Erdtman, G., P. Ceins, R. Melville and C.R. Metcalfe (1969), On the relationships of *Emblingia, J. Linn. Soc. Bot.,* **62**: 169-186.
Esau, K. (1965), *Plant Anatomy,* 2nd edn. John Wiley & Sons, New York.
Estabrook, G.F. and D.J. Rogers (1966), A general method of taxonomic description for a computed similarity measures, *Bioscience,* **16**: 789-793.
Eykman, J.F. (1888), Notes phytochemiques, *Ann. Jard. Bot. Buitenz.,* **7**: 224-234.
Faegri, K. (1980), The problem of polyphyletic origins with special reference to angiosperms, *Taxon,* **29**: 312-314.
Faegri, K. and J. Iverson (1950), *Textbook of Modern Pollen Analysis,* Munksgaard, Copenhagen.
________ (1964), *Textbook of Pollen Analysis,* Munksgaard, Copenhagen; Oxford: Blackwell Scientific Publications.
Faegri, K. and L. van der Pijl (1966), *The Principles of Pollination Ecology,* Pergamon Press, Oxford, Rev. 3rd edn. (1979).
Fagerlind, F. (1947), Strobilus und Blute von Gnetum und die Moglichheit, aus ihrer struktur den Blutenbau der angiospermen Zu deulen, *Arkiv. Bot.,* **33**A: 1-57.
Fairbrothers, D.E. and M.A. Johnson (1961), The precipitin reaction as an indicator of relationships in certain grasses, *in:* D.L. Bailey (Ed.), *Recent Advances in Botany,* Univ. of Toronto Press, Toronto, pp. 116-120.
________ (1964), Comparative serological studies within the family Cornaceae (Dogwood) and Nyssaceae (Sour gum), *in:* C.A. Leone (Ed.,) *Taxonomic Biochemistry and Serology,* Ronald Press, New York, pp. 305-318.
Fairbrothers, D.E. (1968), Chemosystematics with emphasis on systematic serology, *in:* V.H. Heywood (Ed.), *Modern Methods in Plant Taxonomy,* Academic Press, London, pp. 141-174.
Farnald, M.L. (1931), Specific segregation and identification in some floras of eastern North America, *Rhodora,* **33**: 25-63.
Favali, M.A. and F.M. Gerola (1968), Tubular and fibrillar components in phloem of *Brassica chinensis* L. leaves, *Giorn. Bot. Ital.,* **102**: 447-467.
Fernandez, A. (1946), Sur le compartment des chromosomes sur numeraires heterochromatiques pendent la meiose, *Biol. Soc. Broteriana,* **20**: 93-155.
Fernandez-Moran, H. and A.D. Dahl (1952), Electron microscopy of ultra thin frozen sections of pollen grains, *Science,* **116**: 465-467.
Florine, R. (1944), Die Koniferen des oberkarbons und des unteren perms, *Paleontographica,* **85**: 365-654.
Fogg, J.M. (1944), Suggestions for collectors, *Rhodora,* **42**: 145-157.
Foster, A.S. (1944), Structure and development sclereids in the petiole of *Camellia japonica* L., *Torrey Bot. Club Bull.,* **71**: 302-326.
________ (1947), Structure and ontogeny of terminal sclereids in the leaf of *Mouriria Huberi* Cogn., *Amer. J. Bot.,* **34**: 501-514.
Franks, J.W. (1965), *A Guide to Herbarium Practice. Hand Book for Museum Curators,* Part E, Section 3, The Museum Assn., London.
Fritzsche, C.L. (1837), Uberden pollen, *Mem. Sav. Etrang. Acad. St. Petersberg,* **3**: 649.
Frodin, D.G. (1964), *Guide to the Standard Floras of the World,* Univ. of Tennessee Press, Knoxville.
Galston, A.W. (1969), Flavonoides and photomorphogenesis in peas, *in:* J.B. Harborne and T. Swain (Ed.), *Perspectives in Phytochemistry,* Academic Press, London, pp. 193-204.
Gates, B.N. (1950), An electrical drier for harbarium specimens, *Rhodora,* **52**: 129-134.
Gaudet, J. (1960), Ontogeny of foliar sclereids in *Nymphaea odorata, Amer. J. Bot.,* **47**: 525-532.
Gaussen, H. (1946), *Les Gymnosperms, Actuelles et Fossiles, Trav. Lab. Forest,* Toulouse.

Gell, P.G., J.G. Hawkes and S.T.C. Wright (1960), The application of immunological methods to the taxonomy of species within the genus *Solanum, Proc. Roy. Soc.,* **151**: 364-383.

Geesink, R., A.J.M. Leeuwenberg, C.E. Ridsdale and J.F. Veldkamp (1981), *Thonner's Analytical Key to the Families of Flowering Plants,* Leiden Univ. Press, Leiden.

Gibbs, R.B. (1963), History of chemical taxonomy, *in:* T. Swain (Ed.), *Chemical Plant Taxonomy,* Academic Press, London, pp. 44-88.

Gilmour, J.S.L. and W.B. Turrill (1941), The aim and scope of taxonomy, *Chron, Bot.,* **6**: 217-219.

Goebel, K. (1931), Blutenbildung und sprossgestaltung, *Org. der Pflanzen,* Suppl. 2, Fischer, Jena. pp. 242.

Golenkin, M.I. (1927), *The Victors in the Struggle for Existence,* Nauka, Moscow (In Russian).

Good, R. (1931), A theory of plant geography, *New Phytol.,* **30**: 139-171.

_______ (1947), *The Geography of Flowering Plants,* Longman, London, 4th edn, 1974.

_______ (1951), The distribution of the flowering plants in relation to theories of continental drift, *Adv. Sci.,* **8**; quoted from Good (1974).

Goodspeed, T.H. (1945), Cytotaxonomy of *Nicotiana, Bot. Rev.,* **11**: 533-592.

_______ (1947), On the evolution of genus *Nicotiana, Proc. Nat. Acad. Sci.,* **33**: 158-171.

_______ (1954), The genus *Nicotiana, Chron. Bot.,* **16**: 1-536.

Goodspeed, T.H. and P. Avery (1939), Trisomic and other types in *Nicotiana sylvestris, J. Genet.,* **38**: 381-458.

Goodwin, T.W. (Ed.) (1970), *Natural Substances Formed Biologically from Mevalonic acid,* Academic Press, London.

Gotlwald, H. (1977), The anatomy of secondary xylem and the classification of ancient dicotyledons, *in:* K. Kubitzki (Ed.), *Plant Systematics and Evolution,* Suppl. 1, Springer Verlag, New York, pp. 111-121.

Gould, F.W. (1968), *Grass Systematics,* McGraw-Hill, New York.

Graf, A.B. (1961), *Exotica: Pictorial Cyclopaedia of Exotic Plants,* Roehrs Company, New Jersey.

Grant, V. (1949), Pollination systems as isolating mechanisms in angiosperms, *Evolution,* **3**: 82-97.

_______ (1950), Genetic and taxonomic studies in *Gilia.* I. *Gilia capitata, Aliso,* **2**: 239-316.

_______ (1952a), Genetic and taxonomic studies in *Gilia.* II. *Gilia capitata abrontifolia, Aliso* **2**: 361-373.

_______ (1952b), Genetic and taxonomic studies in *Gilia.* III. The *Gilia tricolor* Complex, *Aliso,* **2**: 375-388.

_______ (1954a), Genetic and taxonomic studies in *Gilia.* IV. *Gilia achilleaefolia, Aliso,* **3**: 1-18.

_______ (1954b), Genetic and taxonomic studies in *Gilia.* VI. Interspecific relationships in the leafy-stemmed gilias, *Aliso,* **3**: 35-49.

_______ (1963), *The Origin of Adaptations,* Columbia Univ. Press, London.

_______ (1964), The biological composition of a taxonomic species in *Gilia,* Adv. Genet., **12**: 281-328.

_______ (1965), Evidence for the selective origin of incompatibility barriers in the leafy-stemmed gilias, *Proc. Nat. Acad. Sci. USA,* **54**: 1567-1571.

_______ (1966), The selective origin of incompatibility barriers in the plant genus *Gilia, Amer. Nat.,* **100**: 99-118.

_______ (1971), *Plant Speciation,* Columbia Univ. Press, New York.

Grant, V. and A. Grant (1960), Genetic and taxonomic studies in *Gilia.* XI. Fertility relationships of the diploid cobwebby gilias, *Aliso,* **4**: 435-481.

Grant, V. and K.A. Grant (1965), *Flower Pollination in the Phlox Family,* Columbia Univ. Press, New York.

Gregor, J.W. (1931), Experimental delimitation of species, *New Phytol,* **30**: 204-217.

_______ (1939), Experimental taxonomy-IV. Population differentiation in North America and South American sea plantains allied to *Plantago maritima* L., *New Phytol.,* **38**: 293-322.

Gregor, J.W., V. McM. Davey and J.M.S. Lang (1936), Experimental taxonomy-I. Experimental garden techniques in relation to the recognition of the small taxonomic units, *New Phytol.,* **35**: 323-350.

Grew, N. (1673), *An Idea of a Physiological History Propounded,* Chiswell, London.

Guinochet, M. (1973), Phytosociologie et systematique, *in:* V.H. Heywood (Ed.), *Taxonomy and Ecology,* Academic Press, London, pp. 121-140.

Gulliver, G. (1966), On raphides as natural characters in the British Flora, *Quart. J. Micr. Sci.* (N.S.), **6**: 1.
Guillarmod, A.J. (1976), Use of oderless carrier, a petroleum product, in preparing herbarium material, *Taxon,* **25**: 219-221.
Gunderson, A. (1950), *Families of dicotyledons,* Waltham, Mass., U.S.A.
Guppy, H.B. (1903), *Observations of a Naturalist in the Pacific* Part I, *Venua Levu,* Macmillan, London, Part II, *Plant Distribution* (1906).
_______ (1912), *Studies in Seeds and Fruits,* Williams & Norgate, London.
_______ (1917), *Plants, Seeds and Currents in the West Indies and Azores,* Williams & Norgate, London.
_______ (1919a), Plant distribution from the standpoint of an idealist, *J. Linn. Soc. London,* **44**: 439-472.
_______ (1919b), The island and the continent, *J. Ecol.,* **7**: 1.
Gustafsson, A. (1946), Apomixis in higher plants, Part I. The mechanism of apomixis, *Lunds Univ. Arsskr.,* **42**(3): 1-67.
_______ (1947a), Apomixis in higher plants, Part II. The casual aspects of apomixis, *Lunds Univ. Arsskr.,* **43**(2): 69-179.
_______ (1947b), Apomixis in higher plants. Part III. Biotype and species formation. *Lunds Univ. Arsskr.,* **43**(12): 183-370.
Hagerup, O. (1934, 1936), Zur Abstammung einiger Angiospermen durch Gnetales und Coniferae, *Dansk. Vidensk. Biol. Medd.,* **11**: 1-83; **13**: 1-60.
Hair, J.B. (1962), Basic chromosome numbers in *Cotula, Chromosome Inf. Ser.* No. 3: 41-42.
Hakansson, A. (1945), Uber Zahlige chromosomen in einer Rasse von *Godetia mutans* Hiorth., *Bot. Not.,* **1**: 1-19.
Hall, H.M. (1926), The taxonomic treatment of units smaller than species, *Proc. Int. Congr. Pl. Sci.* Ithaca, New York, **2**: 1461-1468.
_______ (1932), Heredity and environment as illustrated by transplant studies, *Sci. Monthly,* **35**: 289-302.
Hallan, N.D. and T.C. Chambers (1970), The leaf waxes of the genus *Eucalyptus* L. Haritier, *Austr. J. Bot.,* **18**: 335-386.
Hallier, H. (1905), Provisional scheme of the natural (phylogenetic) system of flowering plants, *New Phytol.* **4**: 151-162.
_______ (1908), On the origin of angiosperms, *Bot. Gaz.,* **45**: 196-198.
_______ (1912), L'Origine et la Systeme phyletique des angiospermes exposes a l' aide de leur arbre genealogique, *Arch. Neerl. Sci.,* Ser. IIIB, **1**: 146-234.
Hallock, F.A. (1930), The relationship of *Garrya* and its bearing on the phylogenetic position of the genus, *Ann. Bot.,* **44**: 771-812.
Hamann, U. (1961), Merkmalsbesland und verwandts-schaftsbezienhungen der Farinosae, Ein Beitrag Zum System der Monocotyledonen, *Willdenowia,* **2**: 639-768.
Hanelt, P. (1972), Die infraspezifische variabilitat von *Vicia faba* L. und ihre Gleederung, *Kultur Pflanze,* **20**: 75-128.
Hansen, A. (1920), *Die Pflansandecke der Erde,* W. Englemann, Leipzig.
Hansen, B. and K. Rahn (1969), Determination of Angiosperm families by means of a punch-card system, *Dansk. Bot. Arkiv.,* **26**: 1-44.
Harborne, J.B. (Ed.) (1964), *Biochemistry of Phenolic Compounds,* Academic Press, London.
_______ (1967), *Comparative Biochemistry of the Flavonoids,* Academic Press, London.
Harborne, J.B., D. Boulter and B.L. Turner (1971), *Chemotaxonomy of Leguminosae,* Academic Press, London.
Harling, G. (1951), Embryological studies in the Compositae. Part II. Anthemideae-Chrysantheminae, *Acta Hort. Berg.,* **16**: 1-56.
Harrington, H.D. (1957), Collecting and pressing plants, *in:* H.D. Harrington (Ed.), *How to Identify Plants,* Denver, Sage Books, pp. 90-98.
Harris, T.M. (1951), The relationships of the Caytoniales, *Phytomorphology,* **1**: 29-33.
Hawkes, J.G. and R.N. Lester (1966), Immunological studies on the tuber bearing solanums-II. Relationships of North American species, *Ann. Bot.,* **30**: 270-290.

_______ (1968), Immunological studies on the tuber bearing solanums-III. Variability within *S. bulbocastanum, Ann. Bot.,* **32**: 165-186.

Hayata, B. (1921), The natural classification of plants according to the dynamic system, *Icon. Pl. Formose,* **10**: 97-234.

Hedberg, O. (1958), Cytotaxonomic studies in Scottish mountain plants notably *Deschampsia caespitosa* (L.) P.B. and Lat., *Sv. Bot. Tidskr.,* **52**: 37-46.

Heer, O. (1868, 1878), *Die Fossile Flora der Polarlonder: Flora Fossilis Arctica,* Vols. I & V, Friedrich Schulthess, Zurich.

Hegelmaier, F. (1874), Zur Entwicklungsgeschichte monokotyledonen Keime nebst Bemer Kungen uber die Bildung der Samendeckei, *Bot. Ztg.,* **39**, **44**: 631-639; 648-719.

_______ (1878), *Vergleichende Untersuchungen uber Entwicklung dikotyledoner Kelme mit Berucksichtingung der Pseudomonokotyledonen,* G. Fischer, Stuttgart.

Hegnauer, R. (1963), The taxonomic significance of alkaloids, *in:* T. Swain (Ed.), *Chemical Plant Taxonomy,* Academic Press, London, pp. 389-427.

_______ (1966), Comparative phytochemistry of alkaloids, *in:* T. Swain (Ed.), *Comparative Phytochemistry,* Academic Press, London, pp. 211-230.

_______ (1977), Cyanogenetic compounds as systematic markers in *Tracheophyta, in:* K. Kubitzki (Ed.), *Plants Systematics and Evolution,* Springer Verlag, New York, pp. 191-209.

Henslow, G. (1893), A theoretical origin of endogens from exogens through self-adaptation to an aquatic habit, *J. Linn. Soc. Bot.,* **29**: 485-528.

_______ (1911), The origin of monocotyledons from dicotyledons through self-adaptation to a moist or aquatic habit, *Ann. Bot.,* **26**: 717-744.

Heslop-Harrison, J. (1956), Auxin and sexuality in *Cannabis sativa, Physiol. Pl.,* **9**: 588.

_______ (1957), The experimental modification of sex expression in flowering plants, *Biol. Rev.,* **32**: 38.

_______ , Darwin as a botanist, *in:* S.A. Barnett (Ed.) (1958a), *A Century of Darwin,* Hienemann, London, pp. 267-295.

_______ (1958b), The unisexual flower—A reply to criticism, *Phytomorphology,* **8**: 177-184.

_______ (1964a), Forty years of genecology, *Adv. Ecol. Res.,* **2**: 159-247.

_______ (1964b), *New Concepts in Flowering Plant Taxonomy,* Hienemann, London.

Heywood, V.H. (1959), The taxonomic treatment of ecotypic variation, *in:* A.J. Cain (Ed.), *Function and Taxonomic Importance,* Syst. Assn, London, pp. 87-112.

_______ (1964), List of botanic garden offering seeds of spontaneous plants, compiled on behalf of the international organisation of biosystematists, *Taxon,* **12**: 137-142.

_______ (1967), *Plant Taxonomy,* E. Arnold, London.

_______ Plant taxonomy today, *in:* V.H. Heywood (Ed.) (1968), *Modern Methods in Plant Taxonomy,* Academic Press, London, pp. 3-12.

_______ (1969), Scanning electron microscopy in the study of plant materials, *Micron,* **1**: 1-14.

_______ (1973), Ecological data in practical taxonomy, *in:* V.H. Heywood (Ed.), *Taxonomy and Ecology,* Academic Press, London, pp. 329-348.

Heywood, V.H. and K.M.M. Dakhshini, Fruit structure in Umbelliferae—Caucalideae, *in:* V.H. Heywood (Ed.) (1971), *The Biology and Chemistry of the Umbelliferae,* Suppl. 1 to *Biol. J. Linn. Soc.,* **64**: 215-232.

Heywood, V.H., J.B. Harborne and B.L. Turner (1977), *The Biology and Chemistry of Compositae,* 2 Vols., Academic Press, London.

Hickey, L.J. and J.A. Doyle (1977), Early cretaceous fossil evidence for angiosperm evolution, *Bot. Rev.,* **43**: 3-104.

Hicks, A.J. and P.M. Hicks (1978), A selected bibliography of plant collection and herbarium curation, *Taxon,* **27**(1): 63-99.

Hofmeister, W. (1862), *On Germination, Development and Fructification of the Higher Cryptogamia and on the Fructification of the Coniferae,* Robert Hardwicke, London.

Holland, T.H. (1942-1943), The theory of continental drift, *Proc. Linn. Soc. London,* **155**: 119.

Holmgren, P.K. and W. Keuken (1974), *Index Herbariorum.* Part I: *The Herbaria of the World,* 6th edn., Oosthoek, Scheltema & Holkema, Utrecht.

Holttum, R.E. (1970), The historical significance of botanic gardens in SE Asia, *Taxon,* **19**: 707-714
Hooker, J.D. (1879), Presidential address to the Royal Society in 1878, *Proc. Roy. Soc.,* **28**: 51-55.
_______ (1872-1897), *The Flora of British India,* Vols, I-VII, L. Reeve, London.
_______ (1907), A sketch of the flora of British India, *Imp. Gazetteer,* London.
Hopwood, A.T. (1959), The development of pre-Linnaean taxonomy, *Proc. Linn. Soc. London,* **170**: 230-234.
Howard, R.A. (1963), The vascular structure of the petiole as a taxonomic character, *Adv. Hort. Sci.,* **3**: 7-13.
Howard, R.A., B. Wagenknecht and P.S. Green (1963), *International Directory of Botanical Gardens, Regnum Vegetabile,* Vol. 28, IABG, Utrecht.
Hsu, K.I. (1971), Origin of Alps and Western Mediterranean, *Nature,* **233**: 44-48.
Hubbard, C.E., Gramineae, *in*: J Hutchinson (Ed.) (1948), *British Flowering Plants,* Gawthorn, London, pp. 284-348.
Hughes, N.F. (1961), Fossil evidence and angiosperm ancestry, *Sci. Prog. Lond.,* **49**: 84-102.
_______ (1976), *Paleobiology of Angiosperm Origins,* Cambridge Univ. Press, Cambridge.
Hulten, E. (1937), *Outline of the History of Arctic and Boreal Biota During the Quarternary Period,* Bokfortags Aktiebolaget Thule, Stockholm.
Hutchinson, J. (1926, 1934), *The Families of Flowering Plants,* Vol. I & II,Macmillan, London, 2nd edn (1959), Clarendon Press, Oxford; 3rd edn (1973), Clarendon Press, Oxford.
_______ (1967), *Key to the Families of Flowering Plants of the World,* Clarendon Press, Oxford, 2nd edn (1979).
_______ (1969), *Evolution and Phylogeny of Flowering Plants,* Academic Press, London.
Hutchinson, J.B., R.A. Silow and S.G. Stephens (1947), *The Evolution of Gossypium and the Differentiation of Cultivated Cottons,* Oxford Univ. Press, Oxford.
Hyams, E. and W. Macquitty (1969), *Great Botanic Gardens of the World,* Nelson, New York.
Ikuse, M. (1956), *Pollen Grains of Japan,* Hirokawa, Tokyo; 2nd edn., 1962.
Iverson, T.H. (1970), The morphology, occurrence and distribution of dilated cisternae of the endoplasmic reticulum in tissues of the plants of Cruciferae, *Protoplasma,* **71**: 467-477.
Jaccard, P. and A Frey (1928), *Naturforsch Ges Zurich* **73**: 127, quoted from Gibbs (1963).
Jackson, B.D. (1928), *A Glossary of Botanic Terms: With their Derivation and Accent,* 4th edn., Gerald Duckworth & Co., London.
Jackson, P., J.M. Milton and D. Boulter (1967), Finger print patterns of the globulin fraction obtained from the seeds of various species of Fabaceae, *New Phytol.,* **66**: 47-56.
Jain, S.K. (1969), Comparative ecogenetics of two *Avena* species occurring in central California, *Evol. Biol.,* **3**: 73-113.
Jain, S.K. and R.R.Rao (1977), *A Handbook of Field and Herbarium Methods,* Today & Tomorrow Publ., New Delhi.
Janzen, D.H. (1966), Coevolution of mutualism between ants and acacias in central America, *Evolution,* **20**: 249-275.
_______ (1967), Interaction of the bull's horn acacia *(Acacia cornigenra* L.) with an ant inhabitant (Pseudomyrex ferruginea F. Smith) in eastern Mexico, *Univ. Kansas Sci. Bull.,* **47**: 315-558.
_______ (1975), *Ecology of Plants in the Tropics,* E. Arnold, London.
Jensen, U. (1968), Serologische Beitrage zur Systematik der Ranunculaceae, *Bot. Jahrb.,* **88**: 204-268.
Jensen, S.R., B.J. Nielsen and R. Dahlgren (1975), Iridoid compounds, their occurrence and systematic importance in the Angiosperms *Bot. Not.* (Lund), **128**: 148-180.
Johansen, D.A. (1950), *Plant Embryology—Embryology of the Spermatophyta,* Chronica Botanica Co. Waltham, Mass.
Johanson, B.L. and O. Hall (1965), Analysis of phylogenetic affinities in the *Triticinae* by protein electrophoresis, *Amer. J. Bot.,* **52**: 506-513.
Johanson, M.P. and R.W. Holm (1968), Numerical taxonomic studies in the genus *Sarcostemma* R. Br. (Asclepiadaceae), *in*: V.H. Heywood (Ed.), *Modern Methods in Plant Taxonomy,* Academic Press, London, pp. 199-218.
Johannsen, W.L. (1903), *Uber Erblichkeit in Populationen and reinen Linien,* Gustav Fischer, Jena.
_______ (1905), *Arrelighedslaerens elementer,* Munksgaard, Copenhagen.
_______ (1909), *Elemente der exakten Erblichkeitslehre,* Gustav Fischer, Jena.

Johannsen, W.L. (1911), The genetype conception of heredity, *Amer. Nat.*, **45**: 129-159.
Johri, B.M. (1963), Embryology and taxonomy, *in*: P. Maheshwari (Ed.), *Recent Advances in the Embryology of Angiosperms,* Int. Soc. Pl. Morph. Univ. Delhi. New Delhi, pp. 395-444.
_______ (1967), Angiosperms embryology and taxonomy, *Bull. Natn, Inst. Sci. India,* **34**: 263-268.
Jones, K. (1970), Chromosome changes in plant evolution, *Taxon,* **19**: 172-179.
Jones, S.B. and A.E. Luchsinger (1979), *Plant Systematics,* McGraw-Hill, New York.
Jordan, A. (1846), Observations sur plusieurs plantes nouvelles rares on critiques de la France II, *Ann. Soc. Linneennee de Lyon.*
Jordan, D.S. (1905), The origin of species through isolation, *Science,* **22**: 545-562. n.s.
Jorgensen, C.A. (1923), Studies on Callitrichaceae, *Bot. Tidskr.,* **38**: 81-126.
_______ (1925), Eur Frage der Sytematischen Stellung der Callitrichaceen, *Jahrb. f. Wiss. Bot.,* **64**: 440-442.
Jussieu, A.L. de (1789), *Genera Plantarum,* Paris: Herissan & Barrois.
Just, Th. (1948), Gymnosperms and origin of angiosperms, Bot. Gaz., **110**: 91-103.
Kanai, H. (1964), Improved methods of making dried specimens, *J. Japan. Bot.,* **39**: 12.
_______ (1974), Heat seal: A new technique for mounting herbarium specimens, *J. Japan. Bot.,* **49**: 86-88.
Kapil, R.N. (1962), Some recent examples of the value of embryology in relation to taxonomy, *Bull. Bot. Surv. Ind.,* **4**: 57-66.
Karpechenko, G.D. (1927), Polyploid hybrids of *Raphanus sativus* L. x *Brassica oleracea* L., *Bull. Appl. Bot. Genet. Breed.,* **17**: 305-410.
_______ (1928), Polyploid hybrids of *Raphanus sativus* L. x *Brassica oleracea* L., *Zeitscher. Ind. Abst. U. Vererbungsl.,* **39**: 1-7.
Kawano, S. (1963), Cytogeography and evolution of the *Deschampsia caespitosa* complex, *Canad. J. Bot.,* **41**: 719-742.
Kelsey, H.P. and W.A. Dayton (1942), *Standardized Plant Names,* 2nd edn., Amer. Joint Com. Hort. Nom, Harrisburg.
Kharchenko, V.V. (1928), Systematic importance of the anatomical structure of *Allium* (Abstract), *Proc. All Russ. Congr. Botanists,* Leningrad, p. 135.
King, R.M. and H. Robinson (1970), The new synantherology, *Taxon,* **19**: 6-11.
Klein, G. and G. Pollauf (1929), Der mikrochemische Nachweis der Alkaloide in der Pflanze XII—Der Nachweis des colchicine, *Ost. Bot. Z.,* **78**: 250-256.
Klems (1960), Quoted from Davis and Heywood (1963), op. cit.
Kloz, J. (1971), Serology of the Leguminosae, *in:* J.B. Harborne, D. Boulter and B.L. Turner (Ed.), *Chemotaxonomy of the Leguminosae,* Academic Press, London, pp. 309-365.
Kohler, E. (1965), Die pollen morphologie der biovulaten Euphorbiaceae und ihre lieduting fur die taxonomie, *Grana Palynologica,* **6**: 5-22.
Kolstov, N.K. (1936), *The Organization of the Cell,* Moscow & Leningrad: Nauka (in Russian).
Kowarski, A. (1901), Uber den Nachweis von Pflanzlichen Eiweiss auf biologischem Wege, *Dt. Med. Wschr.,* **27**: 442.
Knudsen, J.W. (1966), *Biological Techniques,* Harper & Row, New York.
_______ (1972), *Collecting and Preserving Plants and Animals,* Harper & Row, New York.
Krassilov, V.A. (1973), Mesozoic plants and the problem of angiosperms ancestry, *Lethaia,* **6**: 163-179.
_______ (1975), Dirhopalostachyaceae—A new family of proangiosperms and its bearing on the problem of angiosperm ancestry, *Palaeontographica Abst.* B. **153**: 100-110.
_______ (1977), The origin of angiosperm, *Bot. Rev.,* **43**: 143-176.
Kraus, R. (1897), Uber specifische Reactionen in Keimfrein Filtraten aus *Cholera, Typhus und* Pestbouillon culturen erzeugt durch homologues serum, *Wien. Klin, Wschr.,* **10**: 736-738.
Krause, K. Liliaceae, *in*: A.H.G. Engler and K. Prantl (Ed.), (1969), *Die Naturlichen Pflanzenfamilien,* 2 Aufl. Bd. 15a, W. Engelmann, Leipzig, p. 227.
Krukoff, B.A. (1972), Notes on Asiatic-Polynesian-Australian species of *Erythrina* II, *J. Arnold Arbor.,* **52**(4): 128-139.
Kubitzki, K. (1969), Chemosystematische Betrachtungen zur Grosgliederung der Blutenpflanzen, *Taxon,* **18**: 360-368.

Kubitzki, K. (1977), *Plant Systematics and Evolution,* Springer Verlag, New York.

Kundu, B.C. and Anima De (1968), Taxonomic position of the genus *Nyctanthes, Bull. Bot. Surv. India,* **10**(3&4): 397-408.

Kuntze, O. (1891), *Revisio Generum Plantarum,* A. Felix, Leipzig.

Kurabayashi, M., H. Lewis and P.H. Raven (1962), A comparative study of mitosis in the Onagraceae, *Amer. J. Bot.,* **49**(9): 1003-1029.

Lakhanpal, R.N. (1970), Tertiary floras of India and their bearing on the historical geology of the region, *Taxon,* **19**: 675-694.

Lam, H.J. (1948), Classification and new morphology, *Acta Bio.,* **8**: 107-154.

_______ (1959), Taxonomy: General principles and angiosperms, *in*: W.B. Turrill (Ed.), *Vistas in Botany,* Vol. 1, Pergamon Press, London, pp. 3-75.

Lanjouw, J. (Ed.) (1961), *International Code of Botanical Nomenclature,* IAPT, Utrecht.

Lanjouw, J. and F.A. Stafleu (1952), *Index Herbariorum,* Part I: *The Herbaria of the World,* 5th edn, 1964, *Regnum Vegetabile,* **31**: 1-251.

Larsen, K. (1963), Studies in the Flora of Thailand, 14. Cytological studies in vascular plants of Thailand, *Dansk. Bot. Ark.,* **20**(3): 211-275.

Lawrence, G.H.M. (1951), *Taxonomy of Vascular Plants,* Macmillan, New York.

Lee, D.W. and D.E. Fairbrothers (1967), Serological and disc electrophoretic studies on North American *Typha, Amer. J. Bot.,* **54**: 660.

_______ (1978), Serological approaches to the systematics of the Rubiaceae and related families, *Taxon,* **27**(2/3): 159-185.

Lesquereux, L. (1891), The flora of Dakota group, *U.S. Geol. Surv. Mon.,* **17**: 1-400.

Levan, A. (1932), Cytological studies in *Allium* I. Chromosome morphological contributions, *Hereditas,* **16**: 257-294.

_______ (1935), Cytological studies in *Allium* VI. The chromosome morphology of some diploid species of *Allium, Hereditas,* **20**: 289-330.

Levitszky, G.A. (1924), *The Material Basis of Heredity,* State Printing Office, Kiev.

_______ (1931), The karyotype in systematics, *Bull. Appl. Bot. Genet. Pl. Breed.* **27**: 220-240.

Lewin, R.A. (1981), Three species concepts, *Taxon,* **30**, 609-613.

Lewis, H. (1951), The origin of supernumerary chromosomes in natural populations of *Clarkia elegans, Evolution,* **5**(2): 142-157.

_______ (1953b), Chromosome phylogeny and habitat preference of *Clarkia, Evolution,* **7**: 102-109.

_______ (1966), Speciation in flowering plants, *Science,* **152**(3719): 167-172.

_______ Taxonomic significance of autopolyploidy, *Taxon,* **16**(4): 267-271.

Lewis H. and M.E. Lewis (1955), The genus *Clarkia, Univ. California Publ. Bot.,* **20**(4): 241-392.

Lewis, H. and P.H. Raven (1958), Rapid evolution in *Clarkia Evolution,* **12**: 319-336.

_______ (1961), Phylogeny of the Onagraceae, *in:* D.L. Bailey (Ed.), *Recent Advances in Botany,* Univ. of Toronto Press, Toronto, 1466-1469.

Lewis, H. and M.R. Roberts (1956), The origin of *Clarkia lingulata, Evolution,* **10**(2): 126-138.

Lindley, J. (1830), *Introduction to the Natural System of Botany,* Longman, Rees, Orme, Brown & Green, London.

Linnaeus, C. (1729), Quoted from Davis & Heywood (1963).

_______ (1730), *Hortus Uplandicus,* T. Haak, Stockholm, rev. edn (1732).

_______ (1735), *Systema Naturae,* T. Haak, Stockholm, 2nd edn (1740).

_______ (1737a), *Critica Botanica,* C. Wishoff, Amsterdam.

_______ (1737b), *Flora Lapponica,* C. Wishoff, Amsterdam.

_______ (1737c), *Hortus Cliffortianus,* C. Wishoff, Amsterdam.

_______ (1737d), *Genera Plantarum,* C. Wishoff; 2nd edn. (1754); 6th edn. (1764).

_______ (1753), *Species Plantarum,* Vols. 1 & 2, L. Salvi, Stockholm, 5th edn (1801).

Linsbauer, K., Die Epidermis, *in:* K. Linsbauer (Ed.) (1930), *Hundbuch der Pflanzenantomie,* Gebruder Borntraeger, Berlin, pp. 27.

Long, A.G. (1966), Some lower carboniferous fructifications from Berwickshire, together with a theoretical account of the evolution of ovules, cupules and carpels, *Trans. Roy. Soc. Edinburgh,* **66**: 345-375.

Longwell, C.R. and W. Bailey (1944), Some thoughts on the evidence for continental drift, *Amer. J. Sci.,* **242**: 218-231

Love, A. (1964), The evolutionary frame work of the biological species concept, *Proc. XI Intern. Congr. Gen.*, pp. 409-415.

Love, A. and D. Love (1956), Cytotaxonomical conceptus of the Icelandic flora, *Acta Horti Gotoburg,* **20**: 65-290.

Mabry, T. (1966), The Betacyanins and Betaxanthins, *in:* T. Swain (Ed.), *Comparative Phytochemistry,* Academic Press, London, pp. 231-244.

Macioz, L.W. (1968), Pollination adaptation in *Pedicularis groenlandica, Amer. J. Bot.*, **55**: 927-932.

MacMillan, B.H. (1968), A method of mounting herbarium in liquid plastic, *New Zealand J. Bot.*, **6**: 514-517.

Magnus, W. (1908), Weitere Ergebnisse der Serum-diagnostik fur die theoretische und angewandte Botanik, *Ber. dt. bot. Ges.*, **26**a: 532-539.

Maheshwari, P. (1950), *An Introduction to Embryology of Angiosperms.* McGraw-Hill, New York.

Maheswari, P. and V. Vasil (1960), *Gnetum. Bot. Mono.*, No. 1, CSIR, New Delhi.

Majumdar, G.P. (1927), *Vanaspati—Plant and Plant Life as in Indian Treatise and Traditions,* Calcutta Univ., Calcutta.

_______ (1946), Genesis and development of plant science in Ancient India, *13th All India Oriental Conf. Technical Science,* Calcutta, pp. 97-120.

Manske, R.H.F. and H.L. Holmes (Eds.) (1950-60), *The Alkaloids,* Vols. I-VII, Academic Press, New York.

Markgraf, F. (1930), Monographie der Gatung *Gnetum, Bull. Jard. Bot. Buitenzorg,* Ser. 3, **10**: 253-310.

Marmey, F. (1958), Contribution a l' etuele morphologique et anatomique du genre *Marrubium* L. an Maroc., *Trav. Inst. Sci. Cherif.*, **14**: 1-93.

Marsden, M.P.F. and I.W. Bailey (1955), A fourth type of nodal anatomy in dicotyledons, illustrated by *Clerodendron trichotomum* Thunb., *J. Arnold. Arbor.*, **36**: 1-50.

Marsden-Jones, E.M. and W.B. Turrill (1930-1945), Reports on the transplant experiments on the British Ecological Society at Potterne, Wilts, *J. Ecol.*, **18**: 352-378 (1930); **21**: 268-293 (1933); **23**: 443-469 (1935); **25**: 189-212 (1937); **26**: 359-389 (1938); **33**: 57-81 (1945).

Marshall, D.R. and S.K. Jain (1968), Phenetic plasticity of *Avena fatua* and *A. barbata, Amer. J. Bot.*, **102**: 457-467.

Mason, H.L. (1950), Taxonomy, systematic botany and biosystematics, *Madrono,* **10**: 193-208.

Mather, K. (1946), *Statistical Analaysis in Biology,* 2nd edn. Chapman & Hall, London.

Martinez, M. (1931), Contribution al estudio de las Digitales (4a nota), *Bot. Soc. Esp. Hist. Nat.*, **31**: 509-520.

Mauritzon, J. (1934), Ein Beitrag zur Embryologie der Phytolaccaceen und Cactaceen, *Bot. Not.*, **1934**: 111-135.

_______ (1939), Die Bedeuntung der Embryologischen Forschung fur des naturliche system der Pflanzen, *Lunds Univ. Arsskr. Adv.*, **35**(15): 1-70.

Mayr, E. (1942), *Systematics and the Origin of Species,* Columbia Univ. Press, New York.

_______ Difficulties and importance of the biological species concept, *in:* E. Mayr (Ed.) (1957), *The Species Problem, Amer. Assoc. Adv. Sci. Publ.* No. 50, pp. 371-388.

_______ (1969a), The biological meaning of species, *Biol. J. Linn. Soc.*, **1**: 311-320.

_______ (1969b), *Principles of Systematic Zoology,* McGraw-Hill, New York.

McClintock, B. (1929), A cytological and genetical study of triploid maize, *Genetica,* **14**: 180-222.

McNair, J.B. (1929), The taxonomic and climatic distribution of oils, fats and waxes in plants, *Amer. J. Bot.*, **16**: 832-841.

_______ (1945), Plant fats in relation to environment and evolution, *Bot. Rev.*, **11**: 1-59.

Mears, J.A. and T.J. Mabry (1971), Alkaloids in the Leguminosae, *in:* J.B. Harborne (Ed.), *Chemotaxonomy of the Leguminosae,* Academic Press, London.

Meeuse, A.D.J. (1961), The pentoxylales and the origin of the monocotyledons, *Koninkl. Nederl. Acad. Van Wetenschappen, Amsterdam,* **C64**: 543-559.

_______ (1966), *Fundamentals of Phytomorphology,* Ronald Press, New York.

_______(1970), The descent of the flowering plants in the light of new evidence from phytochemistry and from other sources, *Acta Bot. Neerl.*, **19**: 61-72, 133-140.

_______ (1975), Floral evolution in the Hamamelidae, *Acta Bot. Nearl.*, **24**: 155-179.

Meglitsch, P.A. (1954), On the nature of the species, *Systematic Zool.*, **3**: 49-65.
Melchior, H. (Ed.) (1964), A.H.G. Engler's *Syllabus der Pflanzenfamilien,* 12th edn. Vol. 2, Gebruder Borntraeger, Berlin.
Melville, R. (1951), On the application of biometrical methods in plant taxonomy, *Proc. Linn. Soc. Lond.,* **162**: 153-159.
_______, Morphological characters in the discrimination of species and hybrids, *in*: J.E. Lousley (Ed.) (1955), *Species Study in British Flora,* Oxford, Bot. Soc. Brit. Is., pp. 55-64.
_______ (1960), A new theory of the angiosperm flower, *Nature,* **2**: 14-18.
_______ (1962), A new theory of angiosperm flower. I. The gynoecium, *Kew Bull.,* **16**: 1-50.
_______ (1963), A new theory of angiosperm flower. II. The androecium, *Kew Bull.,* **17**: 1-63.
_______ (1969), Leaf venation patterns and the origin of angiosperms, *Nature,* **224**: 121-125.
Merrill, E.D. and E.H. Walker (1938), *Bibliography of Eastern Asiatic Botany,* Harvard Univ. Press, Mass.
Merxmuller, H., Summary lecture, *in*: K. Kubitzki (Ed.) (1977), *Plant Systematics and Evolution,* Suppl. 1 Springer Verlag, New York, pp. 397-405.
Metcalfe, C.R. (1936), An interpretation of the morphology of the single cotyledon of *Ranunculus ficaria* based on embryology and seedling anatomy, *Ann. Bot.,* **50**: 103-120.
_______ (1954), An anatomist's view of angiosperm classification, *Kew Bull.,* **3**: 427-440.
_______ (1968), Current development in systematic plant anatomy, *in:* Heywood (Ed.), *Modern Methods in Plant Taxonomy,* Academic Press, London, pp. 45-57.
Metcalfe, C.R. and L. Chalk (1950), *Anatomy of the Dicotyledons,* Vols. 1 & 2, Oxford Univ. Press, Oxford.
Meyer, A. (1926), *Logik der Morpholgie in Rahmen einer Logik der gesamten Biologie,* A Felix, Leipzig.
Meylan, B.A. and B.G. Butterfield (1972), Perforation plate development in *Knightia excelsa* R. Br. A scanning electron microscope study, *Austr. J. Bot.,* **20**: 79-86.
Mez, C. (1926), Die Bedeutung der Serodiagnostik fur die stammesgeschichtliche Forschung, *Bot. Arch.,* **16**: 1-23.
_______ (1936), Morphologie und serodiagnostik, *Bot. Arch.,* **38**: 86-104.
Mez, C. and Ziegenpeck (1926), Der koenigsberger serodiagnostiche stammbeum, *Bot. Arch.,* **13**: 483-485.
Mirov, N.T. (1961), *Composition of Gum Turpentines of Pines,* USDA Tech. Bull. 1239, Washington.
Mohan Ram, H.Y. (1959), Embryological characters in the classification of Acanthaceae, *Proc. 9th Int. Congr. Montreal,* **2**: 267.
Moncrieff, S.R. (1931), The chemical effect of a Mendelian factor for flower colour, *Nature,* **127**: 974-975.
Moore, D.M., The karyotype in taxonomy, *in*: V.H. Heywood (Ed.) (1968), *Modern Methods in Plant Taxonomy,* Academic Press, London, pp. 61-75.
Morishima, H. and H. Oua (1960), The pattern of interspecific variation in the genus *Oryza,* its quantitative representation by statistical methods, *Evolution,* **14**: 153-165.
Moritz, O. (1933), Serologische untersuchungen a Getreidebastarden, *Ber. et. Bot. Ges.,* **51**: 52-57.
_______ (1934), Die botanische serologie, *Beitr. Biol. Pfl.,* **22**: 51-90.
Moseley, M.F. and R.M. Beek (1955), Studies on the Garryaceae. I. The comparative morphology and phylogeny, *Phytomorphology,* **5**: 314-346.
Muhlethaler, K. (1953), Untersuchungen uber die struktur der Pollenmembran, *Mikroskopie,* **8**: 103-110.
Muntzing, A. (1930), Outline to a genetic monograph of the genus *Galeopsis, Hereditas,* **13**: 185-341.
_______ (1932), Cytogenetic investigations on synthetic *Galeopsis tertrahit, Hereditas,* **16**: 105-154.
_______ (1954), The cytological basis of polymorphism in *Poa alpina, Hereditas,* **40**: 459-516.
Murgai, P. (1962), Embryology of *Paeonia* together with a discussion on its systematic position, *in: Plant Embryology—A Symposium.*
Nageli, C.W. von (1883), *Mechanisch-physiologische Theorie der Abstammungslehre,* A Felix, Munchen.
Naik, V.N. (1974), Cytological studies in two species of *Dipcadi* Medik. from India, *Cytologia* **39**: 506-511.

Naik, V.N. (1976a), Chromosome behaviour and evolutionary trends in *Chlorophytum* (Liliaceae), *Bot. J. Linn. Soc.*, **72**: 45-50.

_______ (1976b), Cytotaxonomic studies in two species of *Urginea* Steinh. from India, *J. Indian Bot. Soc.*, **55**: 60-64.

_______ (1977a), Cytotaxonomic studies in six species of *Chlorophytum*, *Bot. J. Linn. Soc.*, **74**: 297-304.

_______ (1977b), *Key to the Angiospermic Families and Certain Genera of Marathwada*, Anthus Publication Aurangabad.

_______ (1979), *The Flora of Osmanabad*, Venus Publishers, Aurangabad.

Naik, V.N. and S.M. Nirgude (1980), Reproductive isolation between *Chlorophytym glaucum* Dalz. and *C. Glaucoides* Blatt., *Proc. Ind. Acad. Sci.* (Plant Sci.), **89**: 465-472.

_______ (1981a), Anatomy in relation to taxonomy of *Chlorophytum* (Liliaceae), *Indian J. Bot.*, **4**(2): 48-60.

_______ (1981b), Vessels in *Chlorophytum* (Liliaceae), *Bull. Mus. Natn. Hist. Nat., Paris*, 4e Ser., 3, Sect. B, *Adansonia* No. 2, pp. 201-212.

Nair, P.K.K. (1965), *Pollen Grains of Western Himalayan Plants*, Asia Publishing House, Bombay.

_______ (1968), A concept on the pollen evolution in primitive angiosperms, *J. Palynol.*, **4**(1): 15-20.

_______ (1970), *Pollen Morphology of Angiosperms*, Vikas Publishers, New Delhi.

Nair, P.K.K. (Ed.) (1980), *Glimpses in Plant Research*-V. *Modern Trends in Plant Taxonomy*, Vikas Publishers, New Delhi.

Natho, G. (1959), Variationshreite und Bastardbildung bei mitteleuropaischen Birkensipppen, *Feddes Rep.*, **61**: 211-273.

Negre, R. (1957), Les *Frankania* du Moroc, *Trav. Inst. Sci. Cherif, Bot.*, **12**: 1-56.

Nelson, A.P. (1965), Taxonomic and evolutionary significance of lawn races of *Prunella vulgaris*, *Brittonia*, **17**: 160-174.

Nelson, C.I. and J.M. Birkeland (1928), A serological ranking of some wheat hybrids as an aid in selecting for certain generic characters, *J. Amer. Agric. Res.*, **38**: 169-181.

Nemejc, F. (1956), On the problem of the origin and phylogenetic development of angiosperms, *Sb. nar. Mus. Praze, Sect. B*, **12**b(2-3): 59-143.

Newberry, J.S. (1895), The flora of Amboy days, *U.S. Geol. Surv. Mon.*, **26**: 1-260.

Newmann, M. (1935), Die Entwicklung des Pollens der Semenanlage und des Embryosacks van Pereskia amapola var. *argentina*, *Osterr. Bot. Ztschr.*, **84**: 1-30.

Nilsson, S. (1967), Pollen morphological studies in the Gentianaceae, *Grana Palynologica*, **7**(1): 46-145.

Nuttall, G.H.F. (1901), The new biological test for blood in relation to zoological classification, *Proc. Roy. Soc. Britain*, **69**: 150-153.

Nygren, A. (1954), Apomixis in the angiosperms, *Bot. Rev.*, **20**: 577-649.

Obermeyer, A.A. (1962), A revision of the South African species of *Anthericum*, *Chlorophytum* and *Trachyandra*, *Bothalia*, **7**: 669-767.

Odum, E.P. (1971), *Fundamentals of Ecology*, 3rd edn., Sounders, London.

Ornduff, R. and T.J. Crovello (1968), Numerical taxonomy of Limnanthaceae, *Amer, J. Bot.*, **55**: 173-182.

Ornduff, R., T. Mosquin, D.W. Kyhos and P.H. Raven (1967), Chromosome numbers in Compositae-VI. Senecioneae-II, *Amer. J. Bot.*, **54**(2): 205-213.

Ornduff, R., P.H. Raven, D.W. Kyhos and A.R. Kruckenberg (1963), Chromosome numbers in Compositae-III. Senecioneae, *Amer. J. Bot.*, **50**(2): 131-139.

Ozenda, P. (1949), *Recherches sur les dictyledones apocarpiques contribution a l'etude des angiosperms dites primitives*, Ecole Normale Super Publ. Lab. Biol., Paris.

Paliwal, G.S. (1965), Development of stomata in *Basella rubra Phytomorphology*, **15**: 50-53.

_______ (1966), Structure and ontogeny of stomata in some Caryophyllaceae, *Phytomorphology*, **16**: 533-539.

_______ (1968), Ontogeny of stomata in some Cruciferae, *Canad. J. Bot.*, **45**: 495-500.

_______ (1969), Stomatal ontogeny and Phylogeny-I. Monocotyledons, *Acta Bot. Neerl.*, **10**: 654-668.

_______ (1970), Epidermal structure and ontogeny of stomata in some Bignoniaceae, *Flora*, **159**: 124-132.

Paliwal, G.S. and N.N. Bhandari (1962), Stomatal development in some Magnoliaceae, *Phytomorphology,* **12**: 409-412.

Paliwal, G.S. and L. Kakkar (1971), Variability in the stomatal apparatus of *Pereskia aculeata* Mill., *J. Indian Bot. Soc.,* **50A**: 164-171.

Pant, D.D. (1958), The structure of some leaves and fructifications of the Glossopteris flora of Tanganyika, *Bull. Brit. Mus.* (Nat. Hist.) *Geol.,* **3**: 125-175.

Pant, D.D. and K. Gupta (1966), Development of stomata and foliar structure of some Magnoliaceae, *J. Linn. Soc. Bot.,* **59**: 265-277.

Pant, D.D. and P.F. Kidwai (1964), On the diversity in the development and organization of stomata in *Phyla modiflora* Michx., *Curr. Sci.,* **33**: 653-654.

_______ (1971), The origin of flowering plants, *J. Indian Bot. Soc.,* **50A**: 242-274.

Pant, D.D. and B. Mehra (1964), Ontogeny of stomata in some Ranunculaceae, *Flora,* **155**: 179-188.

Parkin, J. (1914), The evolution of inflorescence, *J. Linn. Soc. Bot.,* **42**: 511-563.

_______ (1923), The strobilus theory of angiospermous descent, *Proc. Linn. Soc. London,* **153**: 51-64.

_______ (1953), The Durian theory—A criticism, *Phytomorphology,* **8**: 80-88.

Pate, J.S. and B.E.S. Gunning (1972), Transfer cells, *Ann. Rev. Pl. Physiol.,* **23**: 173-196.

Payne, W.W. (1979), Stomatal patterns in Embryophytes: Their evolution, ontogeny and interpretation, *Taxon,* **28**(1, 2/3): 117-132.

Payne, W.W., P.H. Raven and D.W. Kyhos (1964), Chromosome numbers in Compositae-IV. Ambrosieae, *Amer. J. Bot.,* **51**(4): 419-424.

Percival, M.S. (1965), *Floral Biology,* Pergamon Press, Oxford.

Petiver, J. (1899), Some attempts made to prove that herbs of the same make or class for the generality have the like vertue and tendency to work the same effects, *Phil. Trans. Roy. Soc.,* **21**B: 289-294.

Pettet, A. (1964a), Studies on British Pansies-I, Chromosome numbers and pollen assemblages, *Watsonia,* **6**(1): 39-50.

_______ (1964b), Studies on British Pansies-II. The status of some intermediates between *V. tricolor* L. and *V. arvensis* Murr., *Watsonia,* **6**(1): 51-69.

Philipson, W.R. (1974), Ovular morphology and the major classification of dicotyledons, *Bot. J. Linn. Soc.,* **68**: 89-108.

_______ (1977), Ovular morphology and the classification of dicotyledons, *in*: K. Kubitzki (Ed.), *Plant Systematics and Evolution,* Springer Verlag, pp. 123-140.

Pickering, C. (1876), *The Geographical Distributions of Animals and Plants.* Part II. *Plants in Their Wild State,* Naturlist's Agency, Salem, Mass.

Pickering, J.L. and D.E. Fairbrothers (1967), A serological and disc electrophoretic investigation of *Magnolia* taxa, *Bull. Torrey Bot. Club,* **94**: 468-479.

Pijl, L. Van der (1952), Ecological variations on the legume pod, *Indonesian J. Nat. Sci.,* **1/2**: 6-12.

_______ (1960), Ecological aspects of flower evolution-I. Phyletic evolution, *Evolution,* **14**: 403-416.

Pijl, L. Van der and C. Dodson (1966), *Orchid Flowers: Their Pollination and Evolution,* Univ. of Miami Press, Florida.

Pilger, R.K.F. (1922), Uber verzweigung und Blutenstandsbildung bei den Holzgewachsen, *Bibl. Bot.,* **23**: 1-38.

Polunin, N. (1960), *Introduction to Plant Geography and Some Related Science,* Longmans, London.

Porter, C.L. (1959), *Taxonomy of Flowering Plants,* W.H. Freeman & Co, San Francisco.

_______ (1967). Field and herbarium methods, *in*: *Taxonomy of Flowering Plants,* 2nd edn. W.H. Freeman & Co., San Francisco.

Potonie, R. (1967), New phylogenetic facts of fossil spores, *Rev. Paleobotan Palynol.,* **1**: 75-82.

Prat, H. (1932), L' epiderme des graminees. Etude anatomique et systematique, *Ann. Sci. Nat. Bot.* Ser. 10, **14**: 119-324.

Pulle, A.A. (1938), *Compendium Van de Terminologie, Nomenclatur en Systematick der Zaadplanten,* Oosthoek Utrecht, 2nd edn. (1950).

Punt, W. (1962), Pollen morphology of the Euphorbiacae with special reference to taxonomy, *Wentia,* **7**: 1-116.

Puri, V. (1951), The role of floral anatomy in the solution of morphological problems, *Bot. Rev.,* **17**: 471-553.

Puri, V. (1967), The origin and evolution of angiosperms, *J. Indian Bot. Soc.*, **46**: 1-14.

Radford, A.E., W.C. Dickinson, J.R. Massey and C.R. Bell (1974), *Vascular Plant Systematics,* Harper & Row, New York.

Ramayya, N. (1969), The development of trichomes in the Compositae, *in:* K.A. Chowdhury (Ed.), *Recent Advances in the Anatomy of Tropical Seed Plants,* Hindustan Publ. Corp. New Delhi., pp. 85-113.

Rammayya, N. and T. Rajgopal (1968), Foliar epidermis as a taxonomic aid in the flora of Hyderabad. Part I. Portulacaceae and Aizoaceae, *J. Osmania Univ.*, **4**: 147-160.

_____ (1971), Foliar dermotypes of Indian Aizoaceae and their use in identification, *J. Indian Bot. Soc.,* **50**: 355-362.

Rao, T.A. (1957), Comparative morphology and ontogeny of foliar sclereids in seed plants. I. *Memecylon, Phytomorphology,* **7**: 306-330.

Rau, M.A. (1962), Review of recent work on the embryogeny of some families and genera of disputed systematic position, *in:* P. Maheshwari (Ed.), *Plant Embryology—A Symposium,* CSIR, New Delhi, pp. 75-80.

Raven, P.H. and D.W. Kyhos (1961), Chromosome numbers in Compositae-II. Helenieae, *Amer. J. Bot.*, **48**(9): 842-850.

_____ (1965), New evidence concerning the original basic chromosome number of angiosperms, *Evolution,* **19**(2): 244-248.

Raven, P.H., O.T. Solbrig, D.W. Kyhos and R. Snow (1960), Chromosome numbers in Compositae-I. Astereae, *Amer. J. Bot.,* **47**(2): 124-132.

Reeder, J.R. (1957), The embryos in grass systematics, *Amer. J. Bot.,* **44**: 756-768.

Rees, H. (1963), Deoxyribonucleic acid and the ancestry of wheat, *Nature,* **198**(4875): 108-109.

Rehder, A. (1949), *Bibliography of Cultivated Trees and Shrubs,* Macmillan & Co., Mass., Jamaica Plain.

Reichert, E.T. (1913), Differentiation and Specificity of Starches in Relation to Genera, Species, etc., *Carnegie Inst., Washington Publ.*, 173.

Rembert, D.H. (1971), Phylogenetic significance of megaspore tetrad patterns in Leguminales, *Phytomorphology,* **21**: 1-9.

Rendle, A.B. (1904, 1925), *The Classification of Flowering Plants,* Vols. 1 & 2, Cambridge Univ. Press, Cambridge 2nd edn. (1930, 1938).

Ribereau-Gayon, P. (1972), *Plant Phenolics,* Oliver & Boyd, Edinburgh.

Richards, P.W. (1952), *The Tropical Rain Forest: An Ecological Study,* Cambridge Univ. Press, Cambridge.

_____ (1973), The tropical rain forest, *Sci. Amer.,* **229**(6): 58-69.

Rickett, H.W. (1944), The classification of inflorescences, *Bot. Rev.,* **10**: 187-231.

Rivers, L. (1923), Sur l' emplei du serodioagnostic pour la determination de Trifinite au greffage des hybrides de vigne, *C. r. hebd. Seanc. Acad. Agric. Fr.,* **9**: 43-47.

Rohlf, F.J. (1965), A randomization test of the non-specificity hypothesis in numerical taxonomy, *Taxon,* **14**: 262-267.

Rohlf, and R.R. Sokal (1965), Coefficients of correlations and distance in numerical taxonomy, *Univ. Kansas Sci. Bull.,* **45**: 3-27.

Rollins, R.C. (1941), Monographic study of *Arabis* in Western North America, *Rhodora,* **43**: 289-325, 348-411, 425-481.

_____ (1944), Evidence of natural hybridity between guayule *(Parthenium argentatum)* and mariola (Parthenium incanum), *Amer. J. Bot.,* **31**: 93-99.

Rollins, R.C. (1945), Interspecific hybridization in *Parthenium* I. Cross between guayule *(Parthenium argentatum)* and mariola *(Parthenium incanum), Amer. J. Bot.,* **32**: 395-404.

_____ (1946), Interspecific hybridization in *Parenthenium* II. Crosses involving *P. argenitatum, P. stramonium, P. tomentosum* and *P. hysterophorus, Amer. J. Bot.,* **33**: 21-30.

_____ (1949), Sources of genetic variation in *Parthenium argentatum* Gray (Compositae), *Evolution,* **2**: 358-368.

_____ (1958), Taxonomy of higher plants, *in*: W.C. Steere (Ed.), *Fifty Years of Botany,* McGraw-Hill, New York, pp. 192-208.

Royle, J.F. (1833-1840), *Illustrations of the Botany of Himalaya etc.*, W.H. Allen & Co., London.

Sahni, B. (1920), On the structure and affinities of *Acmopyle pancheri* pilger, *Trans. Roy. Philosoph. Soc.* (Lond.), Ser. B, **210:** 253-310.
_______ (1936), Wagener's theory—in the light of Palaeobotanical evidence, *J. Indian Bot. Soc.,* **15**: 319-332.
Saldanha C.J. and C.K. Rao (1975), *A Punched Card Key to the Dicot Families of South India,* Amarind, Bangalore.
Samuelsson, G. (1913), Studien uber die Entwicklungsgeschichte einiger Bicornes Typen, *Svensk, Bot. Tidskr.,* **7**: 97-188.
Samylina, V.A. (1959), New occurrences of angiosperms from the lower cretaceous of the Kolyma basin, *Acad. Nauk USSR (Bot.),* **44**(4): 483-491.
Santapau, H. (1955a), *Botanical Collector's Manual,* Min. Nat. Res. & Scient. Res. New Delhi.
_______ (1955b), *Instructions for Field Collectors of the Botanical Survey of India,* Min. Nat. Res. & Scient. Res., New Delhi.
Santavy, F. (1956), Substances of *Colchicum autumnale* and their derivatives XLVI- Colchicine Like alkaloids in *Littonia modesta, Chem Listy,* **50**: 1861-1862.
Saporta, G. de (1877), *L'ancienne Vegetation Polaire,* C.r. Congr. Int., Sci. Geogr., Paris.
_______ (1894), *Flore fossile du Portugal,* Trav. Geol. Portugal, Lisbon.
Saporta, G. de and A.F. Marion (1885), *Recherches sur les Vegetaux Fossiles de Meximieux,* Lyon-Geneve, Bale.
Sargant, E. (1903), A theory of origin of monocotyledons founded on the structure of their seedlings, *Ann. Bot.,* **17**: 1-92.
_______ (1904), The evolution of monocotyledons, *Bot. Gaz.,* **37**: 325-345.
_______ (1908), The construction of a race of primitive angiosperms, *Ann. Bot.,* **22**: 121-186.
Scandalios, J.G. (1969), Genetic control of multiple molecular forms of enzymes in plants: A review, *Biochem. Genet.,* **3**: 27-79.
Schaffner, J. (1904), Some morphological peculiarities of Nymphaeaceae and Helobiae, *The Ohio Naturalist,* **4**: 83-92.
_______ (1929), Principles of plant taxonomy VII, *Ohio J. Sci.,* **29**: 243-252.
_______ (1934), Phylogenetic taxonomy of plants, *Q. Rev. Biol.,* **9**: 129-160.
Schill, R., W. Barthlott and N. Ehler (1973a), Raster-electronen mikroskopische untersuchungenen cactaceen—Epidermea und ihre Bedeuntung fur die systematik, *Trop. Subtrop. Pflanzenw.,* **4**: 1-13.
_______ (1973b), Micromorphologie der cactaceen—Dornen, *Trop. Subtrop. Pflanzenw.,* **6**: 1-23.
Schimper, A.F.W. (1903), *Plant Geography Upon a Physiological Basis,*Clarendon Press, Oxford.
Schnack, B. and G. Covas (1945a), Hibridicion interspecifica en *Glandularia* (Verbenaceae), Darwiniana, **7**: 71-79.
_______ (1945b), Un hibrido interspecifico del genero *Glandularia (G. peruviana* X *G. megapotamica),* Rev. Argentina de Agro., **12:** 224-229.
Schnack, B. and O.T. Solbrig (1953), El hibrido *Glandularia laciniata* x *G. peruviana* y su anfidiploide artificial., *Rev. Fac. Agro.* (La plata), **29**: 255-266.
Schopf, J.M. (1970), Relation of floras of southern hemisphere to continental drift, *Taxon,* **19**: 657-674.
Schuchert, C. (1932), Gondwana land bridges, *Bull, Geol. Soc. America,* **43**: 875-916.
Schulz, O.E. (1936), Cruciferae, *in*: A. Engler, *Die Naturliche Pflanzenfamilien,* 2nd edn. **17**B: 227-658.
Schwarten, L. and H.W. Rickett (1958-1961), *Abbreviations of Periodicals,* Butterworths, New York.
Scott, D.H. (1911), *The Evolution of Plants,* Black, London.
Scott, R.A., E.S. Barghoorn and E.B. Leopold (1960), How old are the angiosperms? *Amer. J. Sci.,* **258**A: 284-299.
Scully, F.J. (1937), Preservation of plant material in natural colours, *Rhodora,* **39**: 16-19.
Sebastian, C. (1956), Etude du genre *Phillyrea* Tournefort, Trav. Inst. Sci. Cherif., **6**: 1-120.
Seidel, C.F. (1869), Zur Entwicklungsgeschichte der *Victoria regia* Lindl., *Nov. Act. Acad. Caes. Leopoldinocarolinae,* **35**(6): 26.
Selling, O. (1947), *Hawaiian Pollen Statistics,* Vol. II. *The Pollens of the Hawaiian Phanerogams,* Spec. Publ. n. 38, Bishop Mus. Honolulu.

Seward, A.C. (1910), *Fossil Plants.* II. Cambridge Univ. Press, Cambridge.

_______ (1926), The cretaceous plant bearing rocks of western Greenland, *Phil. Trans. Roy. Soc. London,* **215**B: 57-175.

_______ (1933), *Plant Life Through the Ages,* Cambridge Univ. Press, Cambridge.

Sharssmith, H. (1961), The Genus *Hesperolinon* (Linaceae), Univ. California, Publ. Bot., **32**: 235-314.

Sheikh, M.T. (1971), A new laboratory technique for preservation of plant specimens, *Curr. Sci.* **40**: 66-67.

Siethe-von Hoff, A. (1960), Die Harr formen der Gattung Rhododendron L. und die Moglichkeit ihrer taxonomische Verwertung. *Bot. Jahrb.*, **79**: 297-393.

Simpson, G.G. (1943), Criteria for genera, species and sub-species in Zoology and Palaeozoology, *Ann. N.Y. Acad. Sci.,* **44:** 145-178.

_______ (1961), *Principles of Animal Taxonomy,* Columbia Univ. Press, New York.

Simpson, D.R. and D. Janos (1974), *A punch card key to the families of dicotyledons of western hemisphere south of the United States,* Illinois: Field Mus. Nat. Hist. Chicago.

Singh, V., M. Sharma and D.K. Jain (1974), Trichomes in *Salvia* (Labiatae) and their taxonomic significance, *Bull. Bot. Surv. Ind.*, **16**: 27-34.

Sinnott, E.W. (1914), Investigations on the phylogeny of the angiosperms. I. The anatomy of the node as an aid in the classification of angiosperms *Amer. J. Bot.*, **1**: 303-322.

_______ (1916), The evolution of herbs, *Science,* **44**: 291-298.

Sinskaja, E.N. (1948), *Dynamics of Species* (In Russian), Leningrad, Quoted from Davis and Heywood (1963).

_______ (1958), Investigations in the composition of eco-typical and varietal populations. A brief survey of some of our works published in Russian, *Report Scottish Pl. Breeding Stn.,* **1960**: 31-40.

_______ (1960), The most important wild forage plants of North Caucasus (in Russian), *Trud. Priklad. Bot. Genet. Selekc.,* **33**: 149-204.

Sirks, M.J. (1951), The scope of genetics in problems of evolution, *Report Brisbane Meeting Austral. & New Zeal. Ass. Adv. Sci.,* **28**: 170-177.

Sirajeev, G. (1932), Generis Ononis Revisoo Critica, *Beih. Bot. Centr.,* **49**: 381-665.

Skipworth, J.P. and W.R. Philipson (1966), The cortical vasuclar system and the interpretation of *Magnolia* flower, *Phytomorphology,* **16**: 463-469.

Skottsberg, C. (1940), *Vexternas Liv.*, Vol. 5, Kungl. Vet. Acad. Handl., Stockholm.

Smirnov, E.S. (1924), Sur l'analyse de la distribution et de la correleation des caracterres dans les unites systematiques, *C.R. Acad. Sci.*, USSR, Ser. A: 81-84.

_______ (1938), Species construction from a taxonomic point of view (in Russian), *Zool. Zhurn.*, **17**: 387-418.

Smith, C.E. (1971), Preparing herbarium specimens of vascular plants, *Agric. Inform. Bull.*, USDA, pp. 29.

Smith, G.M. (1938), Cryptogamic Botany, Vol. 1, McGraw-Hill, New York.

Smith, P.M. (1968a), The *Bromus mollis* aggregate in Britain, *Watsonia,* **6**: 327-344.

_______ (1968), Serological distinctness of *Bromus pseudosecalinus* P.M. Smith sp. nov., *Reprim Nov. Spec., Regni Veg.,* **77**: 61-64.

_______ (1969a), Serological relationships of *Bromus* L. and *Bolssiera* Hochst. ex Steud. *Reprim Nov. Spec., Regni Veg.,* **19**: 337-345.

_______ (1969b), Serological relationships and taxonomy in certain tribes of Gramineae, *Ann. Bot.,* **33**: 591-613.

_______ (1972), Serology and species relationships in annual bromes (*Bromus* L. Sect. Bromus), *Ann. Bot.,* **36**: 1-30.

_______ (1976), *The Chemotaxonomy of Plants,* Edward Arnold, London.

Snaydon, R.W. (1973), Ecological factors, genetic variation and specification in plants, *in:* V.H. Heywood (Ed.), *Taxonomy and Ecology,* Academic Press, London, pp. 1-30.

Sneath, P.H.A. (1962), The construction of taxonomic groups, *in:* G.C. Ainsworth and P.H.A. Sneath (Eds.),*Microbial Classification,* 12th Symp. Soc. Exp. Microbiol., pp. 289-332.

Sneath, P.H.A. and R.R. Sokal (1962), Numerical taxonomy, *Nature,* **193**: 855-860.

_______ (1973), *Numerical Taxonomy,* W.H. Freeman & Co., San Francisco.

Sokal, R.R. and T.J. Crovello (1970), The biological species concept: A critical evaluation, *Amer. Nat.*, **104**(936): 127-153.

Sokal, R.R. and P.H.A. Sneath (1963), *Principles of Numerical Taxonomy,* W.H. Freeman, San Francisco & London.

Solbrig, O.T. (1966), *Evolution and Systematics,* The Macmillan Co., New York.

_______ (1968), Fertility, sterility and species problem, *in:* V.H. Heywood (Ed.), *Modern Methods in Plant Taxonomy,* Academic Press, London, pp. 77-96.

_______ (1970), *Principles and Methods of Plant Biosystematics,* The Macmillan Co., New York.

Solbrig, O.T., L.C. Anderson, D.W. Kyhos, P.H. Raven and L. Rudenberg (1964), Chromosome numbers in Compositae V. Asteraceae II, *Amer. J. Bot.,* **51**(5): 513-519.

Solereder, H. and F.J. Meyer (1908), *Systematic Anatomy of the Dicotyledons* (Transl. L.A. Boodle and F.E. Fritsch), Oxford Univ. Press, London.

Soo, R. (1953), Die Modernen Grundsatze der Phylogenie im neunen system der Blutenpflanzen, *Acta Biol. Acad. Sci. Hungaricae,* **4**: 257-306.

Sorensen, T. (1953), A revision of the Greenland species of *Puccinella, Parl. Medd. Om. Gronl.,* **136**: 1-180.

Soria, V.J. and C.B. Helser, Jr. (1961), A statistical study of relationships of certain species of the *Solanum nigrum complex, Econ. Bot.,* **15**: 2455.

Sperlich, A. (1939), Das trophische parenchym, B. Exkretionsgewebe, *in:* K. Linsbauer (Ed.), *Handbuch der Pflanzenanatomie,* Gebruder Borntraeger, Berlin, p. 38.

Sporne, K.R. (1948), Correlation and classification in diotyledons, *Proc. Linn. Soc. London,* **160:** 40-47.

_______ (1954), Statistics and evolution of dicotyledons, *Evolution,* **8**: 55-64.

_______ (1956), The phylogenetic classification of the angiosperms, *Biol. Rev.,* **31**: 1-29.

_______ (1969), The ovule as an indicator of evolutionary status in the angiosperms, *New Phytol.,* **68:** 555-566.

_______ (1974), *The Morphology of Angiosperms: The Structure & Evolution of Flowering Plants,* Hutchinson University Library, London.

Sprague, E.F. (1962), Pollination and evolution in *Pedicularis* (Scrophylariaceae), *Aliso,* **5**: 181-209.

Sprague, T.A. (1960), The evolution of angiosperms with special reference to Dicotyledons, *Proc. Cotteswold Nat. Field Club,* **32**(3): 29-42.

Stace, C.A. (1970), Anatomy and taxonomy in *Jancus* subgenus *Genuini, in:* N.B.K. Robson, D.F. Cutter and M. Gregory (Eds.), *New Research in Plant Anatomy,* Academic Press, London, pp. 75-81.

Stace, C.A. (1980), *Plant Taxonomy and Biosystematics,* Edward Arnold, London.

Stafleu, F.A. *et al.* (Ed.) (1978), *International Code of Botanical Nomenclature* as adopted by the XIIth International Botanical Congress, Leningrad (1975), Bohn, Scheltema & Holkema, Utrecht.

Stant, M.Y. (1952), Anatomical evidence for including *Nyctanthes* and *Dimetra* in Verbenaceae, *Kew Bull.,* **1952:** 273-276.

_______ (1970), Anatomy of *Petrosavia stellaris* Becc. a saprophytic monocotyledo, *in:* N.B.K. Robson, D.F. Cutter and M. Gregory (Eds.), *New Researches in Plant Anatomy,* Academic Press, London, pp. 147-161.

Stearn, W.T. (1959), The background of Linnaeus' contribution to the nomenclature and methods of systematic biology, *Syst. Zool.,* **8**: 4-22.

_______ (1960), *Notes on Linnaeus Genera Plantarum:* Prefix to C. Linnaeus, *Genera Plantarum* 1754, *Historia Naturalis Classica Fascimile* V-XXIV, Ray Society, London.

_______ (1964), Problems of character selection and weighting: Introduction, *in:* V.H. Heywood and McNeill (Eds.), *Phenetic and Phylogenetic Classification,* Academic Press, London. pp. 83-86.

_______ (1968), Observations on a computor aided survey of the Jamaican speices of *Columnea* and *Allopectus, in:* V.H. Heywood (Ed.), *Modern Methods in Plant Taxonomy,* Academic Press, London, pp. 219-224.

Stebbins, G.L. (1950), *Variation and Evolution in Plants,* Columbia Univ. Press, New York.

_______ (1951), Natural selection and the differentiation of angiosperm families, *Evolution,* **5**: 299-324.

_______ (1956), Cytogenetics and evolution of the grass family, *Amer. J. Bot.*, **43**: 890-905.
_______ (1957), Self-fertilization and population variability in the higher plants, *Amer. Nat.*, **91**: 337-354.
_______ (1958a), The inviability, weakness and sterility of interspecific hybrids, *Adv. Genet.*, **8**: 147-215.
_______ (1958b), Cytogenetics and evolution of the grass family, *in:* W.C. Steere (Ed.), *Fifty Years of Botany,* McGraw-Hill, New York.
_______ (1959a), Genes, chromosomes and evolution, *in*: W.B. Turrill (Ed.), *Vistas in Botany,* London, pp. 258-290.
_______ (1959b), The role of hybridization in evolution, *Amer. Phil. Soc. Proc.*,**103**: 231-251.
_______ (1974), *Flowering Plants—Evolution Above the Species Level,* Arnold Press, London.
Stebbins, G.H. and G.S. Khush (1961), Variation in the organization of the stomatal complex in the leaf epidermis of Monocotyledons and its bearing on the phylogeny, *Amer. J. Bot.*, **48:** 51-59.
Steenis, C.G.G.J. van (1950), Technique of plant collecting and preservation in the tropics, *in*: Steenis-Kurseman, M.J. van (Ed.), *Flora Malesiana,* Ser. I, **1**: 45-69, Noordhof Groningen, Djakarta.
Steenis, C.G.G.J. van (1962), The land bridge theory in botany, Blumea, **11**: 235-372.
Steudel, E.G. (1821), *Nomenclature botanicus,* J.G. Colfae Stuttgart.
Stix, E. (1960), Pollen morpohologische untersuchungen in compositen, *Grana Palynologica,* **2**(2): 41-104.
Stopes, M.C. (1915), The cretaceous flora Part II. Lower green sand (Aptian) plants of Britain, *Cat. Mes. Plants Brit. Mus.*, pp. 1-360.
Straka, H. (1971), Die pollen kunde in Dienste der pflanzensystematik, *Biol. Uns. Zeit.*, **1:** 143-146, 173-179.
Straw, R.M. (1956), Floral isolation in *Pentstemon, Amer. Nat.*, **90**: 47-53.
Swanson, C.P. (1957), *Cytology and Cytogenetics,* Englewood Prentice-Hall, Englewood Cliff, N.J.
Takhtajan, A.L. (1942), The structural types of gynoecium and placentation, *Bull. Armen. Branch. Acad. Sci.* USSR, **3-4** (17-18): 91-112 (in Russian).
_______ (1943), Correlation of ontogenesis and phylogenesis in the higher plants, *Trans. Erevan State Univ.*, **22**: 71-176 (in Russian).
_______ (1947), On principles, methods, symbols of the phylogenetic construction in botany, *Byull. Mosk. Obshch. Ispyt. Prir. (Bull. Mosc. Soc. Nat.) Biology,* **52**(5): 95-120 (in Russian).
_______ (1948), *Morphological Evolution of Angiosperms,* Nauka Moscow (in Russian).
_______ (1953), Phylogenetic principles of the system of higher plants, *Bot. Rev.*, **19**: 1-45.
_______ (1954), *The Origin of Angiospermous Plants,* Nauka, Moscow (in Russian).
_______ (1958), *Origins of Angiospermous Plants,* Amer. Inst. Biol. Sci. (Transl. from the Russian edition of 1954).
_______ (1959), *Die Evolution der Angiospermen,* Fischer, Jena.
_______ (1961), *The Origin of Angiospermous Plants,* 2nd edn. Nauka, Moscow (in Russian).
_______ (1964a) *Foundations of the Evolutionary Morphology of Angiosperms,* Nauka, Moscow & Leningrad (in Russian).
_______ (1964b), The taxa of higher plants above the rank of order, *Taxon,* **13**: 160-164.
_______ (1966), *A System & Phylogeny of the Flowering Plants,* Soviet Sciences Press, Leningrad (in Russian).
_______ (1969), *Flowering Plants: Origin and Dispersal,* Oliver & Boyd, Édinburgh (English translation by C. Jeffrey).
_______ (1973), *Evolution und Ausbreitung der Blutenpflanzen,* Jena.
_______ (1980), Outline of the classification of flowering plants (Magnoliophyta), *Bot. Rev.*, **46**(3): 225-359.
Tarling, D.H. (1971), Gondwanaland, paleomagnetism and continental drift, *Nature,* **229:** 17-21.
_______ (1972), Another Gondwanaland, *Nature* **238**: 91-92.
Tateoka, T. (1962), Starch grains of endosperm in grass systematics, *Bot. Mag. Tokyo,* **75**: 377-383.
Terentjev, P.V. (1931), Biometrische Untersuchungen uber die morphologischen Markmale von *Rana ridibunda* Pall, *Biometrika,* **23**: 23-51.
Thomas, H.H. (1925), The caytoniales, a new group of angiospermous plants from Jurassic rocks of Yorkshire, *Trans. Roy. Philosoph. Soc.* (Lond.) Ser. B, **213**: 299-363.

Thomas, H.H. (1933), On some pteridospermous plants from the Mesozoic rocks of South Africa, *Phil. Trans. Roy. Soc. B.*, **222:** 193-265.
——— (1936), Palaeobotany and the origin of angiosperms, *Bot. Rev.*, **2:** 397-418.
——— (1955), Mesozoic pteriodosperms, *Phytomorphology*, **5:** 177-185.
——— (1958), *Ligettonia*, a new type of fertile *Glossopteris*, *Bull. Brit. Mus. Nat. Hist.*, **3:** 179-189.
Thompson, W.P. (1918), Independent evolution of vessels in Gnetales and angiosperms, *Bot. Gaz.*, **65**: 83-90.
Thorne, R.F. (1958), Some guiding principles of angiosperm phylogeny, *Brittonia*, **10**: 72-77.
——— (1963), Some problems and guiding principles of angiosperm phylogeny, *Amer. Nat.*, **97**(896): 287-305.
——— (1968), Synopsis of a putatively phylogenetic classification of flowering plants, *Aliso*, **6:** 57-66.
——— (1976), A phylogenetic classification of the Angiospermae, *in*: M.K. Hecht, W.C. Steere and B. Wallace (Eds.), *Evolutionary Biology*, Vol. 9, Plenum Press, New York and London. pp. 35-106.
——— (1977), Some realignments in Angiospermae, *in:* K. Kubitzki (Ed.), *Plant Systematics and Evolution* (Suppl. 1) *Flowering Plants: Evolution and Classification of Higher Categories*, Springer Verlag, New York, pp. 299-319.
Tippo, O. (1938), Comparative anatomy and morphology of the Moraceae and their presumed allies, *Bot. Gaz.*, **100**: 1-99.
——— (1942), A modern classifcation of plant kingdom, *Chorn. Bot.*, **7**: 203-206.
Tomlinson, P.B. (1961), *Anatomy of the Monocotyledons, II. Palmae*, Clarendon Press, Oxford.
——— (1962), *Anatomy of the Monocotyledons III. Scitamineae*, Clarendon Press, Oxford.
——— (1970), Monocotyledons—Towards an understanding of their morphology and anatomy, *Adv. Bot. Res.*, **3**: 207-292.
Tourefort, J.P. de (1700-1716), *Institutiones Rei Herbariae*, Vols. I-III, Typogr. Regia., Paris.
Trecul, A. (1845), Researches sur la structure et le development du *Nuphar luteum*, *Ann. Sci. Nat.* Ser. III Bot., **4:** 286-345.
Treub, H.P. (1974), Liliales—Lily order, *in*: *Encyclopaedia Brittanica* (new edn.) **10**: 971-976.
——— (1975), Class Liliida of superclass Monocotyidra, *Taxon*, **24**: 453-460.
Turesson, G. (1922a), The species and variety as ecological units, *Hereditas*, **3**: 100-113.
——— (1922b), The genotypical response of the plant species to the habitat, *Hereditas*, **3**: 211-350.
——— (1925), The plant species in relation to habitat and climate, *Hereditas*, **6**: 147-236.
——— (1931), The geographical distribution of the alpine ecotype of some Eurasiatic plants, *Hereditas*, **15**: 329-346.
Turner, B.L. (1970), Molecular approach to population problems at the infraspecific level, *in:* J.B. Herborne (Ed.), *Phytochemical Phylogeny*, Academic Press, London, pp. 187-206.
——— (1971), Training of systematics for the seventies, *Taxon*, **20**: 123-130.
Turill, W.B. (1938), The expansion of taxonomy, *Biol. Rev.*, **13**: 342-373.
——— (1953), *Pioneeer Plant Geography: The Phytogeographical Researches of Sir Joseph Dalton Hooker*, Nijhoff, Hague.
Tutin, T.G. (1955), Species problem in plants with reduced floral structure, *in:* J.E. Lousley (Ed.), *Species Studies in British Flora*, Bot. Soc. Brit. Is., Oxford, pp. 21-26.
Uphof, J.C. Th. (1968), *Dictionary of Economic Plants*, 2nd edn. Lehre Verlag van J. Cramer, New York.
Valentine, D.H. (1960), The treatment of apomictic groups in *Flora Europaea*, Feddes Rep., **63**: 114-127.
Valentine, D.H. and A. Love (1958), Taxonomic and biosystematic categories, *Brittonia*, **10**: 153-166.
Valentine, J.W. (1967), The influence of climatic fluctuations on species diversity within the tethyan provincial system, *in:* C.G. Adams and D.V. Ager (Ed.), *Aspects of Tethyan Biogeography*, Systematists Assn. Publ. No. 7, pp. 153-166.
Vidakovic, M. (1957), Forms of *Pinus nigra* in Yugoslavia on the basis of anatomical structure of the needles, *Glasnik Za Sumske Pokuse*, **13**: 111-248.
Vindt, J. (1960), Morphologie des Euphorbiacees du Moruc. Deuxieme partie (Anatomie), *Trav. Inst. Sci. Cherif.*, **19**: i-xxiv, 219-533.

Voughn, J.G. (1968), Seed protein studies of *Brassica* and *Sinapsis* species, *in*: J.G. Hawkes (Ed.), *Chemotaxonomy and Serotaxonomy,* Academic Press, London, pp. 103-110.

Waddington, C.H. (1953), Genetic assimilation of an acquired character, *Evolution,* **7**: 118-126.

Wagner, W.H. (1961), Problems in the classification of ferns, *in:* D.L. Bailey (Ed.), *Recent Advances in Botany,* Univ. of Toronto Press, Toronto, pp. 841-844.

_______ (1962), The synthesis and expression of phylogenetic data, *in:* L. Benson (Ed.), *Plant Taxonomy,* Ronald Press, New York, pp. 415-417.

_______ (1968), Hybridization, taxonomy and evolution, *in:* V.H. Heywood (Ed.), *Modern Methods in Plant Taxonomy,* Academic Press, London, pp. 113-138.

_______ (1970), Biosystematics and evolutionary noise, *Taxon,* **19**: 146-151.

Walker, J.W. (1976), Evolutionary significance of the exine in the pollen of primitive angiosperms, *in:* I.K. Ferguson and J. Muller (Eds.), *The Evolutionary Significance of the Exine,* Academic Press, London, pp. 251-308.

Walter, H. (1971), *Ecology of tropical and subtropical vegetation,* Oliver & Boyd, Edinburgh.

Walters, S.M. (1953), *Eleocharis mamillata* Lindb. f. and allied species, *Ber. Schweiz. Bot. Ges.,* **63**: 271-286.

_______ (1961), The shaping of angiosperm taxonomy, *New Phytol.,* **60**: 74-84.

Wangerin, W.A. (1910), Cornaceae, *in:* A.H.G. Engler's *Das Pflanzenreich.* IV., **229**: 1-110.

Warburg, E.F. (1938), Taxonomy and relationships in the Geraniales in light of their cytology, *New Phytol.,* **37**(3): 189-209.

Warming, E. (1909), *Oecology of Plants,* Clarendon Press, Oxford.

Warmke, H.E. (1941), Chromosome continuity and individuality, *Gold Spring Harb. Symp. Quant. Biol.,* **9**: 1-6.

Watson, L., J.S. Pate and B.E.S. Gunning (1977), Vascular transfer cells in leaves of Leguminosae—Papilionoideae, *Bot. J. Linn. Soc.,* **74**: 123-130.

Webster, G.L. (1967), The genera of Euphorbiaceae in the southeastern United States, *J. Arnold Arbor.,* **48**: 303-361.

Wegener, A. (1924), (Trans. from German by Skerl, J.G.A.), *The Origin of Continents and Oceans* Methuen & Co., London.

Wells, P.V. (1969), Discussion, *in:* P.V. Wells (Ed.), *Systematic Biology,* Nat. Acad. Sci. Publ., **1692**: 206-211.

Wernham, H.F. (1912), Floral evolution: with particular reference to the sympetalous Dicotyledons. IX. Summary and conclusion, *New Phytol.,* **11**: 373-397.

Wettstein, R. Von (1901). *Handbuch der Systematischen Botanik,* Gerbruder Borntraeger, Berlin: 4th edn (1930-1935), Vols. 1-2, Franz Deuticke, Leipzig and Vienna.

Whiffin, T. and A.S. Tombe (1972), The systematic significance of seed morphology in the neotropical capsular-fruited Melastomaceae, *Amer. J. Bot.,* **59**: 411-422.

Whitehead, F. (1963), Experimental studies of the effect of wind on plant growth and anatomy, IV. Growth substances and adoptive anatomical and morphological changes, *New Phytol.,* **62**: 87-90.

Whitemore, T.C. (1975), *Tropical Rain Forests of the Far East,* Oxford Univ. Press, London.

Wiens, D. (1975), Chromosome numbers in African and Madagascan Loranthaceae and Viscaceae, *Bot. J. Linn. Soc.,* **71**: 295-310.

Wight, R. (1838-1853), *Icones Plantarum Indiae Orientalis,* Vols. 1-6, J.B. Pharaoh, Madras.

Williams, L.O. (1970), Field work technique in botany, *in: Field Manual for Museums and Monuments,* 12, UNESCO, pp. 143-154.

Willis, J.C. (1922), *Age and Area,* Cambridge Univ. Press, Cambridge.

_______ (1925), *A Dictionary of the Flowering Plants and Ferns,* 5th edn, Cambridge Univ. Press, Cambridge, 6th edn (1931); 7th edn by H.K. Airy Shaw (1966).

_______ (1940), *The Course of Evolution by Differentiation or Divergent Mutation Rather than by Selection,* Cambridge Univ. Press, Cambridge.

_______ (1949), *The Birth and Spread of Plants,* Conservatoire et Jardin botaniques de la Ville, Geneva.

Winkler, H. (1931), Die Monokotylen sind monokotylen, *Beitr. Biol. Pfl.,* **19**: 29-34.

Withering, W. (1785), *An Account of the Foxglove and Some of Its Medicinal Uses,* Swinney, Birmingham.

Wodehouse, R.P. (1935), *Pollen Grains,* McGraw-Hill, New York.

Woodson, R.E. (1954), The North American Species of *Asclepias* L., *Ann. Mus. Bot. Gard.,* 41: 1-211.

Wulff, E.V. (1943), *An Introduction of Historical Plant Geography,* Chronica Botanica, Waltham Mass.

Wycherley, P.R. (1953), Proliferation of spikelets in British grasses, *Watsonia,* 3: 41.

Yakovlev, M.S. and M.D. Yoffe (1959), On a new type of embryogenesis in *Paeonia* L.,*Proc. 9th Int. Bot. Congr. Montreal,* pp. 437-438.

Zuckerkandl, E. and L. Pauling (1965), Molecules as documents of evolutionary history, *J. Theor. Biol.,* 8: 357-366.

Index